NEWNES INTERNATIONAL MONOGRAPHS ON MATERIALS SCIENCE AND TECHNOLOGY

POWDER METALLURGY
Practice and Applications

NEWNES INTERNATIONAL MONOGRAPHS ON

MATERIALS SCIENCE AND TECHNOLOGY

Advisory Editor

N. L. Parr, C.Eng., M.I.Mech.E., F.I.M.

This new and timely series of monographs provides information on the various aspects of materials science and technology in relation to the needs of engineering design and construction. Allied volumes survey separate areas and give the latest information on processes, structures and properties in order that materials may be employed to maximum benefit. The series is equally suited to the needs of students for use as reading in connection with university or technical college studies. Titles include:

Powder Metallurgy; Practice and Applications, by R. L. Sands, A.I.M. and C. R. Shakespeare, A.I.M., A.C.T.(Birm.)., both of The B.S.A. Group Research Centre, Birmingham.

The Technology and Properties of Ferrous Alloys for High-Temperature Use, by M. G. Gemmill, B.Sc., F.I.M., Generation Design Department, Central Electricity Generating Board.

The Technology of Heavy Non-Ferrous Metals and Alloys, by J. H. Cairns, M.Sc.Tech., Ph.D., A.I.M., and P. T. Gilbert, B.Sc., Ph.D., F.R.I.C., F.I.M., M.Inst.Mar.Eng., both of Yorkshire Imperial Metals Ltd., Leeds.

Mechanical Testing of Materials, by A. J. Fenner, B.Sc.(Eng.), A.M.I.Mech.E., Principal Scientific Officer, National Engineering Laboratory, East Kilbride, Glasgow.

Other titles in preparation

POWDER METALLURGY
Practice and Applications

by

R. L. Sands, A.I.M.

and

C. R. Shakespeare, A.I.M., A.C.T.(Birm.)

LONDON
GEORGE NEWNES LIMITED
TOWER HOUSE, SOUTHAMPTON STREET
LONDON, W.C.2

First published 1966

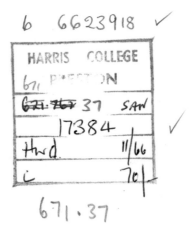
MADE AND PRINTED IN GREAT BRITAIN BY
WILLIAM CLOWES AND SONS, LIMITED, LONDON AND BECCLES

PREFACE

The origins of powder metallurgy are lost in antiquity and yet the same basic techniques are today helping to solve some of the materials problems in the rapidly developing fields of space technology and nuclear energy. A history of powder metallurgy would make interesting reading but, although we have included a brief outline in Chapter 1, this is not a history book. Rather, it is our earnest hope that it is a review of the contemporary 'state of the art'.

Although this is essentially a textbook, which we trust will appeal to the student and budding powder metallurgist, we have planned it in such a way that we hope will also make it of use to designers and engineers in a variety of fields. While we would not presume to attempt to teach powder-metallurgy producers their job, we do believe there is a need for a book that shows the potential user what powder metallurgy can do. For this reason chapters have been aimed at specific types of user.

Concentration on the practical aspects has forced us to limit the theoretical side to that necessary to explain certain processes. However, adequate references are provided for those wishing to study the subject in depth.

Many of the techniques used in powder metallurgy are common to other fields of technology, in particular ceramics. This has meant that there are certain products that are 'border-line cases' because of the difficulty in drawing a line between powder metallurgy and ceramic technology. Thus, although we have included cermets, which may contain only a small amount of free metal, we have left out such products as the magnetic ferrites which contain no free metal. This has been necessary in order to contain the book within reasonable proportions and not because we believe the powder metallurgist should remain ignorant of ceramics. Indeed the two technologies still have much to teach each other and with the advent of new and more complex materials the borders between them will become increasingly blurred.

We acknowledge the help of all those, too numerous to list here, who have provided information, photographs, comment and constructive criticism.

Many of their names appear in references and footnotes, and in acknowledgements to illustrations. We are most grateful for their interest and help. We are particularly indebted to Mrs M. Morris who transformed our many rough sketches into elegant line drawings.

Finally, our thanks are due to our Director of Research, Mr D. A. Oliver, for allowing us to use the many facilities of The B.S.A. Group Research Centre.

R. L. S.

Birmingham   C. R. S.

CONTENTS

PLATES

CHAPTER 1

INTRODUCTION

In subsequent chapters an outline is given of the powder metallurgy industry and the technology upon which it is based. The description 'powder metallurgy industry', implying a single integrated industry, is perhaps a misnomer. It would seem more correct to admit that there are several industries, such as the hard-metal industry and the sintered engineering-components industry, all based upon a common family of techniques. A common technology is then the characteristic which links the various groups of commercial operators together. While the technology is common, the uses to which this is put are widespread and the applications of the end-products astonishingly diverse.

Historical Note

A consequence of this situation is that few firms attempt to cover more than a small range of the important powder-metallurgy products. It is the rule rather than the exception for firms to specialize in one field, with perhaps a secondary interest in one or two allied products. It seems worthwhile examining the history of powder metallurgy to see how the present diversification arose and also to look for a lead as to the likely future of the industry.

The preparation of relatively massive pieces of metal from powders or granules was carried out at least five thousand years ago. Metal was produced in this manner because it was not possible, with the primitive furnaces then available, to obtain temperatures sufficiently high for fusion. It is likely that the first metals to be produced from powder were iron and copper. The general method seems to have been to reduce the ore, probably with charcoal, to give a metal sponge and then to consolidate this by hammering the heated mass. Many articles produced in such a manner have been preserved; easily the most impressive is the iron pillar at Delhi which weighs about 6 tons and was made about A.D. 300.

In time the preparation of articles from iron granules was superseded by fusion methods. Heating techniques improved only slowly of course and, even when it became possible to melt iron, powder metallurgy methods were still required for more refractory metals. For many years platinum had to be consolidated from granules by powder metallurgy. Platinum articles were prepared by the Incas long before the Spanish conquest, using naturally occurring grains of platinum, gold and silver, the gold and silver being important to the process because they formed a low-melting eutectic. Until the end of the eighteenth century all platinum was fabricated from granules by variations of the technique employed by the Incas. 'Pure' platinum was obtained by using metals such as arsenic or lead to form the eutectics, these elements being removed later by oxidation.

At the beginning of the nineteenth century it became possible to prepare platinum metal without liquid-phase sintering, the name of Wollaston being particularly associated with this development. Wollaston[1]* published details of his production method in 1829 and it is clear that he had perceived the importance to the process of such factors as particle size, compacting to a high density and surface activity. Goetzel[2] has said, and rightly so, that in Wollaston's work 'powder metallurgy had its first truly scientific enunciation'.

In the second half of the nineteenth century Wollaston's method for producing platinum articles was superseded by a fusion process. As before, however, there were demands for metals of even higher melting point and again these were consolidated from metal powders. This next phase was closely associated with the advent of the metal-filament electric lamp. As early as 1870 von Welsbach had prepared osmium filaments by extruding osmium oxide with a sugar-syrup binder; the fine threads obtained were fired to carburize and volatilize the binder, reduce the oxide and sinter the metal. A few years later osmium filaments were replaced by tantalum, this being prepared by a similar process to that used for osmium, except that a vacuum treatment was necessary. The final stage in the development of metal filaments was the production of ductile tungsten by Coolidge,[3] whose method involved preparing tungsten briquettes which were sintered and then hot worked; after repeated hot working the metal was sufficiently ductile to be drawn at relatively low temperatures.

The preparation of ingots from powders for the fabrication of metals such as tungsten, molybdenum, tantalum and niobium is today still carried out on a commercial scale. However, a further stage of the cyclic process, which started with iron and copper, may now be taking place with the increasing use

---

* Figures in parentheses refer to references given at the end of chapters.

of melting techniques for the refractory metals. Since there are now no metals that cannot be fused the use of powder metallurgy in primary metal production will be confined in the future to those cases where melting is undesirable.

There is then a continuous link between the current practice for the production of refractory metals and the origins of powder metallurgy some 5,000 years, or more, ago. Out of this direct link there have been 'off-shoots' from which the bulk of present-day commercial powder metallurgy has grown. The earliest developments were in cemented refractory materials. The impetus for one form of these, cemented carbides, came from the need for wear-resisting dies for drawing tungsten. It was perhaps natural that since the high-melting-point metal tungsten had been made by powder metallurgy then a similar technique should be sought for preparing the hard and refractory compound, tungsten carbide. Development of cemented carbides seems to have started about 1914 and Krupp's were marketing these materials by 1927. Another development, which arose directly out of the production of refractory-metal filaments, was cemented tungsten or molybdenum alloys for electrical-contact applications. The first patent for these, dated 1900, mentioned infiltration.

These early developments had followed closely the known techniques of the filament-producing industry and had been mainly confined to high-melting-point materials. The possible use of porous metals had not, however, been ignored and patents for porous bearings were filed in the late nineteenth century. It was not until the 1920s that porous oil-impregnated bearings were commercially produced and the obvious next step, porous metal filters, followed quickly. Iron powder cores were another development of the 1920s. 'Permalloy' cores followed later.

Growth Rate

The final major development was the realization that powder metallurgy could produce certain shapes in some instances more cheaply than the established methods of casting, forging and machining. This led to the growth of the sintered engineering-components industry, starting in the late 1930s. The production of sintered magnets (Alnico) followed. Today the 'sintered-parts' industry is the most vigorous of the major branches of powder metallurgy. Statistics relating to the consumption in the U.S.A. of iron and copper powders, the principal raw materials for parts production, have been collected by the M.P.I.F.[4] The growth rate of the industry can be seen in Figs. 1 and 2. These figures for U.S.A. consumption show that, despite temporary set-backs, there is an undoubted tendency for vigorous expansion. Certainly the rate of growth has been faster than the increase in either steel production or overall business activity. The use of sintered parts, per head of population, is less in Europe than in the U.S.A.; precise figures are not available but

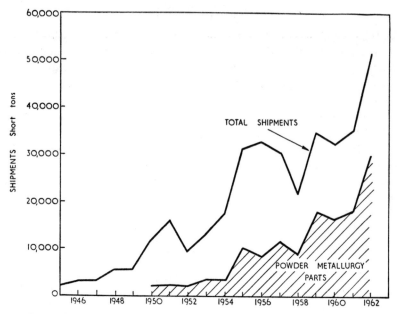

FIG. 1. Annual consumption of iron powders in the United States between
1945 and 1962.[4]

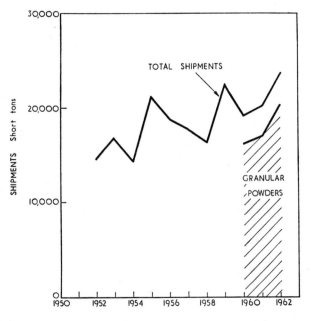

FIG. 2. Annual consumption of copper powders in the United
States between 1952 and 1962.[4] Granular powders are mainly
used for sintered bearings.

current U.K. production seems to have reached about 3,000 tons per annum.

A number of important factors emerge from this brief review. For instance, it is clear that, apart from the production of primary metals (ingots and bar intended for further fabrication), powder metallurgy has been exploited for little over fifty years. During this period the production of refractory metals has been supplanted in importance by the newer powder-metal products. Cemented carbides, porous oil-impregnated bearings and engineering components are now the major industries. Because of these changes most powder metallurgy is now mainly concerned with supplying finished components rather than with material for further fabrication.

The reasons for adopting powder metallurgy have also changed. The emphasis is now on control of structure (cemented carbides, porous metals), production of materials which cannot be made by melting (dispersion-strengthened alloys, metal–non-metal mixtures) and the mass production of complex shapes at low cost (iron and copper-base engineering components, Alnico magnets). There is also an increasing tendency to use loose powder (magnetic cores). The advent of nuclear engineering has also influenced metal-powder technology; not only are exotic combinations of metals and non-metals being called for but it has led to the boundaries between ceramic and metal-powder technology becoming less distinct. Nuclear engineering has set new quality standards in powder metallurgy; the means by which these have been achieved, as well as the resulting technical innovations, promise to widen the scope of the process.

Future of the Industry

What then is the future for powder metallurgy? Certainly some sections of the industry may contract while others expand, but the expansion resulting from the introduction of new types of product seems likely to far outweigh the contraction. Greater emphasis on controlled structures is likely in the future as engineers seek to make improved use of materials in order to achieve better performance and minimize costs; the field of dispersion strengthening is an example of the way in which powder metallurgy will assist these ends. As the cost of manpower becomes an ever greater consideration in total costs, so the use of sintered engineering components should expand, and in this connection techniques such as vacuum sintering, for which capital and operating costs are at present too high, may become competitive and lead to new quality standards and new products. There is also an increasing tendency for metal powders to be the logical product of extraction from ores and to fabricate these directly by powder rolling or extrusion, with the intermediate melting process being omitted. This development may bring powder metal-lurgy back into the field of primary metal production; if so, then the wheel will have turned full circle and the production of such metals as copper may again rely on powder metallurgy.

REFERENCES

1. Wollaston, W. H. *Trans. Roy. Soc.*, **119**, 1 (1829).
2. Goetzel, C. G. *Treatise on Powder Metallurgy*, **1,** 23, Interscience (1949).
3. Coolidge, W. D. *J. Amer. Inst. elect. Engrs.*, **29**, 958 (1909).
4. Roll, K. H. *Progress in Powder Metallurgy*, M.P.I.F., **19**, 195 (1963).

CHAPTER 2

METAL POWDERS, THEIR PROPERTIES AND PRODUCTION

There are many methods available for the preparation of metal powders, and to a large extent the properties of a powder are determined by the method employed for its production. It is convenient, therefore, to consider first the useful properties of a metal powder and the methods of measuring them, and secondly to see how these requirements are met by the various powder production methods.

The chief properties of a powder that need to be considered are: (i) composition, (ii) particle size, (iii) particle shape and (iv) particle structure; the last factor includes micro-structure, porosity, inclusions, etc. These primary properties determine the various other important characteristics of a powder, such as its specific surface (the surface area per unit weight of powder), apparent density and flow properties, as well as its compacting and sintering characteristics. Apart from chemical analysis, which generally follows established techniques, the tests used for the determination of other properties are peculiar to powder technology and will be discussed in more detail.

PROPERTIES AND TESTING

Sampling

Most of the tests carried out on powders require only a relatively small sample and it is therefore essential to ensure that this is truly representative. Many of the techniques established for the sampling of ores and minerals (for example, coning and quartering and the use of various types of riffler) are suitable for metal powders. Batch sizes are generally much smaller than is the case with ores, so that the problems are somewhat different. For instance,

2   7

metal powders are often transported in bins or canisters and during transportation there is a tendency for the finer particles to segregate towards the bottom of the container, so that if the particle-size-analysis sample is to be representative it must include powder from all depths. A method of obtaining such a sample without emptying the container is to insert a narrow bore tube, or 'thief', to the bottom of the bin. The windows in the thief are then opened, and closed again when the thief is full; the tube is then withdrawn. A standard of the American Metal Powder Producers Association[1] recommends three simple sampling techniques for metal powders. Procedure A, for powders blended in mechanical blending equipment, involves taking three samples from the powder stream at intervals during the filling of containers; procedures B and C involve the use of different types of sampling thief.

Composition

Chemical composition is of vital importance to the powder metallurgist; not only does it influence the properties of the final product but it also affects the processing of the powder to that final form. The compacting operation, for example, is vitally dependent upon the plasticity and rate of strain hardening of the metal, and these in turn are related to the chemical composition. Alloy content and impurities also have a great effect on the sintering process by their influence on diffusion rates and, in some cases, the formation of liquid phases at the sintering temperature.

All the established techniques of chemical analysis are used on metal powders; indeed, because of their particulate nature, the analyst's task is often simpler than when analysing bulk materials. However, there are certain special tests which are applied to metal powders. For example, because of their high surface area, metal powders usually have a relatively high oxygen content and this may be determined by wet analysis[2] or, more usually, by weight loss after reduction in a stream of hydrogen.[3] Certain oxides, such as silica (and silicates), alumina, titania, chromium trioxide, magnesia, etc., are not reduced by hydrogen under the conditions of such a test and therefore must be determined by another method. Oxides such as silica (and silicates) that are insoluble in mineral acids may be determined by dissolution of the metal and weighing of the residue.

Although not often used as a production-control technique, X-ray analysis is useful in certain instances; for example, the determination of the ferrite content of certain austenitic stainless-steel powders, the detection of the W_2C phase (indicating undercarburizing) in tungsten-carbide materials, and the detection of certain unreducible oxide phases in various metal powders.

Particle Size, Particle Shape and Specific Surface

These three factors are interrelated since a decrease in particle size or a departure of particle shape from the spherical will lead to an increase in specific surface. The importance of these parameters arises from the influence they have on the basic operations of compacting and sintering. Very fine particles with an irregular shape, and therefore having a high specific surface, are desirable for sintering where high activity is necessary since, as we shall see later (Chapter 4), the driving force for bonding during the sintering operation is the excess energy due to the high surface area. However, very fine powders have certain disadvantages: they tend to have poor flow properties and give low apparent densities, two factors which are of great importance when compacting on automatic presses. Particle shape also affects flow properties and apparent density, spherical particles giving the best properties in both cases. Spherical particles, however, also have the poorest compacting properties since they provide no mechanical interlocking and have the smallest number of point contacts.

Particle Size

The simplest method of determining particle size is by direct measurement on the optical microscope, or by the use of the electron microscope for very fine powders. Although microscopy is resorted to in certain cases it is a slow and laborious technique and, because of the time taken to perform such measurements, it is only possible to use small samples, which means that the sampling technique must be extremely efficient. In practice the chief use of the microscopical method is to check the accuracy of other methods. Particle size is always expressed as a diameter, although only spherical particles have a true diameter, so that when measuring particles on the microscope, it is usual to report an 'average diameter'. With the optical microscope particles down to about 0·3 μ may be measured, whilst the electron microscope permits measurements in the range 10 to 0·001 μ.

All methods, other than microscopy, for the determination of particle size and particle-size distribution rely on some physical property of the particle, such as its ability to pass through an aperture of known dimensions (sieving) or its settling rate in a fluid of known viscosity (elutriation and sedimentation methods).

The most widely used method for determining the particle size of metal powders is sieving. Indeed, metal powders are usually divided into two distinct classes, 'sieve' and 'sub-sieve'. Sub-sieve particles are smaller in size than the aperture of the finest standard wire-mesh sieve, which is about 37 μ. Powders in the sieve range are often designated by the mesh size through which all particles in the batch will pass, for example, minus 100 mesh. Where a size distribution is required, however, this is indicated by giving the percentage of the sample which passes through one sieve but is retained on the next finest sieve, for example, minus 100 plus 150 mesh, 50%, minus 150 plus 200 mesh, 25%, minus 200 plus 270 mesh, 25%.

Woven-wire sieves are usually made of brass or bronze or, in some cases, stainless steel; and recently nylon sieve cloths have been introduced. The mesh number in most standard systems indicates the number of apertures per linear inch, although the nominal aperture for a given mesh number may differ slightly from one system to another because of differences in the wire gauge used. The nominal apertures, of interest in powder metallurgy, of the standard sieves of the Tyler and A.S.T.M. (U.S.) and the British Standards Institution are compared in Table 1.

Table 1. Nominal Apertures of Standard Sieves

Mesh number			Nominal aperture (micron)	Mesh number			Nominal aperture (micron)
Tyler	A.S.T.M.	B.S.		Tyler	A.S.T.M.	B.S.	
—	25	—	707	—	80	—	177
24	—	22	701	80	—	85	175
—	30	—	595	—	100	—	149
28	—	25	589	100	—	100	147
—	35	—	500	—	120	—	125
32	—	30	495	115	—	120	124
—	40	—	420	—	140	—	105
35	—	36	417	150	—	150	104
—	45	—	354	170	170	170	88
42	—	44	351	200	200	200	74
—	50	—	297	—	230	—	63
48	—	52	295	250	—	240	61
—	60	—	250	—	270	300	53
60	—	60	246	270	—	—	52
—	70	—	210	325	325	350	44
65	—	72	208	400	400	—	37

The values given in Table 1 are nominal apertures only; in fact no screen can be woven to the accuracy of a micron. The A.S.T.M. Standard[5] allows for variations in average opening of $\pm 5\%$ between 25 and 70 mesh, $\pm 6\%$ between 80 and 170 mesh and $\pm 7\%$ between 200 and 400 mesh, whilst the maximum permissible variation in individual openings is as much as $+60\%$ for mesh sizes below 170. Although many of the standard sieves have slightly different nominal openings some are, for all practical purposes, equivalents; for example, the A.S.T.M. 30 mesh is equivalent to B.S. 25 mesh and Tyler 28 mesh, while 60 mesh and 100 mesh are equivalent in all three systems. The nominal apertures of successive sieves in the A.S.T.M. series progress in the ratio $\sqrt[4]{2}:1$ and if every sieve in a given range is not used then it is customary to select every alternate or every fourth sieve to preserve a constant ratio.

Woven-mesh cloths are mounted on circular frames, and these are usually of 8 in. diameter for laboratory testing. For use in particle-size analysis sieves are placed in a stack or 'nest' in appropriate order (coarsest at the top) and are subjected to a particular type of vibration by a sieving machine. Such machines, besides shaking or vibrating the nest may also, in certain cases, provide a tapping action which serves to free the sieves of trapped particles that block the mesh. The sample of metal powder to be analysed (usually 100 g) is placed on the top sieve and the stack vibrated for a definite period, generally about 15 minutes. The amount of powder retained on each sieve is then determined by accurate weighing. Such a sieving method is recommended by the American Metal Powder Producers Association and is described in an M.P.I.F. Standard.[6]

It is now possible to produce sieves with accurate apertures down to about 5µ, by electrodeposition of nickel or copper on to photosensitized machine-ruled lines. Such sieves are in fact the subject of an A.S.T.M. Tentative Specification,[7] but they have not yet found wide use in powder metallurgy.

Two particular advantages of sieving for particle-size analysis are that as it uses a larger sample than other methods, it is less subject to sampling error and the method is rapid and easily used for production control. Sieving is a fractionating process, that is, it effectively separates the powder into fractions based on particle size. As such, therefore, sieving is used on a larger scale to process batches of powders so as to eliminate unwanted mesh sizes and to facilitate the reblending of a desired size distribution.

Of the many methods available for the determination of particle size in the sub-sieve range the most important are based on the fact that the settling velocity of a particle in a fluid varies with particle size. This relationship between particle size and settling rate is expressed by Stokes' law as follows:

$$u = d^2 \frac{(\rho_p - \rho_f)}{18\eta} g$$

where u is the terminal velocity of the particle, d the diameter of the particle, ρ_p the density of the particle, ρ_f the density of the fluid, η the viscosity of the fluid and g is the gravitational acceleration.

Stokes' law assumes streamlined flow of the fluid around the particles. Such conditions only apply for very small particles with low settling velocities; at higher velocities the flow becomes turbulent. The criterion of flow conditions is the Reynolds number which is given by:

$$Re = \frac{ud\rho_f}{\eta}$$

Stokes' equation holds if Re is less than 0·2, but at higher values the terminal velocities calculated from the equation will be too high, owing to the dragging effects of turbulent flow. Furthermore, Stokes' law is only strictly true for spherical particles, so that the sizing methods that are based upon it will only give the particle size of an equivalent sphere, i.e. the diameter of a sphere which would behave in the manner observed for the irregular particle, which is not necessarily the same as particles of equivalent mass or equivalent surface area.

Sedimentation methods of particle-size analysis rely on the different settling rates of the different sized particles, usually in a liquid medium. Several such methods have been developed and they differ mainly in the method used to determine the amount of particles having a certain settling velocity. For all these methods the powder sample is thoroughly dispersed in the liquid (usually at a relatively low concentration such as 0·5% by volume) and the amounts of particles with various settling velocities are determined by one of the techniques described below.

Direct weighing is the basis of the sedimentation balance in which a sensitive balance is located at the base of a liquid column containing the suspended particles. The weight of particles reaching the balance pan at various times may thus be determined; since the size of the particles reaching the balance at any particular time can be calculated from Stokes' law a particle-size distribution curve can be obtained.

Direct sampling of the suspension at a certain depth after various time intervals followed by drying and weighing, usually called the pipette method, is a fairly simple way of determining particle-size distribution. The Andreasen pipette is specially designed to carry out this procedure easily and rapidly, and is available commercially. A variation of this technique is to determine the density of the pipette samples using a hydrometer; this avoids the drying stage. The manometric method measures changes in the density of the suspension by measuring pressure changes at a certain depth.

Turbidimetric methods rely on the fact that part of a light beam passing through a suspension will be absorbed and scattered by the particles. In practice, a light beam is transmitted through a dilute suspension at a known depth below the surface and the variation in intensity of the transmitted light with time is measured photo-electrically.

The settling velocity of particles may be greatly increased by centrifuging and several methods have been employed, based on those described above, with the addition of centrifugal force. Such methods are particularly useful for very fine particles.

Whilst sedimentation methods involve the settling of particles in a fluid at rest, elutriation is based on a constant upward flow of fluid (usually air for metal powders); particles with a settling velocity below that of the rate of fluid flow will thus be carried away, while those with higher settling velocities will settle in the column. An elutriation column therefore acts in the same fractionating manner as a sieve since, for a particular flow of fluid, a cut is obtained at a particular particle size. Hence by passing the fluid, containing suspended particles, upwards through columns of different diameters (to vary the velocity) an apparatus analogous to a nest of sieves is obtained: this is the basis of the commercially-available Roller Air Classifier.[8]

Specific Surface

The total surface area of a mass of powder can be used to give an indication of the average particle size, provided certain assumptions are made as to the particle shape, although it gives no indication of the particle-size distribution. Two types of method, sorption and permeametry, are used for the determination of surface area.

Sorption methods rely on the fact that, under certain circumstances, molecules may become adsorbed on to the surface of powder particles to form monomolecular (or sometimes multi-molecular) layers. Thus gas adsorption techniques involve the determination of the amount of a gas required to form a monomolecular layer on the surface of a known weight of powder. It is usually necessary to carry out the determination at low temperatures (e.g. at the boiling point of the gas employed) since at higher temperatures 'chemisorption', rather than the desired physical adsorption, is likely to occur. It is possible then to calculate the number of molecules required to form the layer and from a knowledge of the area covered by a single molecule the total surface area may be obtained.

These methods are typified by that due to Brunauer, Emmett and Teller and known as the BET method. The use of this method and a somewhat improved apparatus have been well described by Lippens and Hermans.[9] The gas adsorption methods available for surface area determination have been ably reviewed by Joy.[10]

Many methods based on the sorption of dyes, radioactive isotopes, fatty acids, etc., from solutions have also been developed, but have not found such widespread use in the field of powder metallurgy as the gas adsorption methods.

Permeametry methods rely on calculation of the surface area from the resistance offered to a flowing fluid by a column of packed particles. The apparatus required is usually fairly simple, consisting of a chamber to contain the powder bed, a pump to force the fluid through the powder and gauges to indicate the fluid flow and pressure drop across the powder bed. The surface area is calculated from Carman's equation as follows:

$$S_0 = \sqrt{\frac{g/k \; K\gamma\epsilon^3}{(1-\epsilon)^2}}$$

where S_0 is the specific surface (cm^2/cm^3), g the gravitational constant (cm/sec/sec), k a proportionality constant with a value of 5, K a permeability constant (cm/sec), and γ is the kinematic viscosity of the fluid (stokes) and ϵ the fractional free volume (ratio of volume of voids to the total volume of the bed). By assuming maximum packing of uniform particles it is possible to derive an expression for the average particle size. Such methods are widely used in powder metallurgy, particularly as an indication of average particle size, because of the simplicity of the apparatus and the speed with which a result may be obtained. The Fisher Subsieve Sizer[11] is a commercially-available permeametric apparatus.

Particle Shape

The particle shape of most metal powders cannot be accurately described. The property is, however, of some importance. As was mentioned earlier it significantly affects compacting properties and, together with particle size, it determines the surface area and hence influences sintering activity. It is the general form (e.g. spherical, angular, irregular, etc.) which is of most importance in compacting, while surface area is related to the amount of fine surface detail as well as the general form. It is sometimes the practice to characterize particle shape by means of a 'shape factor', which is the ratio of surface area to particle size.

Further details of methods for determining the particle size, specific surface, etc., of fine powders are to be found in the book by Orr and Dalla Valle.[12]

Particle Microstructure

The numbers and amounts of the various phases, inclusions, etc., present in the microstructure of a metal particle are largely dependent upon the chemical composition, the composition and the distribution of the phases being determined mainly by the method of powder production. Internal closed porosity is often present in particles and such porosity can have pronounced effects on the behaviour of the powder during processing, particularly if it contains gases or liquids entrapped during the powder-production process. A knowledge of particle microstructure is important in many instances and may indicate the powder's likely behaviour during pressing and sintering.

Examination of particle microstructure follows well established techniques. Particles are usually set in a plastic matrix, ground back and polished and etched in the usual way. Such examination of the internal structure of particles is usually restricted to powders in the sieve-size range, although the structure of finer particles may be examined by use of the electron microscope.

Flow Rate

The rate at which a powder will flow under gravity through an orifice is of great technical importance. In most pressing operations the die is filled by the powder flowing under gravity; the powder must therefore flow quickly and evenly into the die if rapid rates of production and consistent compacts are

to be achieved. Good flow properties are also required of powders for continuous feeding into metal-spraying guns and, since in this case pressing
properties are not important, these powders are usually made as spherical as
possible. However, for most purposes powders which are not spherical are
required, because of their better compacting properties (an exception being
the production of certain filters with controlled porosity where a close graded
spherical powder is desirable). Flow properties are greatly affected by particle
shape and particle size and also by the presence of lubricants, moisture, etc.

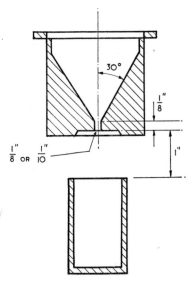

FIG. 3. The Hall Flowmeter and standard cup for determining flow rate
and apparent density. [13]

The standard test[13] for the determination of flow rate is the Hall Flowmeter (Fig. 3) which consists of an accurately machined conical funnel of 60°
included angle. The orifice at the base may be of 0·100 in. or 0·125 in. diam.
depending on the powder being tested. The funnel is usually made of brass
and is supported upon a rigid stand. The time taken for a weighed sample of
powder (usually 50 g) to flow from the funnel into a cup below is determined,
and the flow rate is then expressed in seconds, or in g/min if a non-standard
weight of sample is used.

Apparent Density

The apparent density of a powder is the weight of a unit volume, including
all voids between particles, internal porosity, etc. The value is obtained by

pouring the powder into a container of known volume under standard conditions; thus, in the standard test,[14] a sample of powder is poured through a Hall Flowmeter funnel into a 25-cm³ brass cup. If the powder will not flow freely through the standard Hall funnel then a somewhat similar type (Carney funnel) with a 0·200-in. orifice is used and the powder is agitated or pushed through the orifice with a length of wire.[15] The powder sample is greater than that required to fill the cup so that it overflows; excess powder is then removed by levelling off flush with the top of the cup and the cup tapped lightly to settle the powder and avoid spilling during transfer to a balance for weighing.

A non-standard test is to pour a known weight of powder into a graduated cylinder, tap the cylinder gently until no further settling is observed, and read off the volume. The density figure thus obtained is generally referred to as the 'tap density' and is higher than the 'apparent density' as obtained with the Hall Flowmeter and standard cup. However, tap density figures are not measured as a standard procedure, since they are liable to errors owing to segregation of fines or segregation of materials with different specific gravities.

Pressing Properties

The way a powder behaves when it is compacted in a die is dependent upon a large number of factors, including particle size, particle shape, chemical composition, plasticity and the presence of surface films. However, while the metal-powder parts producer may have a certain academic interest in the reasons for a powder's behaviour, his principal concern is to know exactly how it does behave during processing. In particular, the volume change that occurs on pressing at various loads must be known. The compression ratio, i.e. the ratio of the volume of powder poured into the die to the volume of the pressed part, is a means of expressing this information. Since the weight is the same in both cases this is equal to the ratio of the pressed density (green density) to the apparent density. A typical compressibility curve is shown in Fig. 4. A knowledge of the minimum load necessary to ensure a handleable green compact is also necessary in certain cases. This is termed the 'compactibility' of the powder.] Good compactibility is not necessarily synonymous with good compressibility since a rather brittle powder of low apparent density may have a high compression ratio but give a weak green pressing, and this may also apply to a plastic material, the particles of which have surface films preventing good adhesion.

Green Strength

The strength of a green (i.e. unsintered) compact may be determined in a variety of ways depending on the type of damage the part is likely to be exposed to during handling and transportation. Two types of test have become standard practice. The Rattler test determines the abrasion resistance of the green part by tumbling five standard specimens, $\frac{1}{2}$ in. diam. $\times \frac{1}{4}$ in. long, in a cylindrical barrel of 14 mesh bronze gauze ($3\frac{3}{4}$ in. diam. $\times 4$ in. long, and incorporating a steel baffle) at 87 rev/min for 1000 revolutions. The loss in weight of the specimens, as a percentage of their original weight, is thus a measure of their abrasion resistance. This test gives a good indication of the way sharp edges will withstand handling.

The second type of test determines the transverse-rupture strength of the green part[16] (Fig. 5 (a)). In this test the specimen fails due to surface tensile

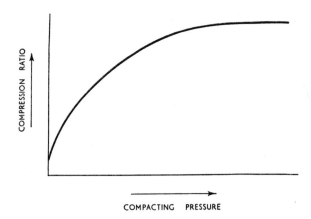

FIG. 4. Typical curve relating compacting pressure and compression ratio for metal powders.

stresses, S, the magnitude of which may be calculated from the simple formula:

$$S = \frac{3WL}{2bd^2}$$

where W is the applied load, L the distance between the outer supports, b the width of the specimen and d is the thickness of the specimen. The radial crushing test,[17] described later, is also used as a measure of green strength.

Green Density

The green density of regular cylinders or bars may be determined simply by calculation from their weights and dimensions or, for more complex shapes, by weighing in air and water. In the latter case it is necessary to seal the part by coating with lacquer or to impregnate with oil.[18] Occasionally the volume of a complex part is determined by displacement in mercury.

Green Spring

When a powder compact is ejected from a die it expands both radially and longitudinally, owing to elastic recovery of residual stresses. As will be shown later (Chapter 3) this may, in certain cases, lead to cracking of the compact. For the production of precision parts, it is essential to know the degree of 'green spring' on ejection in order that the dimensions of the die may allow for this. 'Spring' depends not only on the powder and the compacting load but also on the elastic properties and design of the die.

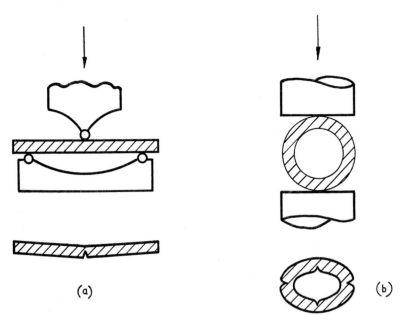

(a)   (b)

FIG. 5. Methods of determining the strength of green or sintered powder metal parts.
(a) Three-point transverse rupture test.
(b) Radial crushing test as applied to cylinders.

Sintering Characteristics

The manner in which a compacted powder behaves on sintering is usually determined by a simple measurement of the change in dimensions of a standard specimen when sintered under standard conditions. This shrinkage (or growth) is then expressed as a percentage of the unsintered length, or, in some cases, as a percentage of the sintered length. Test-pieces for sintering tests may be of any convenient regular shape, such as a rectangular block or a solid or hollow cylinder. However, it is essential to measure both the radial

and longitudinal (pressure axis) dimensions as changes may differ considerably in the two directions. The direct observation of changes during
sintering, for example by dilatometric methods or by changes in electrical
resistivity, is rarely practised in routine production control, although such
methods have been used in research.

Sintered Density

The methods used for the determination of sintered density are the same as
those already described for the determination of green density. A density
determination also indicates the percentage porosity of the material which
may be calculated from the following formula:

$$P=100\left(1-\frac{\rho_p}{\rho_s}\right)$$

where P is percentage porosity, ρ_p the density of the porous part and ρ_s is the
solid density of the material.

Sintered Properties

The transverse rupture[19] and radial crushing[17] tests are widely applied,
the latter particularly in the bearing industry. In the radial crushing test (Fig.
5 (b)) a minimum acceptable breaking load is specified and this is related to
the strength of the material by the following formula:

$$W=\frac{KLT^2}{(D-T)}$$

where W is the minimum acceptable breaking load (lb), K the minimum
acceptable strength constant (lb/in²), L the length of the cylinder (in.), T the
wall thickness (in.) and D is the outside diameter (in.).

When using the above tests it must be remembered that unless the material
is brittle and exhibits negligible plastic deformation to fracture, misleading
results will be obtained. Since many powder metallurgy materials are substantially non-ductile, both tests are very useful, speedy and simple. For
ductile materials a tensile test is to be preferred; machined specimens of
circular cross-section are often used, but pressed 'strip' specimens are usually
preferred for speed and simplicity.

Hardness measurements on powder metallurgy parts are usually misleading because of the effects of porosity. The macro-hardness of a porous body
in fact bears little relationship to the scratch hardness and is certainly no
indication of wear resistance. However, hardness measurements are occasionally specified since they are some indication of local density for a given
material. The Brinell and Rockwell tests are recommended by the American
M.P.I.F.[19]

In addition to the tests described above, special mechanical tests on specific parts may be arranged between producer and customer, such tests being devised from a consideration of service conditions.

Microstructure

The preparation of specimens and the examination of the microstructure of sintered materials follow the usual metallographic techniques. Materials containing residual porosity require certain precautions during both polishing and etching. Smearing of surface layers during grinding and polishing may cover up pores and make the material appear less porous than it actually is. During etching, the etchant tends to be absorbed in the pores and causes staining unless the specimen is washed very thoroughly. Electrolytic etching can overcome this difficulty in some cases, and where chemical etching is necessary staining may be avoided by impregnating the specimen with a resin prior to polishing. Besides indicating the amount and distribution of porosity, metallographic examination will also show the extent to which individual components of the powder mix have interdiffused, i.e. the homogeneity of the sample, the distribution of phases, grain size, the presence of oxides and other inclusions.

THE MANUFACTURE OF METAL POWDERS

The techniques used for the production of metal powders fall into two broad groups: (i) chemical and physico-chemical methods; (ii) mechanical methods. The complete production schedule for any particular metal powder may often involve techniques from both groups. For example, powders which have been obtained by chemical reduction of the oxide or other compounds are often further processed by mechanical comminution.

Chemical and Physico-chemical Methods

Reduction. In terms of total tonnage, reduction methods account for more metal powder than any other single technique. Oxides usually provide the raw material for reduction, although other compounds, such as oxalates, formates and halides, are occasionally used. It is very rare that an ore is sufficiently pure to be reduced directly and extensive concentration and purification is usually required.

Apart from thermodynamic considerations the choice of a reducing agent is largely a matter of convenience and economics. Carbon is the cheapest reducing agent, but it may be inconvenient because of the difficulty of accurately controlling the carbon content of the resulting powder. Hydrogen, and other atmospheres rich in hydrogen, are very convenient to use but are expensive and for very large scale production, as for example in the production of iron powder, the use of carbon is almost certainly an economic necessity. Metallic reducing agents are used in certain cases; for example the use of aluminium in the reduction of Cr_2O_3 and similar aluminothermic processes. Metallic reagents such as magnesium and sodium are also employed to reduce halide vapours such as $TiCl_4$ and $ZrCl_4$. In some cases metal hydrides, such as CaH_2, have been used as a source of very active 'nascent' hydrogen for the reduction of certain stable oxides.

Many reduction processes are carried out at temperatures high enough for the resulting metal particles to sinter together into a 'sponge'. Such sponges are usually easy to crush and mill to a powder suitable for use in powder metallurgy. Where reduction temperatures are not high enough to cause significant sintering as in the case of tungsten, then the resulting powder is only very lightly caked together. The particle size of the powder is then dependent upon a number of factors, the most important of which are: (i) the particle size of the oxide or other compound, (ii) the temperature of reduction and (iii) the reduction time.

In general, powders obtained by reduction methods are of fine particle size and have a high sintering activity. Because of their small particle size, porosity and irregular particle shape, they usually have low apparent densities and poor flow properties. Such characteristics are not necessarily present in powders produced by the comminution of sponges, where particle size and shape are determined by the mechanical treatment.

Displacement. The treatment of metal salts in solution is often a very convenient and economically attractive technique for the production of metal powders, because in many cases ore concentrates may be treated so that powder is produced as part of the extraction process. One method by which metal powders may be produced from solutions containing the metal ions is displacement by a less noble element.

There are a number of possible displacement reactions but only one, the precipitation of copper by iron, has been used on a commercial scale for the production of powders for use in powder metallurgy. Carefully cleaned steel scrap is generally used to displace the copper. It is necessary to control both the acidity of the solution and the flow of solution over the iron. Powders produced by this technique are very fine and of low apparent density.

In recent years, however, the reduction of metal ions in solution using hydrogen under pressure has become established as a viable technique for the production of metal powders. The technique is used for the preparation of nickel, copper and cobalt powders and the plant operated by Sherritt Gordon Mines Ltd., the best known example of this type of process, has been described in detail.[20] This method has also been applied to the production of coated powders,[21] and several ceramic and metal powders, having a coating of nickel on each particle, have been produced. Such powders are potentially useful for the production of cermets and dispersion-strengthened materials and have already proved of value in the spray-coating field.[22] The technique used at the Sherritt Gordon plant involves injecting hydrogen at about 200 lb/in^2 'over pressure' into autoclaves containing the heated purified solution (in the case of nickel this is nickel diammine sulphate at a temperature of 175°C). It is necessary to provide nuclei on to which the metal may precipitate and special 'seed' powder is made by the same process, but using ferrous sulphate as a nucleant. After the first 'densification' the powder produced is left in the autoclave and provides the nuclei for precipitation from subsequent batches of solution. The powder is removed when the desired particle size has been attained. It has been found difficult to produce powder coarser than about 100 mesh, because not only does this coarse powder lose its activity as a nucleant but it is also difficult to maintain it in suspension. Powders produced by this technique are very pure (usually about 99·8%); they have a rather spherical shape (botryoidal, Plate 1) and high apparent densities and flow rates.

Electrolytic Deposition. Metal powders may also be obtained from solutions (or fused salts) by electrolysis. According to the conditions employed the deposit may be either a brittle mass which can be pulverized, or of a loose, fluffy texture, easily converted to powder. In other cases the metal is deposited directly as a powder which falls from the cathode and collects as a sludge in the bottom of the bath. The conditions favouring such deposits (which would, of course, prove disastrous in normal electroplating) are high current density, low concentration of metal ions, high viscosity and high acidity. These conditions lead to a high rate of nuclei formation, suppression of growth parallel to the cathode surface and the evolution of hydrogen at the cathode, all of which favour a loose, fluffy deposit. When dense, brittle deposits for subsequent pulverization are required it is necessary to use a lower current density and an electrolyte of low acidity.

The electrolysis of fused salts always yields a powdery deposit, provided that the temperature of the bath is below the melting point of the metal; sintering of the deposit into a hard cake is prevented by entrapped salt. Very careful control of current density and metal ion concentration is necessary in order to achieve the desired grain size, since subsequent comminution by milling may be difficult owing to the softness of the deposits.

All electrolytically deposited powders must be carefully washed and dried to rid them of electrolyte or salt. Drying is often carried out in an inert atmosphere to avoid oxidation and, in many cases, is combined with an annealing operation.

The particle shape of electrodeposited powders is usually dendritic, and the particle size depends largely on the conditions pertaining during deposition.

PLATE 1

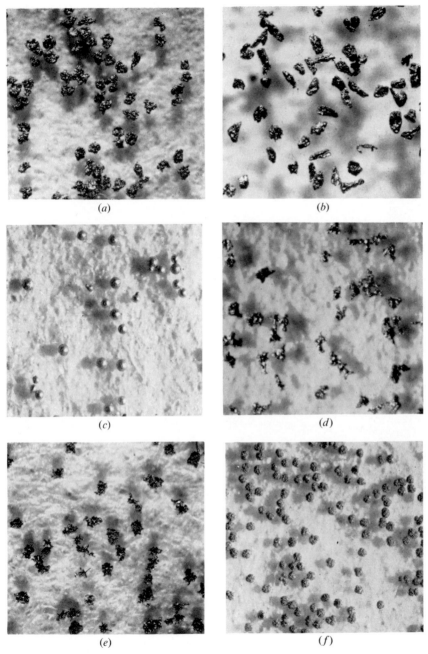

Particle shapes of metal powders produced by various processes (× 30).

(a) sponge iron (b) electrolytic iron
(c) atomized brass (d) atomized stainless-steel
(e) reduced tungsten (f) Sherritt-Gordon nickel

PLATE 2

(*a*) Double-cone blender for mixing metal powders.
(*Courtesy of B.S.A. Sintered Components Ltd.*)

(*b*) Typical die construction showing central hard insert supported by a tough backing ring.

(*Courtesy of B.S.A. Sintered Components Ltd.*)

PLATE 3

(a)

(b)

(a) A sub-press assembly fitted in a double-acting press. (*Courtesy of F. J. Stokes Ltd.*)

(b) Typical mechanical press for use with withdrawal-type tooling. (*Courtesy of Dorst Keramikmaschinen-Bau.*)

(c) Multiple-cam press for ejection-type tooling. (*Courtesy of F. J. Stokes Ltd.*)

(c)

PLATE 4

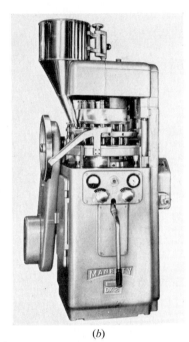

(a) (b)

(a) Modern, fully-automatic, multiple-cam press with two upper and three lower movements. (*Courtesy of F. J. Stokes Ltd.*)

(b) Rotary press for very high speed production. (*Courtesy of Manesty Machines Ltd.*)

(c) Hydraulic press for use with withdrawal tooling. (*Courtesy of Bussman-Simetag.*)

(c)

PLATE 5

(a) A batch-type sintering furnace. (*Courtesy of F. H. D. Furnaces Ltd.*)

(b) Continuous mesh-belt-type furnaces.
(*Courtesy of Royce Electric Furnaces Ltd.*)

PLATE 6

(*a*) Hump-back sintering furnace.
(*Courtesy of Royce Electric Furnaces Ltd.*)

(*b*) Mesh-belt furnace for handling large numbers of sintered engineering components.
(*Courtesy of B.S.A. Sintered Components Ltd.*)

PLATE 7

(a)

(b)

Selection of typical sintered engineering components. (See also Plate 8.)

((a) *By courtesy of B.S.A. Sintered Components Ltd., and*
(b) *S. M. C. Sterling Ltd.*)

PLATE 8

(*a*)

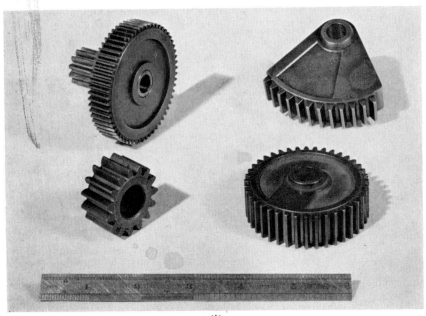

(*b*)

Further selection of typical sintered engineering components.

((*a*) *By courtesy of S. M. C. Sterling Ltd., and*
(*b*) *Sintered Products Ltd.*)

In the case of powders produced from dense, brittle deposits the shape is angular or needle-like and the size is a function of the mechanical methods used for subsequent pulverization. With the exception of powders deposited from fused salts, electrolytic powders are hard and require annealing before use. Perhaps their greatest advantage is their high purity and freedom from non-metallic inclusions, which generally implies good compacting properties.

Precipitation from the Vapour Phase. The reduction of halide vapours, such as $TiCl_4$, by metallic magnesium has already been mentioned under reduction processes. There are other methods, however, whereby metal powders may be obtained directly from the vapour phase; for example, zinc powder may be obtained by condensation of the metal vapour. There are also many possible reactions whereby metals may be obtained in powder or sponge form by the thermal decomposition of vapours. For example, zirconium has been produced by the van Arkel and de Boer method[23] in which the iodide is thermally decomposed on a hot filament. However, the only thermal decomposition process which has achieved commercial success in the powder production field is the carbonyl process for the production of iron and nickel powders. Carbonyls are volatile liquids* obtained by passing carbon monoxide over the metal, in sponge or other finely divided form, at moderate temperature (200°–270°C) and high pressures (up to 200 atm). Carbonyl vapours are decomposed at similar temperatures, but much lower pressures (about atmospheric), and the metal is precipitated in a very finely divided form. The particle size may be increased by subsequent decomposition of carbonyl using the original particles as nuclei. Carbonyl powders of interest in this field fall in the range 100 mesh down to 0.01μ, although most of the powders used lie between 20μ and 2μ. The iron powder produced by this technique is usually spherical, whereas carbonyl nickel powders tend to be somewhat irregular. Since this is a refining process the powders are very pure, except for carbon, oxygen and nitrogen which are picked up during processing and these may be reduced to low levels by an annealing treatment.

Intergranular Corrosion. This process, at one time, appeared promising for preparing alloys, particularly stainless steel, in powder form, but the advent of suitable atomization techniques has largely made the method obsolete. The intergranular corrosion technique, as described by Wulff,[24] consists of carburizing stainless-steel scrap at a suitable temperature (500–750°C) so as to cause precipitation of chromium carbide at the grain boundaries. The boundary areas of this 'sensitized' material are thus made susceptible to attack by corrosive solutions such as copper sulphate–sulphuric acid which, when used boiling, will cause disintegration of the stainless steel into a powder. It was later found[25] that more efficient disintegration could be obtained by making the stainless steel the anode in an electrolytic cell and

* The boiling points of Ni $(CO)_4$ and Fe $(CO)_5$ are 43°C and 107°C respectively.

3

using a copper sulphate–sulphuric acid electrolyte. The particles of this powder are of an angular shape with a size depending on the grain size of the sensitized scrap material.

Oxidation and Decarburization. The reaction between a metal carbide and its oxide, whereby both oxygen and carbon are eliminated as carbon monoxide leaving behind a relatively pure metal powder, has been used for the production of reactive metal powders, notably niobium. A similar reaction is used in the Mannesmann process for the production of iron powder where cast iron is atomized with compressed air. This powder is partially oxidized owing to the controlled conditions of atomization, and if batches of powder are carefully blended to control the carbon and oxygen contents it is possible to eliminate both these elements by heat treatment at about 950°C. The resulting cake of iron sponge is readily broken down by milling.

Mechanical Methods

Production of metal powders by mechanical means is accomplished either by the comminution of solid metals (machining, crushing or milling) or by disintegration of liquid metals.

Machining. Machining solid metals to produce turnings, chips, filings, etc., which may be further comminuted by crushing and milling, is used for the production of beryllium powder and powders of certain reactive metals such as magnesium, where other methods would involve the risk of explosion or fire. The method is, however, far too expensive to find wider application.

Crushing. Few metals are sufficiently brittle to be successfully broken down by crushing, although the method is widely used for the comminution of oxides and similar brittle compounds which may be subsequently converted to metal powders by reduction. Some metals may be embrittled to make them amenable to crushing; the addition of sulphur or a similar impurity, which will form a continuous and brittle grain boundary film, is a typical embrittling procedure. The crushed powder then has a particle size similar to the grain size of the cast (or hot-worked) material.

The metals of Groups IVA and VA are embrittled when heated to moderate temperatures in hydrogen. The brittle 'hydrides' so formed are easily crushed to powder, after which the hydrogen is removed by heating *in vacuo*.

All the usual types of crushing equipment, hammers, jaw crushers and gyratory crushers, may be used for crushing brittle metals. The powders produced are usually angular in shape and generally require further comminution by milling to make them suitable for processing by powder-metallurgy techniques.

Milling. The term milling covers a number of processes which have in common the fact that an impact force is brought to bear on the material being comminuted. In some of these methods, such as ball milling for example, the powder is tumbled in a container together with a number of large, hard, wear-resistant bodies which, by hitting the powder particles, tend to break them down. The mills may be rotated or vibrated in order to effect impact between balls and powder. Vibratory mills are stated to be extremely efficient and to produce equivalent comminution in a much shorter time than the rotary type.

A different type of action is provided by the Hametag Eddy Mill which, by means of rotating fans, imparts a high velocity to the powder particles so that they impact against each other. A similar technique is employed in the Micronizer in which high velocity jets of gas fling the particles against a surface or against each other.

Comminution of ductile metal powders is only achieved when the metal is embrittled by work hardening. The forces involved produce flake-like particles and are sufficient to cause the particles to weld together again. There is thus, for any given conditions, a terminal particle size which is obtained when the rate of breakdown equals the rate of agglomeration. A major feature of milling technology is therefore the control of this terminal particle size.

It is found that by wet milling, and by adding certain surface active agents, much finer sizes may be obtained. In the production of dispersion-strengthened materials extremely fine metal powders are required and the work of Quatinetz, Schafer and Smeal[26] has shown that inorganic salts, such as potassium ferricyanide, aluminium nitrate, cerium nitrate, etc., are more effective than the more usual organic 'surfactants'. In fact, using either cerium or aluminium nitrate and ball-milling under alcohol, these workers were able to reduce 2·5 μ carbonyl-nickel powder to an average particle size of 0·1 μ. The best of the organic surfactants used, stearic acid, gave an average size of 0·3 μ and other organic surfactants were unable to prevent a certain degree of agglomeration. Using potassium ferricyanide as a surfactant several other metal powders, including iron, nickel, silver, copper and chromium, were reduced to sub-micron sizes.

In some cases the milling operation combines comminution and blending; for example, the milling of carbide–cobalt mixtures in the production of cemented carbides causes the cobalt to become coated on to the carbide particles to a certain extent.

Because of the temperature rise, and the continual exposure of fresh active surfaces, metal powders are prone to oxidation during milling unless precautions are taken to eliminate oxygen from the mill. Milling under non-oxidizing liquids or in inert atmospheres will prevent gross oxidation.

The books by Rose and Sullivan,[27],[28] which deal with the theory and practice of milling, should be consulted for more detailed information on this subject.

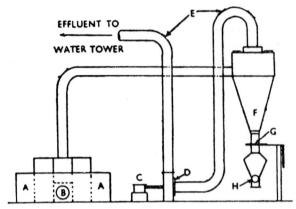

(a) General layout: A. melting furnace, B. atomizing
     unit, C. motor, D. fan, E. explosion vents, F. cyclone,
     G. shut-off slide valve, H. off-take rotary valve.

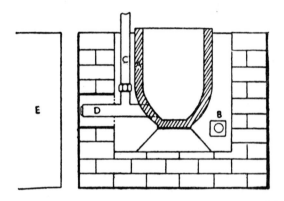

(b) Detail of atomizing unit: A. clay-graphite crucible,
     B. gas burner, C. compressed-air line, D. atomizing
     nozzle, E. collecting trunking.

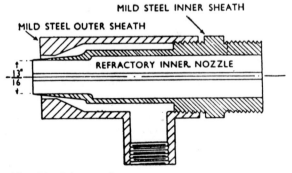

(c) Atomizing nozzle.

(Courtesy of the Institute of Metals)

FIG. 6. Apparatus used by Thompson[29] for investigating the
atomization of aluminium.

Shotting and Granulation. By pouring a molten metal through a screen, or similar device, the metal stream is broken up into a number of droplets. If these droplets then solidify during free fall spherical particles (shot) are obtained. If solidification is caused by contact with water then irregular granules result. Shot and granules are rather coarse and require further mechanical comminution to be suitable for use in powder metallurgy.

Atomization. In the atomization process a stream of molten metal is mechanically disintegrated by a jet (or jets) of high-pressure fluid. Until fairly recently atomization was limited to metals melting below about 1000°C and the atomizing medium was almost always compressed air or another gas. This type of process, which is still widely used, has been well described, as it is applied to aluminium, by Thompson.[29] This apparatus is shown in Fig. 6. Thompson's work is one of the few published studies of the variables involved in atomization and most of his conclusions seem to apply, in a general sense, to all forms of the process. Essentially Thompson concludes that since breaking up a certain amount of a metal into a given number of particles requires a definite amount of energy then (i) an increase in atomizing fluid pressure leads to an increase in atomizing efficiency, i.e. finer powders are produced, while (ii) increasing the metal head or nozzle diameter, both of which increase the metal flow, decreases the atomizing efficiency. However, most of the variables cannot be considered independently; for example an increase in air pressure leads to an increase in metal flow by its suction effect, although this is less apparent as the metal head is increased.

The suitability of atomization for producing alloy powders has led to its extension to the higher melting-point ferrous and nickel-base alloys. Early attempts to use systems similar to that described by Thompson were unsuccessful because of rapid failure of the refractory nozzle. Other methods for the atomization of ferrous and other high melting-point alloys have been reviewed by Watkinson,[30] who also describes a method which has been highly successful for alloy steels and nickel-base alloys. This process originated in Germany where the shortage of copper in World War II led to the development of methods for the production of iron powder by atomization (the usual copper shell driving bands were replaced by sintered iron). One of these, the D.P.G. method, relied on a number of rapidly-rotating blades to break up a stream of molten metal, the resulting droplets being rapidly cooled by a jet of water which surrounded the metal stream. The method was used for a number of years but was eventually abandoned, owing to the inherent disadvantages of metal freezing on the blades and excessive oxide-film formation on the particles. Oxide-film formation is used to advantage in a second German method, the Mannesmann process (Fig. 7). In this a stream of molten, low-silicon, cast iron is atomized by a spiralling annular jet of compressed air. Oxidation of the particle surface occurs but, with careful control of oxygen and carbon contents, a relatively pure iron powder can be produced by a heat treatment at 950°C. The process is still used for the production of iron powders but it cannot be applied to alloys containing reactive metals, such as chromium, aluminium and titanium, which form stable oxides.

The method of atomizing a freely-falling stream of molten metal, using an annular jet of compressed fluid, is the basis of the successful modern technique. If compressed air, or other gas, is used as the atomizing medium then the cooling rate of the molten droplets is sufficiently slow for surface-tension

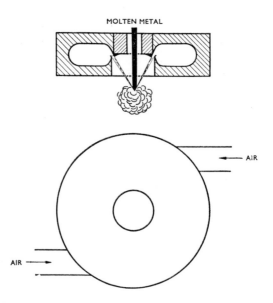

Fig. 7. Schematic representation of the Mannesmann process for atomizing liquid metals. (*Courtesy of the Institute of Metals*)

forces to spheroidize them before solidification occurs. Such spherical particles, although useful in the fields of porous-metal filters and metal spraying, are unsuitable for most powder metallurgy work. If water is used as the atomizing medium the droplet solidifies in its 'as-atomized' form, which is usually ragged or irregular (Plate 1). Even when water is the atomizing fluid nearly-spherical powder can be obtained by superheating the molten metal. Correct control of metal temperature, water pressure and tundish nozzle diameter is therefore necessary to obtain suitable powders.

COMMERCIAL PRODUCTION OF METAL POWDERS

Iron Powders

Most of the iron powder used for powder metallurgy is obtained by reduction and most of this by the Höganäs process. The Höganäs Company is fortunate in having access to relatively pure magnetite concentrates which are reduced by coke. The mixed ore, coke-breeze and limestone (to absorb sulphur) are packed into refractory saggers and heated to 1200°C. The result is a cake of iron sponge which is easily pulverized to powder. In order to provide a high-quality soft powder, for use in powder metallurgy, the pulverized iron is annealed in hydrogen, which, besides eliminating the effects of cold work due to the pulverizing operation, also lowers the carbon and oxygen contents. A similar process is also operated by the same Company's plant at Riverton, N.J.

Another process operated in the U.S.A. is the Pyron process in which carefully selected mill-scale is reduced with hydrogen. At first sight this would appear to be a very expensive method; however, cheap hydrogen may be available at the plant.

The Mannesmann process, which has already been described, is operated in both Germany and the U.S.A. The powder is more expensive than the Höganäs product but has fewer non-metallic inclusions and, therefore, is less abrasive to press tools.

Despite their relatively high cost, electrolytic iron powders find extensive use because of their high purity and outstanding pressing properties. The electrolytic method used by the Swedish Husqvarna Company has been described by Ljungberg.[31] A ferrous chloride electrolyte is used to which is added some ammonium chloride to increase conductivity. Current density is 3–6 amps/dm^2 and the stainless-steel cathodes remain in the bath for 3–6 days. The brittle deposit is stripped, comminuted by ball milling and annealed. Some typical properties of various reduced, atomized and electrolytic iron powders are given in Table 2.

A rather specialized electrolytic method is that used for the production of very fine (200 Å diameter) elongated particles for use in E.S.D. (elongated single domain) magnets. This method has been described by Luborsky, Paine and Mendelsohn.[32] The very fine, elongated dendrites are deposited from a ferrous-sulphate electrolyte into a mercury cathode which usually contains some dissolved tin to control particle shape.

The carbonyl process for the production of iron powders is described in a publication of the International Nickel Co. (Mond) Ltd.,[33] together with details of properties and applications of the powders. Crude iron powder, obtained by reducing crushed iron ore with hydrogen, is reacted with carbon monoxide under pressure, the gaseous iron pentacarbonyl, $Fe(CO)_5$, thus

Table 2. Some Typical Properties of Various Iron Powders

	Reduced	Atomized	Electrolytic
Chemical analysis (%):			
Fe	98	98·5	99
C	0·1	0·1	0·05
O	1·0	0·8	0·5
SiO$_2$	0·2	—	—
Si	—	0·1	0·02
S	0·02	0·03	0·01
P	0·02	0·03	0·01
Sieve analysis (%):			
(mesh)			
+70	—	—	3
−70+100	1	11	13
−100+140	20	25	25
−140+200	26	19	10
−200+230	10	15	10
−230+325	15	16	24
−325	28	14	15
Apparent density (g/cm^3)	2·3	2·5	3·2
Flow rate (sec)	33	25	25
Green density (g/cm^3)*	6·2	6·2	6·7
Sintered strength (tons/in^2)†	9·0	9·0	9·0
Elongation (%)†	8·0	8·0	7·0

* Compacted at 25 tons/in². † Sintered for 1 hour at 1150° C.

formed being subsequently decomposed by injecting into a heated free space. The fine, spherical iron particles collect at the base of the decomposer and the free carbon monoxide is drawn off for re-use.

Copper Powders

The major use of copper powder is in porous bronze bearings and, at present, electrolytic powder is preferred for this application. The production of electrolytic copper powder (E.C.P.) has been described by Mehl[34]; a dilute acid copper sulphate electrolyte and high current densities are employed. The plant is usually attached to an electrolytic copper refinery from which cast anodes are obtained. The cathodes may be copper, aluminium or lead sheets or rods. The 'as-deposited' powder is dendritic in shape and must be carefully washed to remove excess electrolyte. After drying, the powder is usually annealed in either a cracked ammonia or partially-burned town-gas atmosphere. The annealing operation results in some agglomeration and the resulting cake is pulverized by milling. Careful selection of the annealing temperature and milling conditions may thus be used to control the particle size. E.C.P. does not have the high purity usually associated with electrolytic powders, as it often contains a little lead and some silica from dust and anode slag inclusions.

Some copper powder is also produced by an atomization–oxidation–reduction technique. Ingot copper is atomized and then either fully or partially oxidized to a material which is conveniently milled; the oxide is then reduced by hydrogen. Such copper powder has an irregular shape and a spongy texture, and has been successfully employed, when mixed with electrolytic copper powder, for the production of porous bronze bearings.

The Sherritt Gordon process[20] is a potential source of cheap, relatively pure copper powder with properties similar to E.C.P. but, as yet, this has not found widespread use in powder metallurgy.

Copper powder produced by displacement with iron has found some use in the manufacture of sintered friction materials. However, its purity is insufficient for most other powder-metallurgy applications.

Nickel Powders

The chief source of nickel powder for the powder metallurgy industry is the carbonyl process; its main uses, at present, are in sintered magnets, sintered nickel–steels and sintered nickel–silver parts.

The method of production of carbonyl nickel is similar to that used for carbonyl iron. The resulting powder is of high purity, the main impurities being carbon and oxygen, with a particle shape which is rather irregular and spiky and not spherical as is carbonyl iron. Although most of the powders are smaller than 10 μ a special grade is also available in the range $-40/+325$ mesh. This latter powder has a much higher apparent density, $3 \cdot 5 – 4 \cdot 0$ g/cm³ compared with the $0 \cdot 5 – 2 \cdot 5$ g/cm³ of the finer grades. Six grades of carbonyl nickel powder are at present available.[35]

A little atomized nickel powder is produced, mainly for the manufacture of porous-metal filters. Some nickel powder is also produced by the Sherritt Gordon process.

Cobalt Powder

The major uses of cobalt powder are as a binder in cemented carbides and as a constituent of sintered magnet alloys. All the powder used in these applications is produced by reduction with hydrogen. The starting material is usually cobalt oxide but occasionally the oxalate or formate is used. The resulting product is a fine powder of spongy texture and of high purity, particularly if produced from the oxalate or formate.

Tungsten and Molybdenum Powders

Tungsten and molybdenum powders are produced by hydrogen reduction of their oxides WO_3 and MoO_3. In some cases tungstic acid, ammonium paratungstate or ammonium molybdate is used as the starting material. Relatively fine powders are usually required and, therefore, it is necessary to keep reduction times and temperatures to a minimum to avoid particle growth. Typical reduction temperatures are 950°C for tungsten and 1050°C for molybdenum, the exact temperature employed depending largely on the particle size of powder required. When a very fine particle size is required reduction is carried out in two stages: a first stage of 2–3 hours at 400–600°C, followed by about 4 hours at the higher temperature, i.e. about 950°C for tungsten and 1050°C for molybdenum.

Further details of the production of tungsten powder are given in Chapter 6, and Smithells[36] should be consulted for additional information. Commercial tungsten and molybdenum powders are of high purity (99·5–99·9%). Particle sizes vary widely depending on the intended application, but most powders fall in the range 0·1–20 μ.

Titanium and Zirconium Powders

Very little pure titanium or zirconium powder is employed in powder metallurgy, the consumable-electrode arc-melting method having proved so effective that the solid metals are obtained in very good quality by this means. Small amounts of both metals are, however, used in powder form, usually as additions in the preparation of special alloys.

Most of the powders available are produced by the Kroll method of reduction of the tetrachloride with magnesium. In the case of titanium the resulting sponge, which contains some magnesium chloride and magnesium, is crushed and leached with dilute hydrochloric acid. This method is not recommended for zirconium sponge because of its explosive reaction with water. For zirconium a vacuum treatment is used to remove magnesium and its chloride, followed by hydrogenation and crushing of the hydride. The hydride is decomposed by heating *in vacuo*. A pure titanium powder may also be produced by this method.

Miller,[37] reviewing the methods available for the production of these metal powders, also mentions the use of reduction of the oxides with calcium or calcium hydride and electrolysis of fused salts, but neither method is used on a large scale.

Tantalum and Niobium Powders

Considerable amounts of tantalum are processed to wire and sheet by mechanical working of pressed and sintered bars. Some niobium is also processed in this way. The methods of preparation of both metals in powder form are similar and these have been described by Miller.[37] For tantalum the preferred methods appear to be electrolysis of fused potassium–tantalum fluoride, or reduction of the same salt with sodium. The former method gives a rather coarse powder, while sodium reduction provides a much finer product. Both powders are rather high in carbon, oxygen and nitrogen, typical figures being 0·15%, 0·30% and 0·50% respectively.

The major method employed for the production of niobium powder is the production of niobium carbide by heating the oxide with carbon, followed by reaction of the crushed carbide with more oxide under vacuum at 1600°C. Early attempts to produce niobium powder by electrolysis of fused salts gave a poor product, but more recently improved methods have shown great promise in this direction.

High-grade powders of both metals may be obtained by taking the product of one of the reduction methods and subjecting it to a high-temperature vacuum treatment to remove impurities, such as carbon, oxygen and nitrogen. This is then followed by hydrogenation, crushing and milling. A final vacuum treatment at 1200–1400°C removes the absorbed hydrogen.

Beryllium

Because of its extreme brittleness in the cast form, beryllium is usually processed by the techniques of powder metallurgy. Miller[37] discusses two methods for the production of beryllium powder, electrolysis of fused berillium chloride dissolved in sodium chloride and reduction of beryllia with magnesium. In the latter method, however, the temperature is raised, after reduction, to the melting point of beryllium to ensure good separation of metal and salt. The resulting beryllium 'pebbles' are usually melted and vacuum cast, the cast billet then being machined to chips which are subsequently milled to powder in an inert atmosphere.

Aluminium Powder

The use of aluminium powder in powder metallurgy is limited at present to the production of dispersion-hardened aluminium (S.A.P.) and some porous bearings. The aluminium powder used for the production of S.A.P. is a flake-like material produced by milling, usually in the eddy mill. The starting material is obtained by atomization or granulation. Atomization provides a powder suitable for porous bearings.

Lead Powder

Lead powder is produced by an air atomization technique similar to that employed for aluminium powder. Such powder is widely used in the production of bearings and sintered friction materials.

Zinc Powder

There are few uses for zinc powder in powder metallurgy, its high volatility leading to high losses on sintering. The powder is used for certain bearing materials and sometimes for the production of brass parts. Zinc powder may be obtained by condensation from the vapour, although the atomized product is more suitable for the techniques of powder metallurgy.

Tin Powder

Large quantities of tin powder are used for the production of porous bronze bearings and in the manufacture of sintered friction materials. Tin powder may be produced by electrolysis of a stannous–chloride solution, by displacement from solution with zinc, or by atomization. Atomized tin is generally suitable, and is less costly than that produced by other methods.

Alloy Powders

Alloy parts are produced by one of the following methods: (i) mixing individual elemental powders, (ii) using completely homogeneous pre-alloyed powders, each particle having the desired composition or (iii) mixing elemental and 'master-alloy' powders.

Method (i) has several advantages. Elemental powders are usually softer and more plastic than pre-alloyed material and therefore have better pressing properties. If one of the constituents is of low melting point, liquid-phase sintering is possible which leads to high sintered densities. There are, however, many instances where the use of elemental powders must be avoided. For example, one metal may be lost by volatilization, or the interdiffusion during sintering is so slow that a sufficiently homogeneous product is not obtained in economic sintering times. Also, where one component has a high affinity for oxygen, etc., pre-alloying will reduce its activity. Since pre-alloyed powders are expensive method (iii) is an economic compromise used in many instances. This method often has a further advantage in that the master alloy may be a low-melting composition to facilitate liquid-phase sintering.

The most widely-used alloy powders are brass and stainless steel, which are produced by atomization. Atomization is also used for the production of many other pre-alloyed powders, including various nickel- and cobalt-base high-temperature alloys, Stellites and other hard-facing alloys, nickel-copper alloys, certain magnetic alloys such as Permalloy, and high-speed steels. The process can be controlled to give an irregular particle shape for good pressing characteristics.

Because many of the master alloy compositions are extremely brittle they may be conveniently produced in powder form by casting, crushing and milling. In some cases a coarse powder is first produced by atomization which is later comminuted. The chemical and electrolytic disintegration techniques for the production of pre-alloyed powders have now been displaced by atomization.

Electrolytic co-deposition has been used to produce alloy powders, but the products are rarely completely homogeneous and the method is not used on an industrial scale.

Intermetallics and other compounds can be produced by solid-state (or sometimes by metal-gas) chemical reactions. The most important of such compounds are the carbides, and the methods by which these are produced are described in Chapter 6.

TREATMENT OF METAL POWDERS

Metal powders sometimes require pre-treatments to render them more suitable for subsequent processes. Annealing to remove the effects of cold work and increase plasticity is a pre-treatment already mentioned. It is usual to carry out annealing in a reducing atmosphere so that any oxide films which may be present are removed. Hydrogen may be removed from electrolytic or hydrided powders by a heat treatment, sometimes *in vacuo*.

Another form of heat treatment, spheroidization, is concerned with modifying the particle shape. Although irregularly-shaped particles are generally preferred for pressing operations there are certain applications, notably in filter production, where spherical particles are desirable. Since few powder production methods give a spherical particle it is necessary to obtain this by a further treatment. Although spheroidization is not yet carried out on a large scale, the problem has been investigated by several workers. A number of spheroidization methods have been proposed. The most popular method seems to be to allow the particles to fall freely through a heated space in which they melt and spheroidize; further fall through a cooler zone allows solidification of the spherical particle. Wahll, Van Orsdel and Fischer[38] used vertical, molybdenum-wound or carbon-tube furnaces for their work, while with a plasma torch Hedger and Hall[39] were able to spheroidize even molybdenum and tungsten powders.

Where very fine powders have to be used it may be necessary to improve apparent density and flow rate by agglomeration. The usual technique employed is to press the powder into bars, which are subsequently broken down to the desired agglomerate size. It is also possible to achieve a certain degree of agglomeration of ductile powders by ball milling without additions of surfactants, the particles tending to cold weld together into rather flaky agglomerates which then require annealing.

Some form of blending or mixing operation is almost invariably required prior to pressing in order to obtain as homogeneous a product as possible (Plate 2 (a)). Even if all particles are of the same composition it is desirable to blend to ensure that the various mesh sizes are not segregated. Blending powders of different composition may also lead to difficulties if there is a marked difference in their densities. Such problems may be overcome by wet mixing or by the addition of small amounts of organic substances, which cause adhesion between particles and prevent segregation. A mixture of liquid paraffin and petroleum jelly has been used very successfully to prevent segregation of diamond particles from the matrix powder in the preparation of diamond tools.

REFERENCES

1. *M.P.I.F. Standard* 1–61.
2. *M.P.I.F. Standard* 7–61.
3. *M.P.I.F. Standard* 2–48.
4. *M.P.I.F. Standard* 6–54.
5. *A.S.T.M. Standard* E11–61.
6. *M.P.I.F. Standard* 5–62.
7. *A.S.T.M. Tentative Specification* E161–60T.
8. *M.P.I.F. Standard* 12–51.
9. Lippens, B. C. and Hermans, M. E. A. *Powder Metallurgy*, No. 7, 66 (1961).
10. Joy, A. S. *Vacuum* III, 3, 254 (1953).
11. *M.P.I.F. Standard* 32–60.
12. Orr, C. Jun. and Dalla Valle, J. M. *Fine Particle Measurement*, Macmillan (1959).
13. *M.P.I.F. Standard* 3–45.
14. *M.P.I.F. Standard* 4–45.
15. *M.P.I.F. Standard* 28–59.
16. *M.P.I.F. Standard* 15–62.
17. *British Standard* 1131: Part 5.
18. *M.P.I.F. Standard* 8–50.
19. *M.P.I.F. Standard* 13–62.
20. *Powder Metallurgy* No. 1/2, 40 (1958).
21. Meddings, B., Lund, J. A. and Mackiw, V. N. *Canadian Mining and Metallurgy Bull.*, 525 (July 1963).
22. Sheppard, A. J. *British Welding Journal*, **10**, 12, 603 (1964).
23. Van Arkel, A. E. and de Boer, J. H. *Z. anorg. chem.*, **148**, 345 (1925).
24. Wulff, J. in *Powder Metallurgy*, J. Wulff (ed.) A.S.M. Cleveland, 137 (1942).
25. Marshall, P. R. Symposium on Powder Metallurgy, 1954 (*Special Rept. No. 58*), 181, 1956, London (Iron and Steel Institute).
26. Quatinetz, M., Schafer, R. J. and Smeal, C. *Trans. Met. Soc., A.I.M.E.*, 221 (6 Dec. 1961).
27. Rose, H. E. and Sullivan, R. M. E. *A Treatise on the Internal Mechanics of Ball, Tube and Rod Mills*, Constable, London (1958).
28. Rose, H. E. and Sullivan, R. M. E. *Vibration Mills and Vibration Milling*, Constable, London (1961).
29. Thompson, J. S. *J. Inst. Met.*, **74**, 101 (1948).
30. Watkinson, J. F. *Powder Metallurgy*, No. 1/2, 13 (1958).
31. Ljungberg, I. *Powder Metallurgy*, No. 1/2, 24 (1958).
32. Luborsky, F. E., Paine, T. O. and Mendelsohn, L. I. *Powder Metallurgy*, No. 4, 57 (1959).
33. *Inco-Mond Carbonyl Iron Powders*, The International Nickel Company (Mond) Ltd., London (1962).

34. Mehl, E. *Powder Metallurgy*, No. 1/2, 33 (1958).
35. *Mond Carbonyl Nickel Powders*, The International Nickel Company (Mond) Ltd., Publication No. 2600, London (1964).
36. Smithells, C. J. *Tungsten*, Chapman and Hall, London (1952).
37. Miller, G. L. *Powder Metallurgy*, No. 1/2, 53 (1958).
38. Wahll, M. J., Van Orsdel, J. R. and Fischer, R. B. *Powder Metallurgy*, No. 8, 48 (1961).
39. Hedger, J. H. and Hall, A. R. ibid., 65.

CHAPTER 3

SHAPING OF METAL POWDERS

When components are being manufactured from metal powders it is necessary both to shape the powder into the required form and to bond the particles together into a strong useful body. Generally the shaping operation will impart only sufficient strength to facilate handling of the component. It is the subsequent sintering operation that imparts the final strength. Loose sintering and hot pressing are exceptions in that shape and strength are obtained in one operation.

There are many ways of shaping metal powders, although few of them are of much commercial importance. A convenient grouping of the various processes is: (i) pressureless forming, (ii) pressure forming cold and (iii) pressure forming with heat.

The pressureless-forming methods are those in which no external forces, other than the constraint of the mould walls, gravity and atmospheric pressure, are applied. Included in this class are loose sintering, slip casting and slurry casting, and of these only loose sintering finds much application in powder metallurgy.

The cold pressure-forming processes are the most widely used for shaping metal powders; they include pressing in metal dies, vibratory compacting, cyclic compacting, powder rolling, isostatic pressing, explosive forming, forming with binders and cold working of preformed blanks.

Hot forming methods include hot pressing in metal or graphite dies, conventional hot working of preformed blanks or loose powders and hot isostatic pressing.

Of the many shaping methods listed above cold pressing in metal dies is the most widely used industrially, because it lends itself admirably to automation and mass production. Some of the other methods, such as vibratory compacting and hot isostatic pressing, are very much in their infancy and have yet to be used commercially.

PRESSURELESS FORMING

Loose Sintering

Loose sintering is the simplest method of shaping metal powders and it has been used quite widely for the manufacture of highly porous metals. Basically, metal powder is poured or vibrated into a mould which is then heated to the sintering temperature. The form and complexity of shape which can be made by this method depend to a large extent on the flow characteristics of the powder. Additionally, since shrinkage usually takes place during sintering, only shapes where this can occur without mould constraint causing cracking can be used. In this respect the process is analogous to metal casting, and, as in die casting, the component must be removable from the mould after sintering.

The characteristics required of the mould material for loose sintering are: (i) it should be easily machined or formed into the required shape, (ii) it should withstand the sintering temperature without appreciable deformation (or at least contain the metal powder until sufficient strength has been obtained by sintering for self support) and (iii) it should not weld to the powder during sintering. For most applications machined or welded metal moulds are used, although graphite may also be employed where no reaction with the powder is likely, and even here a refractory mould wash may suffice to prevent reaction. Mould washes may also be used to prevent powder welding to metal moulds, although where alloys containing chromium are used a pre-oxidation treatment may be carried out to give an unreducible oxide skin which prevents welding of particles to the mould. Since no pressure is applied to the powder any unreducible oxide skin on the particle will prevent metal-to-metal contact and inhibit sintering. For this reason it is virtually impossible to loose sinter aluminium powder. Although loose sintering is mostly used for the production of highly porous bodies (see Chapter 8), it is also possible to produce high-density components by this method. Careful choice of particle-size distribution can give packed densities of over 80% of the solid, so that shrinkage on sintering to near theoretical density is not too high.

Slip Casting

Slip casting is a ceramic fabrication technique which has been used for many years. Essentially a casting slip is a suspension of fine particles in a liquid medium. The particles are usually finer than 5 μ. Particles coarser than 20 μ are rarely used in slips because of their high settling velocity. Generally

4

deflocculating agents are added to slips to prevent aggregation of particles. According to the theory developed for clay slips, particles develop mutually-repellent charges owing to adsorption of charged ions. Certainly many workers have shown that pH value (a measure of the ion concentration) has a marked effect on viscosity. Deflocculents are usually added to bring the pH to a value giving a minimum viscosity, and by this means a maximum solids content may be employed.

In recent years considerable work has been carried out on the slip casting of non-clay substances, such as pure oxides (see for instance St. Pierre[1]), and this has also been extended to metal powders (see Hausner and Poster[2]). Most slips are prepared with water, but when reactions with the powder are likely, other liquids, such as absolute alcohol, may be used. Prepared slips are poured into absorbent moulds made by casting plaster of Paris around a metal or wooden pattern. The rate at which liquid is extracted from the slip depends on a number of factors, such as the original plaster composition. (Plaster compositions are usually referred to by the weight of water added to 100 parts by weight of plaster. Plasters in the range 70–80 are most generally used.) The initial dryness of the mould also affects liquid extraction rate (or casting rate) and moulds are often wetted so that the casting rate is not too high.

Although solid articles may be slip cast, the process is more often used for hollow shapes when the drain-casting method is used. In drain casting, after the slip has stood in the mould for a time determined by experience, the excess is poured out leaving a hollow casting. Castings are left to dry for some time in the mould, when they shrink away from the mould walls, thus facilitating their removal. Slip casting has not been widely used for metal powders as yet, probably because their plasticity makes pressing more convenient. However, Lidman and Rubino[3] have shown that by using additions of ammonium alginate and polyvinyl alcohol as binders rather coarse stainless-steel powders may be satisfactorily slip cast. The slip-casting process has been more widely used for the production of shapes in metal-ceramic mixtures (cermets).

The disadvantages of slip casting, which have limited its applications so far, are its slowness and relatively high cost. Capital outlay is not high because the equipment is simple, but the process is operated by craftsmen and is not suited to mass production.

Slurry Casting

Slurry casting is really only a version of slip casting, although the slurries usually contain various binders and the moulds may be non-absorbent. Freezing of the liquid medium has been used[4] and slurries have been sucked or injected into the moulds. The advantages and limitations are similar to those of slip casting.

COLD PRESSURE FORMING

Pressing in Metal Dies

As might be expected from the wide commercial application of the process much work, both theoretical and practical, has been carried out in attempts to explain exactly what occurs when a metal powder is compacted in a metal die. Goetzel,[5] and more recently Jones,[6] have provided excellent surveys of this type of work and the reader wishing to delve more deeply into the theoretical aspects of die pressing is recommended to consult these works and the further references contained therein.

When a metal powder is poured into a die it will take on a certain packing density (see Chapter 2), which is to a large extent a function of the powder mixture itself, i.e. particle-size distribution, presence of lubricants, particle shape, etc., but which may also be affected by the shape of the die and the manner of filling. When the first slight pressure is applied by the punch or punches (Fig. 8 (a)) the first densification occurs by movement of particles to provide a better packing density. The extent to which this occurs depends largely on those factors discussed above; for instance, fine powders having poor flow properties are liable to form bridges and the first slight pressure will tend to cause their collapse. An additional effect of interparticle movement is to cause abrasion of the surface films (oxide, adsorbed water vapour, CO_2, etc.), which are present on almost all metal particles. These films must be removed before direct metal contact can take place. Some of the film may be rubbed off by particles moving over each other, while increasing pressure tends to break-up the films which are usually more brittle than the underlying metal. The initial areas of contact between particles are so small that, even at very low punch loads, pressures on these areas are high, which means that surface films at the areas of contact are soon broken.

When metal-to-metal contact is established 'cold welding' takes place, a term used to describe the adhesion which occurs when two clean surfaces are brought into intimate contact without the application of heat. At this stage the compact is beginning to gain some strength, although it is unlikely that this initial bonding would stand the stresses of ejection from the die. Further pressure is now required to cause plastic deformation of the particles, extend the areas of contact and increase strength and density. With some powders density may increase after the initial packing stage without plastic deformation. The sharper asperities of irregularly shaped particles may be sheared off under increasing loads, while particles of brittle or rapidly work-hardening materials displaying little plasticity may also suffer fracture. These phenomena tend to alter particle-size distribution and thereby increase packing density. In fact for very brittle materials displaying no plasticity, particle fracture and repacking is the only mechanism of densification.

A typical plot of pressing load against density is shown in Fig. 8 (*b*). As the punch load increases further densification is increasingly hindered by

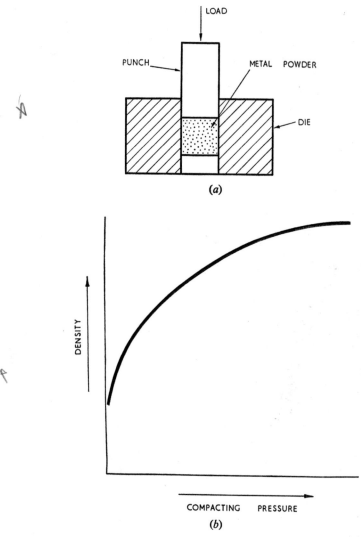

FIG. 8. Die pressing.
(*a*) Apparatus for die compaction.　(*b*) Typical pressure-density curve.

work hardening of the particles and by friction. Work hardening is an inherent property of the material being compacted, and there are only two methods of reducing its effects: (i) by raising the temperature and (ii) by changing to another material. Both methods are used in special cases. Hot pressing is used for difficult materials and where very high densities are required. A change from pre-alloyed to mixed elemental powders may give better pressing properties. Normally work hardening has to be accepted and, if further densification by pressing is necessary, the part is repressed or coined after sintering; sintering serves as an annealing treatment.

Frictional forces between the powder and the die wall can become sufficient to inhibit the transmission of pressing loads throughout the compact and the general effect is a variation in density throughout the compact. The density decreases with increasing distance from the punch face and there is also a density distribution in the horizontal plane due to frictional effects dropping-off away from the die wall. The total effect is to give a density distribution of the general form shown in Fig. 9 (a).

It is apparent that with increasing length to cross-section ratios it becomes increasingly difficult to densify the lower end of the compact. In fact it has been shown that in extreme cases it is possible to form a coherent compact at the top of a die whilst merely supporting the powder in the lower end with a piece of cigarette paper. To improve this situation pressure can be applied from both ends of the die, thus effectively halving the length to cross-section ratio. Fig. 9 (b) shows a typical density distribution when double-ended pressing is used.

The second method of improving pressure transmission is to reduce frictional effects by using a lubricant. Many workers have shown that the application of lubricant to the die walls is as effective in improving green density, as is the admixture of lubricant with the powder, and this implies that interparticle movement is not always a major mechanism in densification. There are many disadvantages in the addition of lubricant to the powder, among which are the following:

(1) Adding the lubricant to the powder is an extra handling operation that increases costs.

(2) If the lubricant is added as a solution for better distribution (Chapter 2) then a further operation is needed to remove the solvent.

(3) Much more lubricant is required to obtain the same effect when it is added to the powder, compared with direct application to the die walls.

(4) Lubricants usually reduce the powder flow-rate and can lead to difficulties in feeding and consistent die filling.

(5) Owing to their essential property of sustaining pressure without breakdown, films of lubricant tend to prevent, or at least to reduce, metal-to-metal contact, thus reducing cold welding and hence lowering green strength. Where the amount of lubricant is high it may become the continuous phase and is then more in the nature of a binder. In this case the strength of the

compact is really the strength of the lubricant. This condition is often met in the pressing of brittle materials such as carbides; as much as 20% of paraffin wax may be added to tungsten carbide–cobalt mixtures, for instance, when the cobalt content is low.

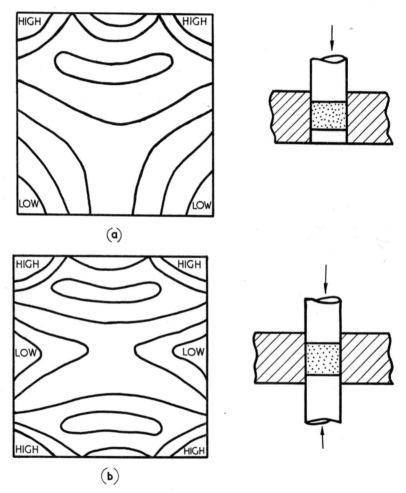

FIG. 9. Density distributions obtained by die compacting.
(a) Single-ended pressing.   (b) Double-ended pressing.

(6) Lubricants usually undergo quite high volume compressions during pressing; this gives rise to high internal stresses which may cause cracking during ejection.

(7) The low density of lubricants in relation to that of metals means that they occupy a relatively large volume of the compact and in some cases this may have the effect of lowering the overall green density. In most cases however, the reduction of friction offsets this effect.

(8) Lubricants are removed either during sintering, when they may contaminate the sintering furnace, or by a separate operation prior to sintering. The latter method (often called de-waxing) has the advantage that it may be possible to recover all or part of the lubricant.

(9) There are many cases where the lubricant or its residue may react with the metal during sintering with possible adverse effects on the properties of the final product.

Despite these disadvantages it is standard commercial practice to mix lubricants with the powder. In the laboratory, and in the production of very large parts where production rates in terms of numbers of components are low, it is perfectly feasible to apply lubricant to the die walls. However, no method has yet been devised whereby die walls may be lubricated satisfactorily during high-speed pressing, other than by the prior addition of lubricant to the powder.

In practice many of the disadvantages mentioned above are minimized by the correct choice of type and quantity of lubricant. Apart from improving density distribution, lubricants are beneficial in other respects. They improve die life and also decrease the load required to attain a specific density, so that overall pressure requirements are lowered. The advantages of lubricants far outweigh their disadvantages and they are added to most industrial powders prior to die pressing. Amongst the lubricants in common use are various waxes such as paraffin wax, 'Acrawax', 'Carbowax',* etc., and stearic acid and various stearates, such as those of calcium, lithium, aluminium, magnesium, lead and zinc. Graphite also provides good lubrication, although its use is restricted to those instances where carbon additions are required, or the presence of carbon does not adversely affect the properties of the part.

A powder mass does not behave like a true fluid in that the applied pressure is not transmitted uniformly throughout the compact. Besides the effects on density already discussed this also affects the radial pressure transmitted to the die walls. If the die contained a fluid the pressure on the die walls (Pr) would equal the applied pressure (Pa), i.e. true hydrostatic conditions. With metal powders the stress distribution within the compact is quite complex and it is virtually impossible to calculate accurately the radial pressures exerted on the die. Some interesting theoretical and practical work has been carried out, particularly by Long[7, 8] and Bustamante and Sheinburg[9] who have shown that the Pr/Pa ratio can reach quite high values and in

---

* 'Acrawax' is a trade name of Glyco Chemicals Inc., 'Carbowax' is a trade name of Union Carbide Corp.

some instances approaches unity (hydrostatic conditions). It is apparent
from the above work that Pr/Pa increases with increasing density, i.e. as compaction proceeds the percentage of the applied load transmitted to the die
walls increases. The radial pressures developed lead to elastic deformation of
the die and compact, while the compact also deforms plastically (in most cases).
When the punch load is released the elastic deformations will try to recover
and it is likely that the radial elastic contraction of the compact will be less
than that of the die, since some of the compact expansion is due to plastic
deformation. Because of this the die grips the compact tightly which inhibits
the axial elastic expansion of the compact and gives rise to the following
effects: (i) a definite pressure is needed to eject the compact from the die,
(this is somewhat reduced by the use of lubricants), and (ii) radial and axial
expansions of the compact occur as it is ejected. Such expansions must be
allowed for when die dimensions and punch movements are determined.
Jones[6] gives some typical figures for elastic expansion of compacts made in
electrolytic copper and Swedish sponge-iron. These figures, which represent
the increases in length and diameter of compacts compared with the dimensions of the unstrained die cavity, are shown in Table 3.

Table 3. The Relationship between Elastic After-expansion and Compacting Pressure
for Iron and Copper Powders[6]

	Compacting pressure (lb/in²)	Increase in length (per cent)	Increase in diameter (per cent)
Copper	11,200	0·599	0·168
	44,800	0·368	0·172
	89,600	0·660	0·258
Iron	11,200	0·465	0·156
	44,800	0·835	0·280

Elastic expansion on ejection can lead to cracking of the compact if the
release of stresses and the sudden expansion break the interparticle bonds.
Brittle materials are prone to a particular form of cracking, known in the
pharmaceutical field as 'capping'. Capping takes the form of a cone-shaped
piece of the compact which breaks away as shown in Fig. 10. Long[7] maintains that this type of cracking is due to the centre of the compact being
relatively free to expand axially, while expansion of the outer portions is
restricted by die-wall friction. When cracking occurs in ductile metal compacts it generally takes the form of laminations parallel to the punch faces.
Powder blends containing large percentages of fine particles are more prone
to the defect, probably due to the large volume of air entrapped in them. As
mentioned previously, lubricants may aggravate cracking tendencies, because
they have a large volume expansion on release of pressure and they also

lower compact strength. However, they lower die-wall friction and so tend to reduce internal stresses. Pressing cracks may be minimized and ejection made easier by incorporating a slight taper in the die mouth, so that elastic expansion takes place progressively. Also anything which increases green strength (see Chapter 2) will minimize this type of cracking.

Tool and Press Design

Tooling Principles. As shown earlier, owing to the effect of die-wall friction it is usually necessary to apply pressure to both ends of a compact in order to obtain as uniform a density as possible. Only very thin parts, such as discs and washers, may be satisfactorily compacted by single-ended pressing.

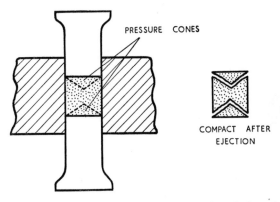

PRESSURE CONES

COMPACT AFTER EJECTION

Fig. 10. Illustration of the mode of compact failure in 'capping'.

There are three basic methods by which the 'double-action' effect (pressing from both ends) may be obtained, as shown in Fig. 11. In the first method (*a*) the press applies pressure to both upper and lower punches, a special type of press known as the double-acting type being required. In the second, (*b*) the die may be supported by means of springs. If the springs are just strong enough to support the die (floating-die) and to return it to the filling position after ejection, then as compaction proceeds the increasing frictional force between powder and die will move the die downwards over the lower punch. The total effect is the same as that achieved at (*a*). The third shown at (*c*), is known as the 'withdrawal' method and involves the application of a controlled downward movement to the die instead of relying on friction. In the last two methods ejection is achieved by continued downward movement of the die while the upper punch is retracted. Ejection in a double-acting press is achieved by upward movement of the lower punch.

The powder-metallurgy industry since World War II has grown up around two distinct schools of thought on tooling methods. The American industry is based almost exclusively on the double-action method using special presses. On the other hand, most European manufacturers have based their process on relatively simple presses using the floating die and withdrawal methods, with the various punch, die and core rod movements built into a complex die set.

To illustrate powder-metallurgy tooling, the methods used to produce some typical forms will be described. It should be borne in mind that one of

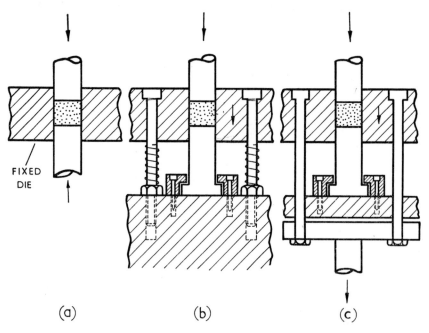

FIG. 11. Various methods of achieving double-ended pressing.
(a) Ejection (double-acting press) method.   (b) Floating-die method.
(c) Withdrawal method.

the major objectives in tool design is to obtain as uniform a density as possible in the part, and this entails keeping the effects of friction to a minimum and maintaining as uniform a compression ratio as possible when compacting parts of varying thickness. A further consideration is the avoidance of undue stresses in ejection which might tend to fracture a delicate section.

In the examples that follow only relative movements between die, punches and core rods will be considered as these are generally similar whichever pressing method is used. In the diagrams the motions indicated are those which would be obtained by the double-action method as these are the simplest to illustrate.

Simple cylinders or other prismatic parts are relatively easy to produce, because a single punch in each end of the die is all that is required. The only limitations on this type of part are (i) maximum diameter imposed by available press capacity, (ii) maximum length-to-diameter ratio imposed by frictional effects and (iii) a limitation on certain cross sections which might seriously weaken the die, as discussed later. Hollow prismatic shapes are fairly easily made using core rods of the desired contour, although there is a minimum limit on wall thickness of the part since the very thin punches required would be excessively weak.

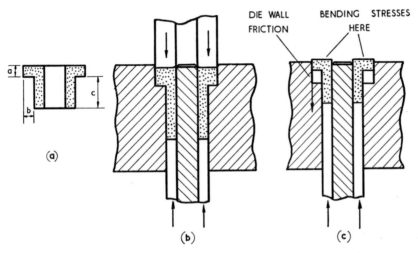

Fig. 12. Method of compacting a flanged part in a shouldered die.

When the section thickness varies, some means of maintaining a constant compression ratio must be considered. Although small changes in section may be pressed using contoured punches it is normally necessary to use other methods, such as the shouldered-die technique which is widely used for the pressing of flanged bushes (Fig. 12). With the shouldered-die technique the effective pressure from the top punch is really limited to the flange itself, so that a low-density region is likely to occur immediately below the flange. This is overcome to some extent by non-simultaneous motions of the upper and lower punches so that final compaction of the flange takes place only after the remainder of the part has been fully pressed. In addition, as the flange is subjected only to single-action compaction, flanges thicker than about a quarter of an inch have low density regions on their lower faces. The biggest limitation to the shouldered-die technique, however, occurs on ejection. The flange is unsupported and therefore liable to breakage, owing to the bending stresses caused by die-wall friction (Fig. 12 (c)). There is, therefore, a maximum flange overhang (generally considered to be 1·5 times the flange thickness) which may be satisfactorily produced in a shouldered die. Thick flanged parts or flanges with large overhang therefore require two lower movements, or a movable die insert.

The limitations of the shouldered die are eliminated by introducing a second lower punch (Fig. 13). The second punch is either spring supported for

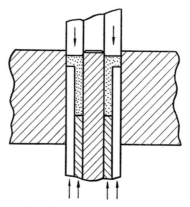

FIG. 13. The use of two lower punches to compact a flanged part.

filling or has its own separate motion, so that equal compression may be applied to both sections. When the part to be produced does not have a flat upper face (essential to filling) then it becomes necessary to use multiple upper punches, unless the changes in height of the upper profile are slight. Furthermore, since filling to a flat upper face is still necessary, then transfer of the powder within the die is required, after the cavity has been sealed by the upper punches. Fig. 14 shows the sequence of events for the compaction of a component with a profiled upper face. Similar considerations apply to the pressing of components having curved faces. The number of punches used to form a curved face is determined by tooling economics and the uniformity of density necessary in the part.

In American practice the punch movements discussed above would, where possible, be linked directly to available press motions. European practice, on the other hand, is generally to use floating lower punches where extra movements are required. These punches are supported on springs in the 'fill'

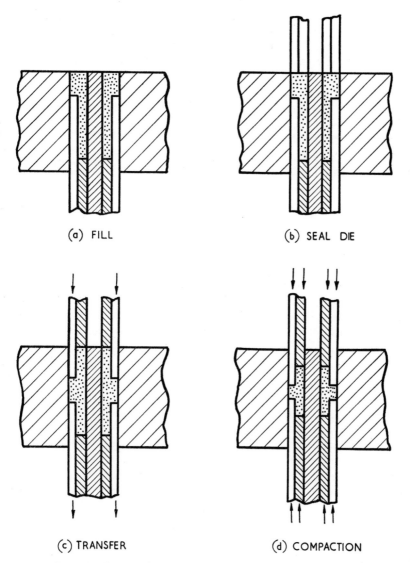

(a) FILL   (b) SEAL DIE

(c) TRANSFER   (d) COMPACTION

FIG. 14. The use of powder transfer to form a central flange.

position and move down on to stops during compression. Die sets for the European technique may be extremely complex and many devices are employed to actuate the various movements. Rollers and forks are used to remove stops, and compressed air is often used to float dies or core rods and to provide ejection movements. In general the European system is somewhat more versatile than the American, and in the United Kingdom, where both systems are in wide use, there has been a slight swing in recent years in favour of the European system. There is much to be said for a combination of the two systems with the press providing some movements and others being incorporated in the tooling. Also, when a very close fit between punch and die is required, as when pressing very fine powders, it is necessary to use a die-set to achieve the essential degree of alignment. Such sub-press assemblies are often used in double-acting presses (Plate 3 (a)), although the punch movements are still provided by the press.

The design of pressing tools for powder-metallurgy parts is a subject in itself for which the *Höganäs Iron Powder Handbook*[10] is an excellent source of detailed information.

Presses. Powder-metallurgy presses may be either mechanical or hydraulic. In general the mechanical type is chosen for high-speed production of small- and medium-sized components, while hydraulic presses are more popular for large components where high specific pressures are required but fast production is not so necessary.

The presses possessed by a component producer will, to a large extent, determine the types and sizes of component he is able to produce. For instance the press imposes maximum limits on powder-fill depth and specific pressure, which then limit the height and cross-sectional area of a component which may be produced. (These limits vary for powders of different compression ratios and different compactabilities.) On double-acting presses the number of movements available imposes some limitations on complexity, although many of these may be overcome by incorporating floating punches and by using European tooling techniques.

Many types of mechanical press have been designed for powder compacting. Operative mechanisms include simple crankshaft, toggle action, cams and many combinations of these. Although the European tooling system was originally developed for use with fairly simple presses, the growth of the industry has been such as to necessitate increased complexity, even in presses for this tooling method. A typical press designed for use with withdrawal tooling is shown in Plate 3 (b). This is a combined toggle -and cam-action press of 100-tons capacity. The upper ram movement is controlled by the toggle action, while other movements, such as the die withdrawal and feed shoe motion, are controlled by a system of adjustable cam and lever mechanisms. This press is designed to give non-simultaneous compaction and after the upper punch has closed the die, the punch and die speeds are constant for a predetermined period, so that pressure is exerted from the bottom only. The die movement then ceases and the upper punch pressure redistributes the density so that the neutral zone is moved to the centre of the compact.

The multiple cam press shown in Plate 3 (c) is typical of the type of mechanical press used for American or ejection tooling. The press shown here has provision for one upper and two lower movements which are all controlled from a single camshaft fitted with adjustable cams. Cam motion is transmitted to the rams by means of pivoting arms which are forked to fit round the ram. Pressure is exerted through adjustable nuts on the ram. The cams themselves have replaceable sections so that the individual cycles of upper and lower punches may be varied to give simultaneous or non-simultaneous compression. Such presses are extremely versatile and have been extensively developed over the years. The latest of a long line of these presses, shown in Plate 4 (a), is fully automatic, and has two upper and three lower movements.

A hydraulic overload device, which regulates the maximum pressure on the punches and prevents overloading should slight overfilling of the die occur, is shown on the press illustrated in Plate 3 (a).

The maximum output of mechanical presses of the types discussed above is generally in the range 5–35 compacts per minute, depending mainly on the size of the part. Small, simple parts may be compacted, however, at rates up to 500 per minute by using a rotary press. These presses are widely used in pharmaceutical work, but have also been adapted for use with metal powders. A rotary press consists of a circular die table containing a number of dies, usually up to about fifteen for metal powder work. Discs above and below the die table carry the punches and the whole of this assembly rotates at speeds of up to about 50 rev/min. The action of the punches is controlled by fixed guides or cams, except near the position of maximum pressure where rollers usually take over. Since a number of tool sets have to be made for these presses, tooling costs are high and hence only where very large numbers of a component are required is the use of the rotary press an economic proposition. A typical press of this type is shown in Plate 4 (b). This is a 10-ton capacity machine with thirteen die stations and an output of 260–520 compacts per minute.

Mechanical presses of the cam and eccentric types are generally limited to about 100 tons capacity, though toggle-action presses of 300 tons are in use. However, the modern trend in powder metallurgy is towards still larger parts which need presses of higher capacity, and it is in this field that the hydraulic press is preferred. A feature of hydraulic presses is that they usually compress to a predetermined pressure (unlike mechanical presses which normally have a predetermined stroke). Because of this characteristic very consistent densities from part to part are obtained. Slight differences in die filling lead to differences in height of the compact, so that where dimensional accuracy is more important than consistency of density it is necessary to equip hydraulic presses with limit switches, or some such means of pressing to constant volume, to achieve the same effect as in compacting with mechanical presses.

Hydraulic presses can be constructed with independently-operated upper and lower cylinders and a fixed die table for use with ejection-type tooling. Such presses are in use, but their major disadvantage is their considerable height which necessitates a high working platform or a pit to take the lower cylinder. It is usually more convenient to adapt hydraulic presses for use with single-action or with floating-die or withdrawal tooling. A typical hydraulic press for use with withdrawal tooling is shown in Plate 4 (c). The die movement is controlled by adjustment of the upward pressure of a lower (low-pressure) ram. The modern hydraulic powder-metallurgy press has vastly increased speeds compared with its slow-moving forerunners, and presses such as the 200-ton model illustrated in Plate 4 (c) are capable of compacting up to ten parts per minute.

An important feature of most presses is the provision of means for filling

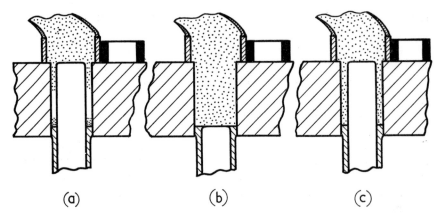

(a)   (b)   (c)

Fig. 15. The use of core rod withdrawal to facilitate the
filling of thin-walled cavities.

the die with powder. On most rapid-production presses the powder is held in a hopper and transferred to the die via a feeder shoe. This shoe is moved across the die table after the ejection of the previous compact and pushes this compact clear of the die mouth, then as the shoe moves over the die mouth, powder is able to fall freely into the die cavity. Clearly the flow characteristics of the powder are very important in this method of filling the die, and some presses have a vibrator fitted to the shoe to assist powder flow.

Various methods are also used to ensure that all parts of the die cavity are adequately filled with powder. For instance, the lower punch may be retracted whilst the shoe is over the die mouth so that powder is 'sucked' into the die. Where the cavity to be filled is deep and narrow, as with the thin-walled bush shown in Fig. 15, then bridging of the cavity may easily occur, powder failing to flow freely to the bottom (Fig. 15 (*a*)). In such cases it is best to retract both the punch and core-rod and to fill the whole cavity (i.e. overfilling, Fig. 15 (*b*)) and then to raise the core-rod to its position for pressing, thus pushing the surplus powder out of the cavity (Fig. 15 (*c*)).

This method of die filling with top-levelling is, of course, a constant-volume method and it depends critically on consistent packing properties of the powder mix. Die filling by means of a weighed charge, while theoretically giving much better uniformity from part to part, is not easily carried out on rapid-production presses. Though, no doubt, rapid weighing methods could be devised, the constant-volume method is very much simpler and, in practice, can give weight tolerances from part to part of less than $\pm 1\%$.

Tool Construction. The principal requirement of a die is that it should be an accurate negative of the part to be produced, due account being taken of the various expansions on ejection and dimensional changes on sintering. A die must also have sufficient strength to withstand the stresses imposed in pressing and, if it is to be used to produce a large number of parts, will need adequate abrasion resistance to prevent undue wear. For dies which are required to produce many thousands of parts at high compacting pressures no one material combines the necessary properties. It is therefore common practice to use abrasion-resistant inserts in a strong, tough backing ring (Plate 2 (*b*)). Because many of the parts produced by powder metallurgy are of complex form the ease with which the negative forms may be generated in the die material is also of great importance. A simple shape, such as a cylinder, can easily be drilled in a single piece of annealed steel, while more complex prismatic shapes may also be slotted or broached in a single piece. The introduction of such techniques as electro-erosion has enabled toolmakers to machine dies from a single piece in both hardened steels and cemented carbides. However, it is usually more convenient to split complex dies into a number of inserts, and this type of construction makes such operations as milling and grinding much more convenient. Inserts may be held together by screws in a clamping ring or, more usually, by a shrink ring. The shrink-ring method has the advantage of a much sturdier construction and, further, the compressive stresses induced in the die tend to counteract the radial stresses of pressing, thus reducing the elastic over-expansion of the die. Inserts held in clamping rings are, however, easier to remove for regrinding or replacement, but this system is unusual in a production die which, if well designed in the right material, may produce several hundreds of thousands of parts. Where the part being produced is fragile and subject to breakage on ejection, dies may be of a split construction to facilitate removal of the piece after pressing. Such a technique is obviously too slow for the rapid production of small components but it is useful where larger, more expensive, parts are being made. Refractory metals and carbides are often moulded by this

5

method. The clamping rings holding the die together must be substantial and may need to be supplemented by horizontal press rams.

Materials forming the die walls must have high strength to resist bursting and high hardness for abrasion resistance. For these reasons high-alloy tool steels or cemented carbides are chosen for production dies. Softer materials may be used in some instances where the anticipated production is low and the powder to be pressed soft and relatively non-abrasive. Development dies are often made from easily machined materials such as cast iron, and although such materials will not withstand high pressures a die may be made quickly which will give valuable information to the designer concerning the dimensions of the production die. The compositions of some typical die materials are shown in Table 4.

Table 4. Typical Die Materials

Type	No.	Composition (weight per cent)								
		C	Si	Mn	Cr	Mo	V	W	Co	Others
High-alloy non-deforming tool steels	1	1·65	0·30	0·5	13·0	0·7	0·3			
	2	2·10			13·0		4·0	1·4		
High-speed tool steels	3	1·20			4·5		3·8	13·5		
	4	0·83			4·0	5·0	1·9	6·5		
	5	0·82			4·8		1·6	20·0	10·5	
	6	1·20			4·5	3·5	3·0	10·0	10·0	
Cemented carbides	7								6–12	Balance WC

The types of material in Table 4 are given in order of increasing cost. Although the cost of the raw material can be a major factor in the overall cost of a die it is most important to choose a material which will last for the expected production run, particularly if the die shape is complicated and machining costs high. It is clear that cemented carbides, which are expensive as raw materials and are also costly to shape and finish (as they require diamond grinding) will only be chosen for very long production runs or where abrasive conditions are such as to preclude other die materials. Of the steels in Table 4 the high-chromium types, numbers 1 and 2, are very popular for general work on a wide range of powder materials. They are cheaper than the high-speed steels, possess similar wear resistance and are less likely to deform on heat treatment. High vanadium content combined with high carbon (e.g. steels 2, 3 and 6) gives rise to the presence of the very hard vanadium carbide which increases wear resistance, though at the expense of impact resistance. Such steels may also give trouble in machining and grinding.

All the steels in Table 4 are heat treated to a hardness in excess of 60 Rc for use as die materials, and in fact 65 Rc is a more usual figure. The cemented carbides, of course, have much higher hardness, being the equivalent of 72 Rc and above. One of the major advantages of the cemented carbides is their high modulus of elasticity ($\sim 80 \times 10^6$ lb/in^2 compared with 30×10^6 lb/in^2 for steels) which greatly reduces over-expansion of the die during pressing and thus lowers ejection pressures and compact spring back. Risks of cracking on ejection are also reduced.

In order to increase wear resistance, various surface treatments, such as nitriding, hard-chromium plating and flame-plating, have been used on die steels. Flame-plating[11] of tungsten carbide (with about 8% Co) is a fairly recent process and it shows great promise as a method of combining the toughness of steel with the wear resistance of cemented carbide.

Materials used for shrink rings and die reinforcement must have adequate toughness and a high yield strength in order to support the hard and brittle inserts. Shrink rings are therefore usually made from a low alloy, non-deforming steel, of medium or high carbon content, tempered to between 25 and 40 Rc. Too soft a steel will lack strength, which means that the required dimensions will give a die of excessive weight, while too hard a steel will lack ductility.

The outside dimensions of a die for a given strength are usually calculated assuming that the majority of the applied pressure is transmitted radially. In most cases this gives a die which is bigger than it need be, but as Long[8] has shown there are cases where this assumption is justified. Calculations of die strength must include allowances for the effect of shrink fits, etc., and an excellent account of such calculations is given in the *Höganäs Iron Powder Handbook*.[10]

Core rods form the internal faces of a part and therefore have to withstand more or less the same conditions as dies. They require hardness and abrasion resistance, although toughness may also be necessary, particularly when the rod is rather slender and prone to breakage. Core rods are therefore made from similar materials to those used for dies; high-speed steels are popular and are sometimes nitrided. Surface treatments or coatings are usually restricted to the actual wearing portion of the core rod; below this portion the rod is left uncoated and may be tempered to a lower hardness to give greater toughness. The wearing portion of slender core rods is sometimes made of cemented carbide which is brazed or mechanically attached to the lower part of the rod. For large (over $\frac{7}{8}$ in. diam.) core rods, however, it is more usual to fit a carbide sleeve. Steel core rods are preferably hardened to 67–65 Rc but this is reduced for more slender rods. *Höganäs Iron Powder Handbook*[10] recommends that full hardness is only used where the length to diameter ratio is 12:1 or less; above a ratio of 20:1 60–58 Rc is recommended and this should be reduced to 45–40 Rc below the wearing portion.

Whereas core rods and dies form the inner and outer profiles of a part, the punches form the end faces (and, where multiple punches are used, part of the profile). Powder movement across punch faces is small, so that abrasion resistance is not usually a major consideration. Punches are mainly subjected to compressive loads so that they tend to deform radially. Since this expansion must be elastic and no permanent upsetting is permissible, a high compressive strength is required. Also, since punches, particularly lower punches, are often long and slender, considerable toughness is required to avoid breakage due to slight non-axial loading; thus a compromise must be reached between strength and ductility. The usual materials employed are low-alloy, manganese, nickel–chromium and nickel–chromium–molybdenum, non-deforming steels. Carbon contents vary depending on design; where sections are thin or the punch faces have to form a chamfer then carbon contents may be as low as 0·35%, but where short stubby punches of simple form are used carbon may approach 1·0%. Punches are usually tempered to about 56 Rc at the face and 45 Rc on the relieved portion. It is unusual to heat treat punches to a hardness greater than 58 Rc. Although these lower hardness figures lead to more frequent refacing this is a much cheaper operation than punch replacement due to breakage.

It is good practice to relieve punch dimensions behind the forming face so that any powder escaping through the clearance between punch and die (or core rod and punch) will not be so easily trapped and cause scoring. The land, or fully-dimensioned portion of the punch, should be kept to a minimum, usually $\frac{1}{8}$–$\frac{3}{8}$ in., this applying particularly to lower punches.

Punch facings of cemented carbide have been used on occasions with good results. Difficulties in attachment have restricted their use in general but a recent process,[12] developed by the F. J. Stokes Corporation, shows some promise. The process, called 'fusion tipping', involves induction heating of the shank, tip and brazing material whilst applying axial pressure, followed by heat treatment of the whole assembly. The process is said to eliminate 'mushrooming' of either the shank or brazing material under pressures of up to 50 tons/in².

After heat treatment and final grinding, tools are polished to give the required degree of surface finish. Hand lapping with rouge or diamond paste is usually the only satisfactory method of obtaining the desired mirror-like finish. On dies this lapping should be carried out in the direction of punch travel to reduce friction to an absolute minimum. In general a surface finish of 5 μ in. r.m.s. is considered desirable.

Sizing and Coining. Sizing and coining are pressing operations carried out after sintering. Sizing, as the name suggests, is an operation designed to correct warping and other forms of distortion which may take place during sintering. Although some products are well within tolerance after sintering, such parts as bearings, cams, etc., which have to be a close fit on a shaft or in a housing, usually need sizing before being put into service. Sizing does not give rise to a great deal of deformation and density changes are only slight.

Coining, on the other hand, involves the application of considerable pressure and is designed to increase the density and strength of the parts; it also acts as a sizing operation. It is often possible to obtain significant improvements in density by coining since the sintering operation removes the work hardening effects of compacting.

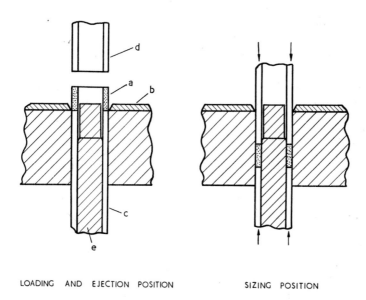

LOADING AND EJECTION POSITION   SIZING POSITION

Fig. 16. Typical sizing operation for a plain bush.

Tooling for sizing and coining is similar to, but not as complex as, that required for compaction since the total tool movements are generally shorter and there are no problems of powder transfer. The usual sizing or coining operation involves forcing the part into a die, very often over a core rod, and finally compressing it between upper and lower punches. A typical sizing operation for a plain bush is shown in Fig. 16. The bush *a* is positioned over the die by the location plate *b* and supported by the lower punch *c* which is in the raised position. As the upper punch *d* descends, the lower punch is retracted and the part is forced into the upper portion of the die. Only the outside diameter is sized at this stage, because the upper portion of the fixed core rod *e* is undersize. As the part is pushed further into the die the bore is sized over the full diameter portion of the core rod, and compression between the two punches sizes the length. Finally the lower punch is raised to eject the part.

As in compacting, lubrication is vital if reasonable pressures and economic die lives are to be realized. However, since the part is rigid, lubrication is somewhat simpler than with powder. Liquid lubricants, i.e. oils or solutions of stearates in oils may be used and are usually applied by spraying. It is important to avoid the absorption of lubricant into the interior of the part, because once in the pores it acts as a hydraulic cushion resisting the pressures exerted by the tools. Liquid lubricants should therefore be used sparingly and applied immediately before the sizing or coining operation. Where solid lubricants are used they may be applied by a tumbling operation; this method is not particularly effective on long, narrow holes.

The presses designed for the compacting of metal powders are quite suitable for sizing and coining and are widely used for these operations. However, as the requirements are simpler, special sizing and coining presses have been designed which are generally cheaper than the compacting presses.

Component Design Considerations

Since cold die pressing is by far the most widely used method of shaping metal powders it is pertinent to consider the limitations to component form imposed by the use of a rigid metal die.

It is important to realize that it is not often possible to take a component which has been designed for production by machining or casting and to manufacture it in that form by powder metallurgy. As was shown earlier, available press capacity limits the maximum cross-section and this, together with die-fill depth limits the length. There are also certain limits, because of friction considerations, on features such as flange sizes when using shouldered dies, etc. These problems may be overcome, for instance, by the aquisition of larger presses or by more complex tooling. There are, however, certain design features which are virtually impossible to produce economically by die pressing. Experience has shown that in such cases it is usually possible to redesign the part so that it fulfils the same function but is capable of being produced by die pressing.

The features which are undesirable in components for manufacture by die pressing fall into two groups: (i) those forms which are ruled out by powder flow and ejection considerations, and (ii) forms for which the tooling required would be insufficiently strong. The first group includes holes not in the direction of pressing. Holes at right angles to the direction of pressing are often required, and various tooling tricks have been devised to produce these, but it is usually much cheaper to machine them after sintering. Other troublesome forms are re-entrant angles and curves, threads, etc., which require sideways powder-flow and which make ejection by the normal process impossible. Again, these features must be machined after sintering. A selection of such forms is shown in Fig. 17. While machining is a way of overcoming certain pressing problems, the amount of machining which may be economically combined with die pressing is limited. A point is reached where the part is more economically produced completely by machining, assuming, of course, that powder metallurgy is not essential for some reason, such as with porous materials (e.g. bearings).

The second group includes parts with very thin walls or deep narrow splines etc., which would require weak punches or weak die constructions.

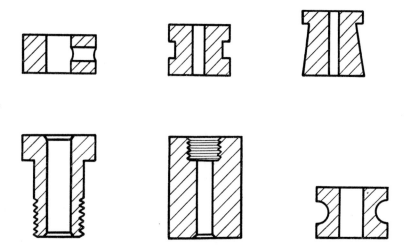

Fig. 17. Forms impossible to produce by die compacting.

Such parts should be redesigned if possible as shown in Fig. 18. It is generally considered that the thinnest practical punch wall thickness is $\frac{1}{32}$ in., so that the step in (b) and the lower wall thickness in (c) should be increased to this minimum value. The part shown in (a) would involve a die with long, narrow, weak splines; the re-design shown would give a much stronger die construction. It must also be remembered that parts with very thin walls, long narrow projections, feather edges, etc., are very liable to damage during handling in the green state. Chamfered edges may be produced provided that the angle to the pressing axis is at least 45° and a small flat is incorporated to eliminate the feather edge (Fig. 19). Sudden large changes in section or uneven cross-sections (Fig. 20) should be avoided, because these not only give trouble in pressing but also lead to distortion during sintering. Very thin core rods are liable to deviate from the vertical under load and are also easily broken.

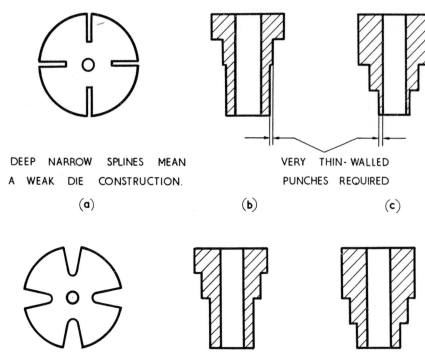

DEEP NARROW SPLINES MEAN
A WEAK DIE CONSTRUCTION.

(a)

VERY THIN-WALLED
PUNCHES REQUIRED

(b)   (c)

Fig. 18. Forms leading to weak die or punch constructions (*top*) and
suggested redesigns to give adequate tool strength (*bottom*).

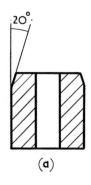

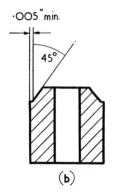

(a)   (b)

SMALL   CHAMFER   ANGLE
MEANS   FINE FEATHER EDGE
ON   PUNCH

LARGER   ANGLE AND FLAT
ELIMINATES   FEATHER   EDGE

Fig. 19. Modifications to chamfers to eliminate punch weakness.

Deep, small-diameter holes, therefore, are best machined after sintering. Complex profiles on core rods are often necessary but where possible re-designing to round holes greatly simplifies tool making.

Another feature which must be considered is the tolerance specified on die-

(a)   (b)

FIG. 20. Forms leading to distortion.
(a) Sudden large changes in cross section.
(b) Very uneven cross-sections.

pressed parts. After sintering, tolerances approaching ± 0.0008 in. per inch in the radial direction are usually attainable, but in the direction of pressing tolerance limits are wider, being around ± 0.005 in. per inch. These limits depend on the powder material, the intricacies of the component shape, sintering conditions, etc. Where higher degrees of accuracy are required it is necessary to resort to sizing, machining or grinding.

Vibratory Compacting

In recent years it has been shown that the application of vibration during compacting will considerably reduce the pressure required to attain a given density. Both low-frequency, high-amplitude[13] and high-frequency, low-amplitude[14] vibrations have been used with good effect. Although the method seems more applicable to carbides, cermets and similar brittle materials, the Russian work[14] also reports good results with ductile metal powders.

The main advantages appear to be a greatly reduced pressure requirement (as little as one hundredth of that required without vibration) resulting in a large increase in die and punch life, negligible over-expansion of the die, low internal stresses and very little trouble with cracking on ejection or during sintering. Furthermore, it seems that quite complex, multi-section parts may be produced using simple, single-punch, tooling.

Although the method shows great promise it remains to be seen whether it can be effectively applied to high-speed production. However, it may prove extremely useful in the production of very large parts since the required press capacity is greatly reduced. It may also be possible with vibratory compacting to use multi-cavity dies, because of the simple tooling and low loads required.

Cyclic Compacting

The elimination of expensive machining operations and the ability to produce porous materials are among the advantages made most use of in powder metallurgy, but the production of standard forms, such as bar, sheet and strip, from powders may also be attractive for a variety of reasons. For instance, many metals by reason of their mode of extraction are readily available as powders (nickel is an example), and direct fabrication would eliminate the processes of melting, casting, ingot fettling, hot rolling and descaling. The soft magnetic alloys, some of which are best prepared by powder metallurgy, are also often required in strip form.

Other materials which are conveniently produced, or may only be produced, by powder metallurgy and which are likely to be required in bar or similar forms, are cermets, dispersion-hardened alloys, refractory metals and alloys, and carbide tool materials.

Cyclic compacting is one method of producing fairly long lengths of strip or bar from metal powders. The method was developed at the Westinghouse Electric Corporation and has been described by Deibel, Thornburg and Emley.[15] Essentially the process is an extension of single-action die pressing in which the die is replaced by a U-shaped channel which contains the powder, and the punch by a specially shaped 'shoe' As the name indicates the process is not truly continuous but proceeds in a series of steps or 'cycles'. The sequence of operations is shown in Fig. 21. The result of the specially shaped punch is that whilst the flat surface compacts the powder to the desired density, the angled portion produces a gradual increase in density from the loose powder to that produced by the flat surface. The amount by which the powder is moved forward should be less than the length of the flat portion of the punch to ensure that some of the fully compacted powder remains under this 'finishing area'. Repetition of the cycle will produce a continuous bar. The various steps would seem to be quite easily automated and fairly rapid rates of production can be envisaged.

Relatively thick bars or plates may be produced (Deibel et al.[15] report thicknesses up to 1 in.) in lengths suitable for further conventional working after sintering. The limitation on thickness is essentially the same as in single-action die pressing, i.e. due to wall friction. Maximum width would be limited by press capacity.

Powder Rolling

The compaction of metal powders into continuous lengths by rolling has been widely studied, particularly over the past decade. Evans and Smith,[16,17,18] for example, have investigated the rolling of copper powders, and further work is reported by Hunt and Eborall.[19] The rolling of nickel powders has been studied by Worn and Perks,[20] and the rolling of stainless-

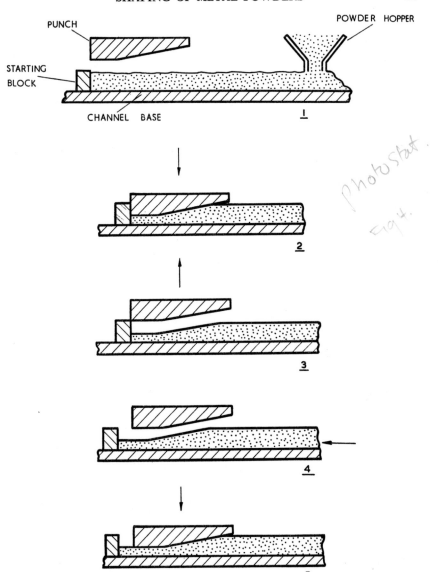

PUNCH

POWDER HOPPER

STARTING BLOCK

CHANNEL BASE

1

2

3

4

5

FIG. 21. The various stages in the cyclic-compacting process.

steel powders by Storcheim *et al.*[21] Worn[22] has also provided a review of the subject, while Marshall[23] has given the plant requirements for the process. The principle of the roll compacting process is comparatively simple;

powder is fed into the roll gap of a simple mill where it is compacted into a coherent strip. The mill rolls may be in the same vertical or the same horizontal plane, the former being easier for strip handling while the latter is perhaps more convenient for powder feeding. As in conventional rolling, friction between the roll and the work material plays a very important part, because it controls the amount of powder carried into the roll gap. This is analogous to the rolling of solid material where the entry of material between the rolls is limited by the condition that the contact angle θ (Fig. 22) must be less than the friction angle f, where $\tan f = \mu$, the friction coefficient between rolls and stock. That is the force tending to draw the work into the rolls ($F \cos \theta$) must exceed the horizontal component of the roll pressure ($P \sin \theta$) which tends to force the work out of the roll gap. Entry becomes impossible when $F \cos \theta - P \sin \theta = 0$, and since $F/P = \tan f$, entry is impossible when $\theta = f$.

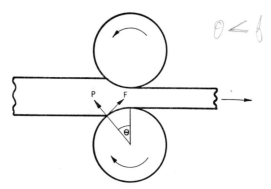

FIG. 22. Angular relationships between the forces involved in rolling.

Thus in the roll compacting of metal powders the maximum thickness of handleable green strip which may be produced is related to the friction between rolls and powder and the diameter of the rolls, which determines 'contact angle'. However, Evans and Smith[18] show that, due to slipping between powder particles, the actual angle at which the powder is gripped is much lower than the calculated friction angle, f. As a result it is found that in order to roll compact a certain thickness of strip it is necessary to use very much larger diameter rolls than are required for producing similar strip from solid material. Roll diameters of between 50 and 150 times the strip thickness thus seem to be required.

One way of increasing the maximum strip thickness is to increase μ by roughening the roll surface, although, during rolling, the roughened surface tends to become polished so that the conditions change. A further method of increasing friction is to force-feed the powder into the roll gap. Archimedean screw devices have been tried and, although Evans and Smith[18] had little success with these, Hunt and Eborall[19] report improvements on strip thickness for very fine copper powders using such methods. However, despite the use of such devices, it would appear that, even using the largest feasible roll diameters, the thickest strip that may at present be produced from any metal powder is about $\frac{1}{4}$ in.

A further limitation of this process is the very low rolling speed. Conventional strip production often entails finishing speeds of 1500 ft/min or more, but powder rolling is usually limited to about 25 ft/min. This is mainly due to the difficulties associated with the feeding of powders into the roll gap. When gravity feeding is employed the controlling factor is the natural flow rate of the powder. Forced-feeding mechanisms overcome this difficulty, but a further factor which imposes a limit on the rate of powder feed is the rate at which air is expelled from the powder. In fact, Worn and Perks[20] point out that when rolling a nickel powder of $1\cdot0$ g/cm³ apparent density at 8 ft/min (about 1 lb/min), a litre/min of air needs to escape. A back flow of air from the roll gap will obviously impede the flow of powder and Worn and Perks show that by substituting a gas of low viscosity (e.g. hydrogen) for air the situation may be improved.

At the present time it appears that powder rolling is limited to the production of relatively thin strip at fairly low speeds, so that its advantages over conventional methods are in the elimination of a large number of passes and intermediate anneals.

Isostatic Pressing

Isostatic pressing is the compaction of powders by means of a pressurized fluid. Most usually the process is operated at room temperature with oil or water as the fluid and thus the term 'hydrostatic pressing' is often used. In order to produce the desired form the powder is packed into a shaped, flexible envelope which is sealed before pressing. Flexible envelopes, which must be completely impervious to the pressurizing fluid, are usually made from rubber or plastics. The advantages of isostatic pressing compared with compacting in dies are the complete absence of die-wall friction and the uniform application of pressure in all directions, which result in uniform density throughout the part. Because of the absence of die-wall friction, and the use of a flexible mould which does not interfere with ejection, it is possible to produce shapes, such as long slender rods, undercuts, etc., which cannot be made by die pressing. The principal disadvantage of the process is the difficulty in holding close dimensional tolerances. This arises from the difficulty of packing the powder to a uniform density before pressing; any non-uniformity in packing density leads to dimensional differences since the pressed density is uniform. Also the flexible moulds which must be used are insufficiently rigid to maintain the shape accurately while being filled with powder. The latter problem may be overcome to some extent by supporting the flexible mould, during packing and pressing, by a mesh or perforated container.

Moulds may be sealed by a rubber bung or a preformed rubber or plastic lid. Rubber solutions or other adhesives are used to seal the lids to the moulds, or, in the case of plastics, a welding technique may be employed. Where a rubber bung is used it is often convenient to 'push-seal' the bung so that it clamps the mould against the supporting tube (Fig. 23).

Entrapped air can be removed from the packed envelope by inserting a hypodermic needle and evacuating with a vacuum pump; the hole made by the needle is self sealing. Van Buren and Hirsch[24] have demonstrated,

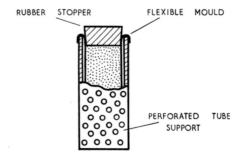

FIG. 23. Flexible mould for isostatic compaction, with perforated support tube.

however, that results are not always improved by de-airing; they found that with fine powders de-airing generally gave a higher green density, but with coarse iron and tungsten powders green density was adversely affected.

The liquid pressurizing media for room-temperature isostatic pressing include water, glycerine and various oils. Hydraulic oils are usually the most satisfactory since they are easy to handle and do not corrode the pressure vessel. Pressurization of the chamber may be effected by means of a high-pressure pump (Fig. 24) or, where such a pump is not available, it may be more convenient to seal the container with a piston as shown in Fig. 25 and force the piston against the liquid by a press.

Pressures of 100,000 lb/in^2 are readily available by isostatic pressing and such pressures will give green densities of 90% or more in ductile powders.[24] In general the pressure required for a given green density is lower for isotatic pressing than for die pressing. Pressing cracks occur infrequently in isostatic pressing and brittle powders such as ceramics, which are virtually impossible to die press without binders, may be satisfactorily compacted by this method.

Green density and strength are often high enough for compacts to be machined in the green state, an operation which is often necessary owing to the inherent lack of accuracy of the method. Shrinkage on sintering is very uniform, however, so that loss of accuracy during sintering owing to differential contraction is slight.

The major application of isostatic pressing to metal powders has been in the production of dense slugs for further working, e.g. by extrusion. The method is particularly useful for the preparation of extrusion billets in the refractory metals such as tungsten, molybdenum, niobium and chromium, and for dispersion-hardened materials.

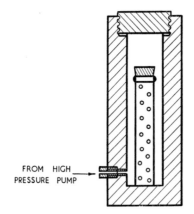

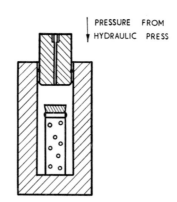

FIG. 24. Apparatus for isostatic pressing using a high-pressure pump.

FIG. 25. Apparatus for isostatic pressing using a hydraulic press.

A rather elegant method of isostatic pressing in which the mould also acts as the pressure-transmitting medium has been described by Penrice[25] and more recently by Highriter, Curcio and Kaempf.[26] This method employs a mould made from a reversible gel which may be cast around a metal pattern. The mould is then filled with powder, sealed and pressed in a conventional compacting die. The gel serves to transmit the pressure isostatically to the powder (Fig. 26). Metal cores may be used to produce hollow parts and Penrice claims to have produced tubes with a wall thickness of only 0·015 in. A variation of this process has been described by Weber et al.[27] Their process, which they term the 'rubber stopper method', uses a die to form the outside of the component and a rubber stopper as a core (Fig. 27). The expansion of the core during compression approximates to isostatic pressing. The method is obviously useful for the compaction of crucible-type shapes. Various plastics materials such as p.v.c. have been successfully employed in place of rubber or reversible gels in both the above processes, and despite their extra 'stiffness' the degree of isostatic transmission of pressure is usually adequate for most purposes.

Explosive Forming

In the forming of sheet metals advantages have been found in the use of very high pressing rates. Such high pressing rates are commonly achieved by the use of explosives and the method has been quite widely used with success

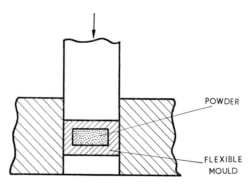

FIG. 26. Isostatic pressing in a metal die using a thick-walled flexible mould as the pressure-transmitting medium.

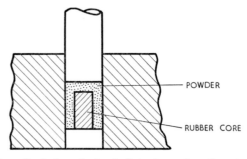

FIG. 27. A method of producing hollow shapes in a die using an elastic core to transmit pressure isostatically.

on a number of 'difficult' materials. Generally a liquid medium (usually water) is employed to transmit the pressure wave from the exploding charge to the metal sheet, which is held over an open (or evacuated) die.

A similar method[28] for the compaction of metal powders uses a 14-inch naval gun barrel partially filled with water. After sealing, a charge is detonated inside the barrel and pressures up to 66,000 lb/in^2 are claimed. Since such pressures are easily obtained by conventional isostatic pressing any advantages of this method would have to be due to the very high rate of pressing.

Explosive charges have also been used to drive punches (or pistons) into dies containing loose powder. Such die sets have been described by La Rocca and Burkhardt,[29] and using them the authors claim to have compacted sponge cobalt and ductile titanium powder to densities of 95% of theoretical. A survey of explosive-forming methods and their potential application to the compacting of metal powders is given by Cooley.[30]

Forming with Binders

For centuries it has been known that the natural clays are plastic when mixed with water and that in this state they may be formed very easily by hand. During recent times clays have also been formed by techniques, such as extrusion, which require the application of pressures in excess of those used by the potter. By the addition of various binders and plasticizers, powders which are not naturally plastic (in the ceramic sense) may be given clay-like properties and then formed in the same way as the natural clays. Many organic materials have been suggested in the ceramic and patent litera-ture as binders and plasticizers for non-clay materials, including various gums, starches, waxes, ammonium alginate, polyvinyl alcohol, resins, nitrocellulose, and shellac. Hyde,[31] for example, gives a list of proprietary materials suitable for use as plasticizers in the extrusion of various ceramic powders, such as Al_2O_3, SiC, BeO, etc.

Suitable mixtures may be shaped by hand but extrusion seems to be the main process by which these plasticized materials have been formed. Although ceramics and cemented carbides have been extruded by this technique little use has yet been made of the method for the shaping of metal powders. This is presumably due to their true plasticity which enables them to be extruded or hot worked by other processes without the use of binders. It is worth noting, however, that the first osmium and tungsten wires for lamp filaments were prepared by this technique using such materials as sugar or dextrin as binders and extruding through a diamond die. The process was used for about ten years at the turn of the century until it was replaced by the Coolidge process (see Chapters 1 and 11).

The extrusion of cemented-carbide compositions with suitable binders is practised commercially and is capable of producing quite complex shapes including twist-drill forms.

Injection moulding of intricate parts using various plastics as binders is another process which has found commercial application in the ceramic field[32] but, as far as is known, has not yet been used for metal powders.

The major disadvantage of techniques employing binders and plasticizers is the large amount of these materials required in the mixture. As much as 50% of additives may be required to give a workable mixture, all of which must be removed, either before or during sintering, which leaves a very

6

porous body requiring high shrinkage if reasonable density is to be achieved. In fact all the problems associated with the use of lubricants are encountered in a more exaggerated form. Nevertheless such techniques would appear to be useful in the shaping of the more brittle metals and carbide materials.

Cold Working of Preformed Blanks

The cold consolidation of sintered compacts in dies has been described under sizing and coining. Conventional cold working methods such as rolling and drawing in which the metal is unsupported may also be used on pressed and sintered blanks. The cold working of porous metals must be carried out very carefully, particularly in the early stages, owing to their lack of ductility. As the density increases the degree of reduction between anneals may be increased.

A much better technique, in most cases, is to hot work the preformed blank until density and ductility are such as to allow considerable cold deformation between anneals. The material may then be treated as a conventional wrought product, although internal oxide films may still cause some trouble. The avoidance of internal oxidation during hot working, by canning, etc., is discussed later.

PRESSURE FORMING WITH HEAT

Hot Pressing

In cold pressing, densification is increasingly retarded due to the effects of work hardening within the powder particles, so much so that it is impossible fully to densify most metal powders by pressing at room temperature. However, if during pressing the temperature is maintained above the recrystallization temperature the effects of work hardening are eliminated. Thus, in one operation, it is possible to produce a highly dense component to precise dimensions without the necessity for further sizing or coining. Furthermore, by hot pressing it is possible to form dense compacts from materials which at room temperature display little or no plasticity.

Early work on the hot pressing of metal powders has been reviewed at length by Goetzel,[5] while Williams[33] has studied the effects of load, time and temperature on the densities of various metal powders. In the field of ceramics, carbides and intermetallics, important papers on the subject have been presented by Murray, Livey and Williams,[34] Jackson,[35] and Thomas and Jones.[36] The major commercial applications of hot pressing in powder metallurgy at present are in the preparation of diamond tools and some cemented carbides (see Chapter 6).

While the hot-pressing technique has important advantages, outlined above, there are definite practical difficulties and disadvantages. For most metal powders the first problem is that of preventing oxidation of the powder; it may be necessary to maintain a protective atmosphere not only during heating and pressing but also during cooling after ejection. This makes the process slow, cumbersome and fairly expensive (though it must be remembered that the sintering operation is eliminated). The use of elevated temperatures limits the choice of die materials. High-speed steel dies will operate satisfactorily up to about 500°C, but die wear increases rapidly above this temperature. Above 500°C it is necessary to use the superalloys based on nickel or cobalt (e.g. the Stellites and Nimonics*) or cemented carbides. Above 1000°C the field is limited to graphite, oxides, uncemented carbides and possibly other high-temperature compounds, such as nitrides, borides and silicides. Of these graphite is the almost universal choice because it is cheap, easy to machine and has excellent thermal-shock resistance. It may be used up to 3000°C and, being an electrical conductor, it allows direct heating of the die by either resistance or induction heating. In addition, graphite provides its own protective atmosphere of carbon monoxide (though this may also be carburizing and reducing which in some cases may prove troublesome). Disadvantages associated with the use of graphite are, first it may react with the material being pressed; this is usually overcome by using a mould wash of a substance such as boron nitride. Secondly, graphite dies are limited to loads of about 2 tons/in², but since its strength does not decrease with temperature such loads may be employed above 2000°C. Furthermore, 2 tons/in² is usually sufficient to densify even the hardest and most refractory materials, provided that the correct temperatures are employed.

For most metal powders the hot-pressing temperatures are below 1000°C and metallic dies are usually adequate. An exception is the preparation of large blanks in beryllium (see for example, Martin, Knight and Ellis[37]), which is carried out under vacuum in graphite dies.

Other Hot Working Processes

The hot rolling of loose copper powders has been studied by Evans.[38] The powder was heated to temperatures up to 300°C during passage down a heated chute between hopper and rolls. Despite difficulties due to powder sticking to the chute, Evans showed that a much stronger final strip was produced than when cold rolling. Sintering of the strip, however, was still necessary.

For other hot working processes where the powder must be supported in some way a simple approach is to pack into a metal container or 'can', which is then sealed and hot worked in the conventional manner. Such canned powders may be hot worked by forging (i.e. by upsetting or in closed dies), extrusion, rolling and swaging. An excellent review of these techniques for the

* 'Nimonic' is a trade name of Henry Wiggin & Co. Ltd.

consolidation of metal powders is provided by Williams.[39] Apart from supporting the powder during consolidation the can also prevents oxidation of the powder, particularly if it is evacuated before sealing. Difficulties are often encountered in the working of canned powders, owing to a large amount of deformation of the can being necessary before the powder is fully densified. This may lead to excessive wrinkling of the can or even bursting, with, consequently, detrimental effects on the accuracy and purity of the product. Such difficulties may be overcome by building up a composite can having thicker walls where these are required. A typical example is the 'picture frame' technique often used for the hot rolling of powders, Fig. 28. Here thick side walls are used to support the powder laterally. The preferred method is to cold compact a blank before canning, so that the amount of deformation necessary

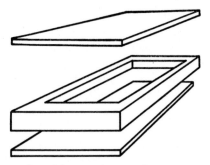

FIG. 28. A 'picture frame' for canning powder compacts prior to rolling.

for densification is reduced. This is particularly useful in hot extrusion where the can is unable to expand outwards and tends to wrinkle into the powder giving a poor surface on the final product.

The hot extrusion process is extremely useful in the production of rods, tubes and similar shapes from powders, since the amount of deformation obtained in one operation is very high and theoretical densities are usually obtained with only moderate extrusion ratios. The process as applied to metal powders has been described by Loewenstein, Aronin and Geary,[40] who discuss the extrusion of loose powders, compacted blanks, canned loose powders and powders precompacted and canned or compacted directly into the supported can. Amongst the powder materials which have been consolidated by such techniques are dispersion-strengthened materials (including S.A.P.), refractory metals, beryllium, cermet fuel materials (e.g. UO_2 in a stainless-steel matrix) and magnesium alloys. When extruding refractory metals where the extrusion temperature is very high (often 1400°C or above) a convenient method is to use a thick outer container of, say, mild steel which

' to a lower temperature of about 1100°C. The canned billet of
tal powder is preheated separately to its required extrusion

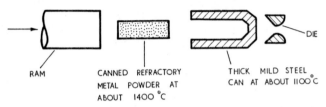

RAM   CANNED   REFRACTORY   THICK   MILD STEEL
       METAL POWDER AT   CAN AT ABOUT 1100°C
       ABOUT   1400 °C

FIG. 29. Typical scheme for the extrusion of refractory metal powders at
very high temperatures.

temperature, placed inside the mild-steel container and the composite billet
extruded as shown in Fig. 29.

Hot Isostatic Pressing

The application of heat to the isostatic pressing process had until recently
received little attention because of some formidable technical problems. It is
necessary to use metal envelopes to contain the powder, and pressure trans-
mitting media must be either gases or liquid metals. The process has been
termed 'gas pressure bonding' where a gas is used to transmit the pressure.
However, despite the problems, recent work at the Battelle Memorial
Institute[41] has established the process as a feasible method of consolidating
powders.

The early work at Battelle made use of a stainless-steel hot-wall autoclave
using helium gas as the pressurizing medium. Such autoclaves, however, were
limited in terms of maximum pressure and temperature, so that the next step
was the construction of a cold-wall autoclave with an internal heater. This
type of apparatus is capable of pressures of up to 10,000 lb/in² at temperatures of up to 1570°C. In a paper by Hodge[42] the possibility is mentioned
of obtaining pressures of up to 50,000 lb/in² and temperatures of up to
3000°C in the near future. The choice of envelope materials is obviously
limited at such temperatures.

REFERENCES

1. St. Pierre, P. D. S. in *Ceramic Fabrication Processes*, W. D. Kingery (ed.),
   45, John Wiley (1958).
2. Hausner, H. H. and Poster, A. R. in *Powder Metallurgy*, Leszynski (ed.),
   461, Interscience, New York (1961).
3. Lidman, W. G. and Rubino, R. V. *Prec. Met. Mold.*, **14** (8), 40 (1956).
4. Grala, E. M. in *Powder Metallurgy*, Leszynski (ed.), 507, Interscience, New
   York (1961).

5. Goetzel, C. G. *Treatise on Powder Metallurgy*, Interscience, New York (1949).
6. Jones, W. D. *Fundamental Principles of Powder Metallurgy*, Arnold, London (1960).
7. Long, W. M. *Powder Metallurgy*, No. 6, 73 (1960).
8. Long, W. M. in *Special Ceramics 1962*, 327, Academic Press, London (1963).
9. Bustamante, S. J. and Sheinburg, H. *Powder Metallurgy*, No. 6, 36 (1960).
10. *Höganäs Iron Powder Handbook*, Höganäs Billesholm, Stockholm.
11. Haycock, H. J. and Frazer, R. J. *Machinery*, 738 (Sept. 27th, 1957).
12. *Precision Metal Molding*, **20** (6), 84 (June, 1962).
13. Bell, W. C., Dillender, R. D., Lominac, H. R. and Manning, E. G. *J. Amer. Ceram. Soc.*, **38**, No. 11, 396 (Nov., 1955).
14. Likhtman, V. I., Gorbunov, N. S. and Shatalova, I. G. *Doklady Akademii Nauk, SSSR*, **134**, 5, 1150 (1960).
15. Deibel, C., Thornburg, D. R. and Emley, F. *Powder Metallurgy*, No. 5, 32 (1960).
16. Evans, P. E. and Smith, G. C. Symposium on Powder Metallurgy, 1954 (*Special Rept. No. 58*), 131, 1956, London (Iron and Steel Institute).
17. Evans, P. E. and Smith, G. C. *Powder Metallurgy*, No. 3, 1 (1959).
18. Evans, P. E. and Smith G. C. ibid., 26.
19. Hunt, D. G. and Eborall, R. *Powder Metallurgy*, No. 5, 1 (1960).
20. Worn, D. K. and Perks, R. P. *Powder Metallurgy*, No. 3, 45 (1959).
21. Storcheim, S., Nylin, J. and Sprissler, B. *U.S. Atomic Energy Comm.* 1954, *S.E.P.—161.*
22. Worn, D. K. *Powder Metallurgy*, No. 1/2, 85 (1958).
23. Marshall, A. F. ibid., No. 5, 24 (1960).
24. Van Buren, C. E. and Hirsch, H. H. in *Powder Metallurgy*, Leszynski (ed.), 403, Interscience, New York (1961).
25. Penrice, T. W. *Powder Metallurgy*, No. 1/2, 79 (1958).
26. Highriter, H. W., Curcio, R. and Kaempf, L. in *Powder Metallurgy*, Leszynski (ed.), 443, Interscience, New York (1961).
27. Weber, B. C., Thompson, W. H., Bielstein, H. O. and Schwartz, M. A. *J. Amer. Ceram. Soc.*, **40** (11), 363 (1957).
28. Anon. *Iron Age*, 56 (Sept. 25th, 1952).
29. La Rocca, E. W. and Burkhardt, L. A. *Bull. Amer. Phys. Soc.*, Ser. 11, 2, 263 (1957).
30. Cooley, R. A. in *Powder Metallurgy*, Leszynski (ed.), 525, Interscience, New York (1961).
31. Hyde, C. in *Ceramic Fabrication Processes*, W. D. Kingery (ed.), 107, John Wiley (1958).
32. Anon. *Ceramic Ind.*, 52 (Nov., 1961).
33. Williams, J. Symposium on Powder Metallurgy, 1954 (*Special Rept. No. 58*), 112, 1956, London (Iron and Steel Institute).
34. Murray, P., Livey, D. T. and Williams, J. in *Ceramic Fabrication Processes*, W. D. Kingery (ed.), 147, John Wiley (1958).
35. Jackson, J. S. *Powder Metallurgy*, No. 8, 73 (1961).
36. Thomas, A. G., Jones, H. J. *Powder Metallurgy*, No. 6, 160 (1960).
37. Martin, A. J., Knight, R. A. and Ellis, G. C. ibid., No. 7, 268 (1961).
38. Evans, P. E. in *Powder Metallurgy*, Leszynski (ed.), 553, Interscience, New York (1961).
39. Williams, J. *Powder Metallurgy*, No. 1/2, 94 (1958).

40. Loewenstein, P., Aronin, L. R. and Geary, A. L. in *Powder Metallurgy*, Leszynski (ed.), 563, Interscience, New York (1960).
41. Hodge, E. S., Boyer, C. B. and Orcutt, F. D. *Ind. and Eng. Chem.*, **54**, 30 (Jan., 1962).
42. Hodge, E. S. *Metals Engng Quart.*, **1**, 4, 3 (1961).

CHAPTER 4

SINTERING

A mass of loose powder may be cold shaped in any of the ways described in Chapter 3, but the shaped body will be very fragile unless it has been compacted at a high pressure. Even bodies of high density compacted at high pressures may be unable to withstand small applied stresses (other than compressive stresses) because of the limited degree of interparticle bonding. To produce a useful body, able to withstand working stresses, it is necessary to induce strong bonding between particles; sintering is the process by which the additional bonding is achieved.

While sintering is a vital step in most powder-metallurgy processes it is by no means mandatory. In certain cases particle bonding would be detrimental and sintering has to be omitted; instances of this are soft magnetic dust-cores and single-particle domain magnets. When sintering cannot be employed, bonding agents, such as plastics, may be used to impart strength to the powder body.

Sintering may be defined as heating a particulate body, below the melting point of at least one major constituent, in order to cause interparticle bonding. In addition to causing particle bonding, sintering can also lead to the following important effects: (i) chemical changes, (ii) dimensional changes, (iii) relief of internal stresses, (iv) phase changes and (v) alloying. When a compacted powder body is sintered a simple measure of particle bonding is its macro-strength. Fig. 30 (a) shows schematically how strength and some other properties may vary with sintering temperature. Each of the curves in Fig. 30 (a), except that for conductivity, consists of three sections. In the first portion of each curve the property is either constant or increases very slowly with increasing sintering temperature; this is followed by a range where a rapid increase in the property occurs for only a small increase in the sintering temperature, and in the third stage the values of all properties appear to approach a saturation level. What is particularly important is that the start of the second sintering stage, where the rapid changes commence, is at a different temperature for each of the properties considered. For instance, an appreciable increase in strength may be obtained before a significant dimensional change occurs, while the ductility continues to increase at sintering temperatures above which strength and dimensions are virtually constant.

One consequence of the relationships described above is that there is rarely a unique sintering temperature for a material, but usually a range of sintering temperatures. Conversely, it is often necessary for the sintering temperature to be closely controlled. This apparently paradoxical situation arises because a property frequently needs to be controlled at some particular level, or perhaps the best compromise between two or more properties needs to be achieved. A good example of this is the situation which often occurs when producing sintered engineering components (Chapter 5); these must be held to close dimensional tolerances, which means that more than about 1% shrinkage cannot be tolerated. On the other hand, maximum strength and ductility are usually needed. The practice is therefore to sinter at the highest temperature possible without excessive dimensional change.

The remarks above apply to the sintering of single elemental powders. Single-phase alloy powders behave in a somewhat similar manner; Fig. 30 (*b*) gives some experimental results obtained with an austenitic stainless-steel powder and the characteristic features of Fig. 30 (*a*) are evident. When two or more elemental or alloy powders are sintered together it is difficult to give rules for the changes which occur. Clearly, except in those cases where at the sintering temperature no solubility is possible between the phases present, alloying will occur, although diffusion is unlikely to proceed sufficiently for equilibrium to be attained unless the sintering time is protracted. In some cases a liquid phase will be formed and this constitutes an important difference between the sintering of duplex and elemental systems. When a liquid phase is present all changes proceed at a much faster rate than when only solid phases are involved. As a general rule, if porosity must be eliminated then commercial practice is to use liquid-phase sintering (with which infiltration may be included), unless it is economically possible to supplement the normal sintering forces as in hot pressing.

So far the effects of sintering have been considered as functions of temperature, time and alloy system. A further most important process variable is the sintering atmosphere. All metal powders are sintered in controlled neutral or reducing atmospheres, while non-metals such as oxides may need to be sintered in controlled oxidizing atmospheres. The first requirement of a sintering atmosphere for metal powders is that it should displace the air from around the powder and thereby prevent oxidation. Gross oxidation can occur rapidly in powder bodies because of the large surface area, and even

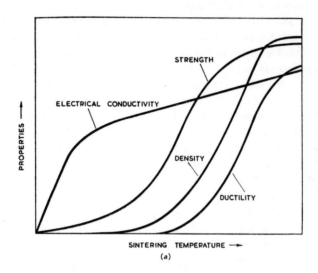

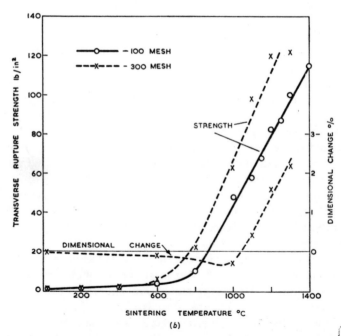

Fig. 30. The influence of sintering temperature on (a) the properties of a typical sintered body and (b) the strength and dimensional change of sintered stainless-steel. (Diagram (b) by *courtesy of C. A. Wright and M. J. Handy*.)

slight oxidation can prevent the desired properties being attained in a sintered body. Elimination of oxygen from the sintering furnace by displacing air with another gas can be achieved fairly easily; a gas which does nothing more than this is termed 'neutral'. The usefulness of neutral gases is limited, and reducing gases are usually preferred to decompose the compounds which are frequently present on the particle surfaces. In certain cases vacuum sintering is necessary.

In this introduction some features of sintering have been presented. It will now be appreciated that sintering is a complex process in which physical, chemical and metallurgical effects interact.

FUNDAMENTALS OF SINTERING

The tendency for a system to assume its state of lowest energy is the driving force for sintering. In a powder mass there is excess energy due to the large free surface. The amount of excess surface energy, however, is not large. Kuczynski[1] has calculated that one gram-mole of $1\ \mu$ diameter spherical copper powder will have only about 10 calories of excess energy. During sintering, the surface area is decreased by an increase in interparticle contact area and by smoothing of the particle surfaces. Thus the energy available to continue the process becomes less and the rate of change slower. To enable sintering to proceed it is necessary that the atoms have sufficient mobility to move to new positions; atomic mobility is a function of temperature and thus sintering is markedly temperature dependent. Since the energy for sintering is derived from the excess surface energy, more energy will be available from fine, irregular powders than from coarser spherical materials.

Consider the pertinent characteristics of a powder mass prior to sintering. If the powder has not been deformed during shaping (the process only having served to pack the particles) there will be only slight interparticle adhesion, principally resulting from van der Waals' attractive forces. In a body which has been compacted the situation will be different. The application of pressure may have disrupted the surface films and will have caused plastic deformation of the particles, particularly at the contact areas. As a result there will be definite contact between individual particles, the contact area will be strained and therefore of high energy. Thus, before sintering, a powder body consists at best of particles adhering to each other at small contact areas and at worst of particles separated by surface films of oxides, etc., or adsorbed gases.

Particle Bonding and Shrinkage

The phenomena which sintering theory must seek to explain are the occurrence and extent of particle bonding and the dimensional changes which cause porosity to decrease. Consider first the case of two spherical particles which are just touching, the shaping process not having caused any particle deformation. Fig. 31 shows two cases of a neck forming between particles. In Fig. 31 (a) the particle centres have not moved closer together, and thus the material supplied to the neck has been obtained by distortion of the particles. In this case, since the particle centres are still at the same distance apart, a gross dimensional change has not occurred. The situation in the second case (Fig. 31 (b)) is different. Here the particle centres have moved closer together and, if these spherical particles had been part of a larger powder mass, macroscopic shrinkage would have been observed.

Kuczynski[1] has considered the stresses which may arise in the neck formed between two spherical particles due to surface tension forces, and has also shown their implications. If the radius of the neck between two

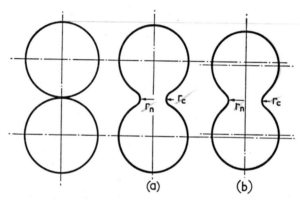

FIG. 31. Sintering of spherical particles: (a) when there is no overall shrinkage and (b) when shrinkage occurs.

particles, r_n, is much greater than the radius of curvature, r_c, then the stress, σ, acting in the neck (whose magnitude is related to the surface tension, γ) is approximately:

$$\sigma = \frac{\gamma}{r_c} \tag{1}$$

This stress is directed outwards (tensile stress) from the neck. For the case of 40 μ diameter copper powder having $r_c = 5 \times 10^{-6}$ cm and taking the surface tension of copper as 1400 dynes/cm, σ is of the order of 400 lb/in^2, a substantial stress in copper when acting at the sintering temperature.

One result of this stress in the neck is that the equilibrium vapour pressure above the neck will be slightly greater than that over the particle surface remote from the neck. If the equilibrium vapour pressure remote from the neck is P, then it can be shown that the equilibrium pressure over the neck $(P+\Delta P)$ is given by:

$$\frac{\Delta P}{P} = \frac{\gamma V}{RTr_c} \tag{2}$$

where V is the molar volume of the solid, R the gas constant and T the absolute temperature. Because of the difference in equilibrium vapour pressure it is possible for material to be transported by evaporation from some parts of the particle surface, and simultaneous condensation at the neck to occur with the result that the neck between the particles will grow.

A similar argument will show that a gradient exists in the concentration of vacancies between the neck and the adjacent solid. If C is the equilibrium concentration of vacancies in the solid and ΔC the excess concentration in the neck then:

$$\frac{\Delta C}{C} = \frac{\gamma V}{RTr_c} \tag{3}$$

Thus there will be a vacancy concentration gradient between the neck and the remainder of the particle which can result in a flow of material towards the neck; the mechanism for this flow may be either surface or volume diffusion.

Summarizing these findings, at the junction between two particles there exists a stress which is acting in a manner to cause the neck to grow. This stress also causes vapour pressure and vacancy concentration gradients which can result in neck growth by the evaporation and condensation mechanism, or by a vacancy diffusion process.

It is not certain whether in practical metal-powder systems interparticle necks do grow by the direct action of the tensile stress. In Newtonian solids viscous flow might be expected to occur according to the well known relationship:

$$\sigma_s = \eta \frac{de}{dt} \tag{4}$$

where η is the viscosity, de/dt the strain rate and σ_s the shear stress (which is proportional to the tensile stress σ). Frenkel[2] has examined the sintering of glass (a Newtonian solid) and found that it obeys eq. (5), indicative of viscous flow. (r_p is the particle radius and t is the time.)

$$\frac{r_n^2}{r_p} = \frac{3}{2}\frac{\gamma}{\eta}t \tag{5}$$

In a metal (Bingham solid) viscous flow does not occur, instead the applied stress must exceed a critical flow stress for plastic flow to occur. While it is established that plastic flow does occur in 'hot pressing' where the applied pressure is additive to σ, the occurrence of plastic flow is not unambiguously established for the sintering of metals. Mackenzie and Shuttleworth[3] have argued that the rates of densification observed when sintering metals are too high to be due to a diffusion process alone, and they have postulated the existence of a strain field associated with each particle. From their model they deduced that the interaction of these strain fields results in stresses sufficient to cause plastic flow. This concept has not, however, been unchallenged and, as shown later, the presence of grain boundaries acting as 'sinks' for vacancies can reconcile the observed rates of densification with a diffusion process.

The process of evaporation and condensation can lead to neck growth but not to densification. The rates of neck growth which this process can cause seem to be lower than those actually observed, except for substances having a high vapour pressure at their sintering temperatures. Equation (6) has been derived for the growth rate of a neck due to evaporation and condensation. (M is the molecular weight of the substance.)

$$\frac{r_n^3}{r_p} = \left(\frac{9\pi}{2MRT}\right)^{1/2} V\gamma Pt \tag{6}$$

Kingery and Berg[4] have examined the sintering of sodium chloride and found it to obey the above equation. They concluded that evaporation and condensation was the sintering mechanism in this case.

For metals the most important sintering mechanism is vacancy diffusion. The flow of vacancies away from the neck results in material being transported to the neck from the particles. For the process to cause appreciable movement of material, the vacancy gradient must be maintained and the vacancies moving away from the neck must be eliminated at some suitable sink. If the vacancies move by surface diffusion, that is they diffuse along the free surface of the particle, the pore itself will act as the sink. Surface diffusion cannot, however, lead to a reduction in total porosity, but only to neck growth and change in the shape of the pores. The alternative process, volume diffusion, requires a movement of vacancies from the neck into the interior of the particle. In their consideration of the rate of densification, Mackenzie and Shuttleworth claimed that volume diffusion could not be the dominant process, owing to the long distances over which vacancies had to diffuse and, as noted earlier, they concluded that plastic flow was the most important mechanism. More recently, however, the work of Kuczynski[1] and Alexander and Balluffi[5] has given strong support to the volume diffusion theory and has also shown how the relatively fast rate of densification can be reconciled with the theory. Kuczynski, using the idealized system of spheres sintered to plates and models prepared by winding wires on to spools, has demonstrated that many metals obey the derived relationship given below for neck growth by volume diffusion:

$$\frac{r_n^{5}}{r_p^{2}} = \frac{K\gamma V}{RT} \cdot D_v t \tag{7}$$

where K is a constant which depends upon the geometry of the system and D_v the volume self-diffusion coefficient. Kuczynski also observed that in the case of fine powders sintered at high temperatures the rate of neck growth approached a seventh power function with respect to time. Since for surface diffusion eq. (8) should be obeyed, he concluded that this process also contributes to the sintering of metals.

$$\frac{r_n^{7}}{r_p^{3}} = \frac{56\gamma V d}{RT} \cdot D_s t \tag{8}$$

(d is the interatomic distance and D_s the coefficient of surface self-diffusion.)

Alexander and Baluffi[5] demonstrated how the strong support for volume diffusion arising from the work of Kuczynski can be reconciled with the observed rates of densification. They showed that densification ceases if grain boundaries are removed from the system and concluded from this that the grain boundaries act as the vacancy sinks. Because the distance over which diffusion is required (neck to grain boundary) is much shorter than was considered by Mackenzie and Shuttleworth, the volume diffusion process is able to account for the observed effects. Since the work referred to above there has been further confirmation of the role of grain boundary sinks and of the paramount importance of volume diffusion as the mechanism of densification in the sintering of metals.

Summarizing the present state of sintering theory, metals sinter by a diffusion process except where an external stress is applied to cause plastic flow (hot pressing). There is also the possibility of an evaporation and condensation process operating for certain metals, but the great weight of evidence suggests that volume diffusion is the dominant process of densification, although surface diffusion contributes to bonding in some cases.

Porosity

In a loose powder mass it is possible for 70% or more of the total volume to be comprised of pores, while in a compact pressed from a ductile powder the porosity may be less than 10%. During sintering important changes will occur in both the amount of porosity and in the shape and size of the pores.

When considering porosity it is necessary to differentiate between (i) interconnected (or open) porosity and (ii) closed porosity. The former refers to pores which interconnect with each other and which are connected to the compact surface; closed pores do not connect with the surface. Prior to sintering most of the porosity is interconnected. When shrinkage occurs not only will the total porosity decrease but some of the previously interconnected pores will become isolated. In general, the amount of closed porosity either increases or remains substantially constant as sintering progresses. Arthur[6] has shown how the porosity of copper compacts varies during sintering. His results show that when total porosity is reduced to about 5%, interconnecting pores have virtually disappeared and all the remaining pores are isolated. An important finding of Arthur's work is that the relationship between closed, interconnected and total porosity is independent of compacting pressure and therefore of green density.

Prior to sintering the pores are extremely irregular in shape due to the many sharp cornered crevices formed by the particle contact areas. It is in these crevices that the neck radius is a minimum, and thus the sintering forces due to surface tension are the greatest. Therefore, during sintering, material transport will take place in such a manner that the smallest crevices will be filled first and there will be a tendency for the pores to assume a spherical form. Transport mechanisms, such as surface diffusion and evaporation and condensation, which cannot contribute to densification, can cause pore spheroidization. When a pore attains a spherical form its excess surface energy is a minimum and there will thus be a greatly reduced driving force for further sintering.

In many cases it may not be permissible to allow a large dimensional change, i.e. only a very small degree of densification can be allowed. In such porous material, if maximum strength and ductility are required, it is an advantage to obtain spherical pores since these have the least stress-raising effects. Spheroidization of pores can be assisted by the activated sintering technique developed by Eudier.[7] In activated sintering a halide is present in the sintering atmosphere and also possibly as a liquid phase within the pores. The halogen component speeds up the spheroidization process, possibly by increasing the vapour-phase transport of material. It is also claimed that activated sintering may promote homogenization in multi-phase systems.

In a powder body there usually exists a wide range of pore sizes. The range of pore sizes present depends upon the shape and particle size distribution of the original powder and the degree to which it has been packed. A detailed investigation of the way in which the pore size distribution changes during sintering has been made by Rhines, Birchenhall and Hughes.[8] The results of this investigation show that (i) for a given sintering temperature there is a critical pore size below which pores are unstable and disappear, (ii) as the sintering temperature increases the mean pore size increases, (iii) during sintering large pores can grow at the expense of small pores and (iv) the change in pore size distribution and shape is dependent upon the sintering atmosphere as well as the temperature. The preferential growth of large pores can be reasonably explained in terms of the volume diffusion mechanism discussed earlier, by postulating that the large pores act as sinks for the vacancies diffusing away from the smaller pores. The Mackenzie and Shuttleworth theory is unable to explain this type of pore size change.

As was noted earlier, rapid densification can only occur when there is a grain boundary near to the neck; if grain growth occurs the rate of densification will be greatly reduced. Significant grain growth does not occur, however, until porosity is fairly low, the pores themselves acting as growth inhibitors.

Multi-component Systems

The aspects of sintering phenomena so far discussed have been limited to pure metals. It is now necessary to consider the sintering of multi-component systems, i.e. systems in which more than one metal is involved. Two characteristics of such systems are important: (i) diffusion processes will no longer be limited to self-diffusion and (ii) in many cases the sintering temperature will be above the melting point of one constituent which will lead to liquid phase formation.

In the discussion of interparticle bonding it was clear that volume self-diffusion was probably the most important mechanism for the sintering of metals, the driving force for this being vacancy gradients due to the tensile stress at the interparticle neck. In multi-component systems, however, heterogeneous diffusion will occur, e.g. the diffusion of component A into component B and vice versa. In heterogeneous diffusion the driving force is the concentration gradient across the interface. Concentration-activated diffusion causes material interchange between particles and it may therefore result in bonding but not necessarily in shrinkage.

The mass flow which occurs during heterogeneous diffusion is related to the concentration gradient and the diffusion coefficient D as follows:

$$\text{mass flow} = D \times \text{concentration gradient.}$$

This relationship (Fick's law) is more usually expressed in the form:

$$S = A D \frac{dc}{dx} \tag{9}$$

where S is the amount of material diffusing in unit time through an area A, and dc/dx is the concentration gradient. The diffusion coefficient D is not a constant but varies with both concentration and temperature. The temperature dependence of D is given by the relationship:

$$D = D_0 e^{-Q/RT} \tag{10}$$

where Q is the activation energy for diffusion and D_0 a constant. A relation

7

between D_0 and Q is given by the well known Dushman–Langmuir equation:

$$D_0 = \frac{Qd^2}{hN} \tag{11}$$

or

$$D = \frac{Qd^2 e^{-Q/RT}}{hN} \tag{12}$$

where d is the interatomic spacing, h is Planck's constant and N is Avogadro's number.

The principal mechanism by which atoms diffuse is (for substitutional solid solutions) vacant site diffusion. Thus an atom and a vacant site change place producing diffusion in the opposite direction to the vacancy movement. In alloy systems in which the solute normally occupies the interstitial sites, for instance carbon in iron, diffusion will always be interstitial. There is a proportionality between the activation energy for diffusion Q and melting point T_m or sublimation energy E, at least for cubic metals, as is shown in Table 5. The proportionality is obeyed well by f.c.c. metals.

Table 5. Proportionality between Activation Energy for Diffusion (Q), Melting Point (T_m) and Sublimation Energy (E)
(*after Le Claire*[9])

Metal	Q (kcal)	T_m (°K)	E	Q/T_m	Q/E
Copper	57·2	1356	81·2	42	0·70
	61·4	1356	81·2	45	0·76
(polycryst)	45·1	1356	81·2	33	0·56
(single cryst)	49·0	1356	81·2	36	0·60
Gold	51·0	1336	92·0	38	0·55
	62·9	1336	92·0	47	0·68
	53·0	1336	92·0	40	0·58
Lead	28·05	600	47·5	47	0·59
Silver	45·9	1234	68·0	37	0·68

When two dissimilar particles are sintered not only will there be bulk diffusion in both directions but diffusion along the particle surfaces will also occur. If the activation energy is the energy necessary for atoms to move through an almost perfect lattice then diffusion along a surface, which will be in a less perfect state, will require a smaller activation energy. From similar considerations diffusion along a grain boundary should be easier than through the lattice.

The results of Brattain and Becker,[10] given in Fig. 32, show how D varies with temperature for bulk, surface and grain boundary diffusion; it is obvious that surface diffusion will proceed much faster than bulk diffusion with grain boundary diffusion occupying an intermediate place. Not only does diffusion proceed faster through the less perfect lattices of the surface and grain boundary but it also commences at a lower temperature. Huttig,[11] in discussing the role of self-diffusion in sintering in terms of Tammann temperature (fraction of absolute melting point), states that self-diffusion through the lattice (volume diffusion) proceeds at an appreciable rate above $0.33 \, T_m$, while surface diffusion becomes important above $0.23 \, T_m$. The presence of porosity naturally decreases diffusion by reducing the available cross-section (Fig. 33).

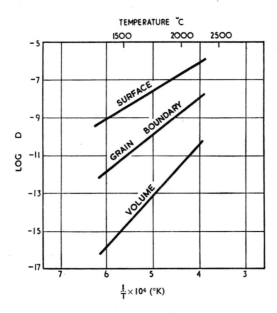

FIG. 32. Comparison of the rates of surface, grain boundary and volume diffusion of thorium in tungsten.[10]

The experiments, referred to earlier, in which models were made by winding wires on to spools, have also been carried out with dissimilar wires. In these experiments the importance of surface diffusion has been confirmed. The Kirkendall effect was also noted (the diffusion of A into B is faster than the diffusion B into A, with the consequence that micro-porosity occurs in A because of the net material transport away from this metal). Although metals are invariably sintered at temperatures higher than $0.33 \, T_m$, it is unusual when sintering a mixture of dissimilar powders for diffusion to proceed sufficiently fast for complete homogenization. Some diffusion data relevant to powder metal processes are given in Table 6.

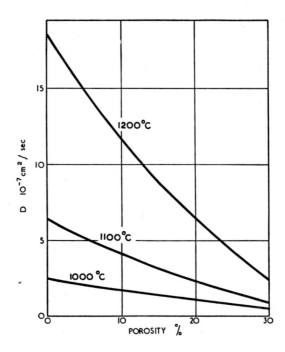

FIG. 33. Variation of diffusion rate of carbon in iron with porosity.[12]

Table 6. Diffusion Data for some Powder Metallurgy Systems

Base metal	Diffusing element	Temperature (°C)	D (cm²/sec)	D_0 (cm²/sec)	Q (kcal)
Copper	Nickel	950	$2 \cdot 1 \times 10^{-10}$	$6 \cdot 5 \times 10^{-5}$	29·8
	Tin	400	$4 \cdot 8 \times 10^{-13}$		
		760	$1 \cdot 4 \times 10^{-9}$	$4 \cdot 1 \times 10^{-3}$	31·2
		850	$3 \cdot 9 \times 10^{-9}$		
	Zinc	500–900		$2 \cdot 4 \times 10^{-3}$	30·2
Iron	Carbon	1100	$4 \cdot 5 - 8 \cdot 3 \times 10^{-7}$		
		1250	$2 \cdot 8 \times 10^{-6}$	$4 \cdot 9 \times 10^{-1}$	36·6
	Chromium	1150	$6 \cdot 8 \times 10^{-10}$		
		1350	$2 \cdot 2 - 5 \cdot 3 \times 10^{-8}$		13·5
	Copper	800–1200	—	3·0	61·0
	Manganese	1400	$9 \cdot 6 \times 10^{-8}$	—	—
	Nickel	1200	$9 \cdot 3 \times 10^{-11}$	—	—
Nickel	Copper	890	$1 \cdot 92 - 2 \cdot 4 \times 10^{-10}$	$1 \cdot 0 \times 10^{-3}$	35·5
Tungsten	Carbon			$2 \cdot 75 \times 10^{-3}$	112

Liquid-phase Sintering

An important characteristic of multi-component systems is that it is often possible to choose a sintering temperature at which liquid and solid phases coexist. The characteristics of liquid-phase sintering which have led to its wide application are: (i) the possibility of obtaining complete elimination of porosity under suitable conditions, (ii) the high rates of diffusion through the liquid phase which may speed homogenization, (iii) stable high-melting point metals, which would otherwise require very high sintering temperatures, may be bonded into dense bodies and (iv) where a two-phase alloy is required, and the components are not soluble in each other, liquid-phase sintering enables a dense coherent body to be produced.

When the temperature of a multi-component system is raised so that a liquid phase is formed the degree to which the liquid wets the solid particle will largely determine the characteristics of the subsequent sintering. If the amount of liquid phase is small and the solid particles are not wetted, bonding will be by solid-state diffusion between adjacent solid particles, the same as for solid-phase sintering. Only when the liquid phase wets the solid particles does it greatly influence the sintering process.

Since wetting is of such importance to the liquid-phase sintering process it is worthwhile considering some of the elementary facts relating to this phenomenon. Consider Fig. 34 (*a*), at equilibrium:

$$\cos \theta = \frac{\gamma_{SG} - \gamma_{SL}}{\gamma_{LG}} \qquad (13)$$

where θ is the contact angle, γ_{LG} the liquid–gas interfacial energy, γ_{SG} the solid–gas interfacial energy and γ_{SL} is the liquid–solid interfacial energy. When the liquid phase completely wets the solid and thereby completely envelopes the solid particles the contact angle is zero. If θ is greater than 90° then the total surface energy of the system is reduced by removal of the liquid phase from the system (and it has been found that in non-wetting liquid-phase sintering systems the liquid phase will 'sweat out' of the compact as predicted).

Surface energy considerations also determine whether a liquid phase will penetrate between two grains and, for instance, separate two solid particles which have sintered together. The factors governing penetration of a liquid-phase alloy into a grain boundary (Fig. 34 (*b*)) are:

$$\gamma_{LS} < \gamma_{GB}, \text{ complete penetration}$$
$$\text{of grain boundary by liquid alloy} \qquad (14)$$
$$\gamma_{LS} = \gamma_{GB}, \ \phi \text{ will be } 120° \qquad (15)$$
$$\gamma_{LS} > \gamma_{GB}, \ \phi \text{ will be } 180° \qquad (16)$$

where γ_{GB} is the grain boundary energy, γ_{LS} the liquid–solid interfacial energy and ϕ is the dihedral angle. One of the most important practical effects of these surface energy considerations is the effect on grain growth during liquid-phase sintering. The low liquid–solid interfacial energy which accompanies complete wetting also encourages grain-boundary penetration. Thus, where complete wetting occurs, any solid-state bonds will usually be destroyed and very little grain growth will occur. On the other hand, incomplete wetting may leave intact many solid bonds and grain growth may occur.

When a liquid phase has been formed which completely wets the solid phase, the particles will be rearranged under the action of surface energy

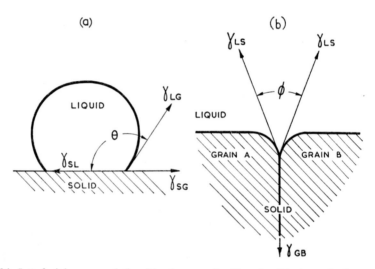

FIG. 34. Interfacial-energy relationships between liquid and solid phases in the case of (a) a liquid droplet on a solid surface and (b) a liquid phase at a grain-boundary junction.

forces to give a higher density. According to Kingery,[13] the surface-tension forces cause a negative pressure in the pores which is equivalent to placing the whole system under hydrostatic pressure. The pressure P is related to the surface tension of the liquid (γ_L) and the pore radius (r) as follows:

$$P = \frac{2\gamma_{LG}}{r} \tag{17}$$

As an example of the magnitude of the pressures developed, Kingery uses the iron–copper system and obtains the results given in Table 7.

As the rearrangement process takes place the pore size remains small, and thus the pressure high, throughout the sintering process. Porosity can only

Table 7. Pore Pressures developed in the Liquid-phase
Sintering of Iron–Copper
(*after Kingery*[13])

Pore radius (microns)	Pressure	
	dynes/cm²	lb/in²
100	$0 \cdot 26 \times 10^6$	3·7
10	$2 \cdot 6 \times 10^6$	37
1	$25 \cdot 6 \times 10^6$	370
0·1	256×10^6	3700

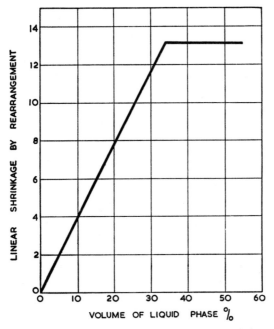

FIG. 35. Relationships between the volume of liquid phase and the amount of linear shrinkage which can occur due to particle rearrangement.

be completely eliminated by particle rearrangement if there is sufficient liquid phase to fill the interstices between the solid particles at maximum packing density. Fig. 35 shows how the maximum density due to particle rearrangement is related to the amount of liquid phase formed for the case where the maximum packing density of the solid phase is 65%. In practice it is found that complete densification can occur at liquid phase contents lower than that predicted by the considerations used in obtaining Fig. 35. For this to occur it is necessary for material of the solid phase to be transported through the liquid phase so that solid particles can change their shape and thereby alter the packing density. Therefore, complete densification with small liquid phase content only occurs when the solid phase is soluble to some extent in the liquid. The process of solution and re-precipitation was first suggested by Price, Smithells and Williams[14] who believed that the driving force was due to the higher solubility of small particles compared with larger particles. Kingery,[13] however, has shown that this explanation is inadequate since the difference in solubility of a small particle compared with that of a flat surface is insufficient to account for the observed transport. Furthermore, Kingery notes that transfer from a flat surface to a highly curved surface has also been observed. Kingery suggests that the stresses due to surface tension forces (and which cause the particle rearrangement) are concentrated in areas where the solid grains are separated by only a thin liquid film. One effect of this stress concentration is to cause a change in the chemical potential or activity. This difference in activity between the highly stressed areas and the other parts of the particle surface is believed to result in solution of the solid phase at the area of stress concentration, and this is followed by precipitation in the areas of lower stress. This theory suggests a mechanism whereby a change in particle shape occurs which allows packing to a higher density and ultimately elimination of porosity.

Infiltration

The infiltration process is of importance in powder metallurgy both as a method of eliminating porosity and of preparing two-phase structures. A porous metal skeleton is first prepared and is then brought into contact with a molten metal (the infiltrant) which fills the pores. Capillary forces are responsible for the complete filling of the skeleton. Infiltration is strictly a post-sintering process rather than true sintering. However, in practice, infiltration is related closely to liquid-phase sintering, particularly since the time for which the compact is maintained at the infiltration temperature is usually longer than is necessary for complete penetration. The conditions which exist after penetration are similar to those which are found in liquid-phase sintering.

The first requirement of a suitable infiltrant is that its melting point must be considerably below that of the skeleton metal. Other requirements are that it does not form high melting-point compounds with the skeleton metal and that it must wet the skeleton metal. It is also desirable that skeleton metal and infiltrant have only limited solubility in each other; this require-ment is chiefly of importance when the individual melting points are relatively close together.

Schwarzkopf,[15] discussing the mechanism of infiltration, has pointed out that while wetting is necessary in order for the infiltrant to displace the air within the compact and completely to fill all the interconnected porosity, it is not essential that the dihedral angle is zero. Complete wetting, although not essential, produces structural changes, because with a zero dihedral angle the liquid infiltrant will penetrate the grain boundaries and separate the skeleton particles which have previously sintered together.

The simplest infiltration technique is to place a compact or sheet of the required infiltrant metal in contact with the skeleton compact and to pass this through a sintering furnace. A disadvantage of this method is that if the skeleton metal is soluble in the infiltrant it may be badly eroded at the contact surface. This effect may be overcome by using an alloy infiltrant whose composition corresponds to its solubility limit in the skeleton metal. An alternative way of combating erosion is the 'bridge' method. A piece of porous metal (bridge) is placed between the infiltrant and the skeleton, and after passing through the bridge the infiltrant is saturated with the skeleton metal. It is also possible to infiltrate by immersing the sintered part in a bath of molten infiltrant.

Chemical Reactions

Sintering is almost invariably performed in a controlled atmosphere. Neutral atmospheres merely displace air from around the compact, while reducing atmospheres also bring about chemical decomposition of surface compounds.

Before discussing the various types of sintering atmospheres and their applications and limitations, it will help to consider some of the relevant characteristics of a 'green' compact. Surface oxides or nitrides may be present on powder particles and there will be adsorbed gas layers. These characteristics are retained in a compact and, in addition, there will be air which has become mechanically entrapped during the compacting process. Surface oxides are usually continuous, thin films, but in some cases discrete particles, resulting from the powder production process, may be present. Where a continuous film is present this may be ruptured at the particle contact points during compacting. Also covering the particle surfaces will be the layers of adsorbed gases. While it may, in some cases, be possible to prevent the formation of surface oxides, it is virtually impossible to obviate these adsorbed layers.

There are two distinct types of adsorption depending on the forces involved, namely, physical (or van der Waals') adsorption, and chemisorption. Physically adsorbed gases form films many molecules thick, and these gas films can usually be removed by heating *in vacuo*. The forces causing this physical adsorption are the same as the attractive forces which cause departure from ideal gas laws, liquefaction, etc. Heats of physical adsorption are usually low (less than 5 kcal/mole). According to Trapnell[16] physical adsorption does not usually occur unless p/p_0 exceeds 0·01 (p is the gas pressure at a certain temperature and p_0 the saturation vapour pressure at that temperature). Gases which are chemisorbed are much more strongly bound to the metal surface than those which are physically adsorbed. Ordinary chemical affinity is no guide to chemisorption. For instance, tungsten, which does not form a stable nitride, chemisorbs nitrogen; whereas aluminium, which forms a stable nitride, does not. In chemisorption, electron transfer occurs between the adsorbent and the adsorbate. Heats of chemisorption are usually greater than 10 kcal. Whereas physical adsorption may give an adsorbed film many molecules thick, chemisorption is essentially monomolecular. Chemisorbed gases are difficult, if not impossible, to remove from metal surfaces. Tomkins[17] cites the example of oxygen on tungsten where heating to 1500°C for one year in high vacuum does not remove the chemisorbed layer, and although heating to 2200°C will drive off the oxygen this occurs by rupture of the W—W bonds not the W—O link.

An interesting study of gases mechanically entrapped in pores during compacting has been made by Williams.[18] The technique used enabled him to distinguish between gases mechanically entrapped and adsorbed gases. Powder was compacted in air in a conventional die set and it was found that about 80% of the air present in the loose powder prior to compacting was retained in the compact. A consequence of this is that the gas within the pores is at a pressure greater than atmospheric. After compacting at 80 tons/in², Williams found an internal gas pressure of 15·5 atm. Due to the internal pressure the gas effused but only slowly. Williams' data also showed that at low compacting pressures (12 and 22 tons/in²) the amount of adsorbed gas is equal to that entrapped. The amount of adsorbed gas decreases as the surface area is reduced by increasing the compacting pressure.

It is against this background that the chemical interaction between the sintering atmosphere and the compact must be viewed. If the principal mechanism by which a neutral atmosphere works is physical displacement of the air from within the pores, it is apparent from Williams' data that this process will achieve little unless the furnace is first held under a reduced pressure for a considerable time to draw out the air contained within the pores. Unless this is done it seems inevitable that, so far as most metals are concerned, the composition of the gas within the pores will be such that compound formation is likely to occur during sintering.

The likely presence of oxides in the powder, or formation of oxides during sintering, shows why reducing atmospheres are to be preferred and thus the characteristics of reducing reactions are of importance. Consider the typical reaction:

$$FeO + H_2 \rightleftharpoons Fe + H_2O \tag{18}$$

The velocity of the forward (reduction) reaction (V_f) is:

$$V_f = [FeO][H_2] \times K_f \qquad (19)$$

where [FeO] and [H_2] are the activities.

Similarly the velocity of the reverse reaction is:

$$V_b = [Fe][H_2O] \times K_b \qquad (20)$$

At equilibrium $V_f = V_b$ and therefore,

$$\frac{[Fe][H_2O]}{[FeO][H_2]} = K, \text{ the equilibrium constant} \qquad (21)$$

More usually this is written:

$$\frac{P_{Fe}P_{H_2O}}{P_{FeO}P_{H_2}} = K \qquad (22)$$

where the prefix P denotes the concentration in atmospheres. Since the above equation involves two solids which have negligible vapour pressures, this approximates to:

$$K \simeq \frac{P_{H_2O}}{P_{H_2}} \qquad (23)$$

If the reaction involves a change of volume such as:

$$C + CO_2 \rightleftharpoons 2CO \qquad (24)$$

then

$$K = \frac{P^2_{CO}}{P_{CO_2}} \qquad (25)$$

Thus from knowledge of the equilibrium constant, K, for various reactions, and the way in which it varies with temperature, it is possible to calculate gas compositions to give reducing conditions. The temperature dependence of K can be calculated from the relationship:

$$\Delta G_T = -RT \log K \qquad (26)$$

Values of ΔG_T are tabulated in many references and are often given in the form:

$$\Delta G_T = A + B \log_{10} T + CT \qquad (27)$$

where A, B and C are constants.

The energies of reaction may be added accordingly to Hess's principle, for instance for the reaction:

$$Fe_2O_3 + 3H_2 \rightleftharpoons 2Fe + 3H_2O \qquad (28 (a))$$

the ΔG_T may be obtained by combining the ΔG_T values for Fe_2O_3 and H_2O, e.g.

$$3(H_2) + 1\tfrac{1}{2}(O_2) = 3H_2O \qquad\qquad (28\ (b))$$

and

$$2Fe + 1\tfrac{1}{2}(O_2) = Fe_2O_3 \qquad\qquad (28\ (c))$$

thus

$$G_T\Delta\ (a) = \Delta G_T\ (b) - \Delta G_T\ (c)$$

A thorough treatment of the thermodynamics of such reactions is given by Kubaschewski and Evans.[19]

The usual reducing atmospheres used in sintering are based on hydrogen or hydrocarbon derivatives. Reduction with pure hydrogen or dissociated

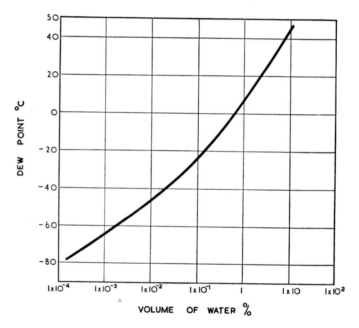

FIG. 36. Variation of water content with dew point.

ammonia (the nitrogen can usually be considered inert) is fairly straightforward and readily interpreted in terms of the elementary theories discussed above. The principal important impurity in commercial hydrogen is water vapour (or oxygen whose reaction with hydrogen to form water is readily catalysed) and since water is also the product of reduction reactions the purity of hydrogen (and hence its reduction ability) is often described in terms of dew point. Fig. 36 gives the relationship between dew point and water content.

With the second type of reducing atmosphere, that obtained by burning hydrocarbons, the situation is rather more complex. For instance, combusting methane with various ratios of air will give atmospheres containing varying amounts of unreacted methane, carbon monoxide, carbon dioxide,

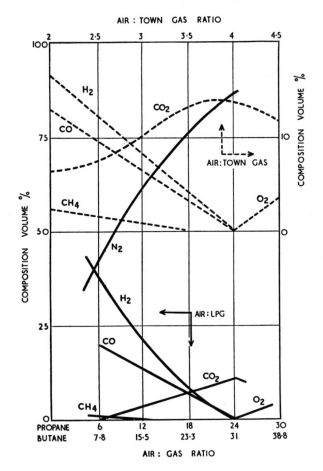

FIG. 37. The influence of air:gas ratio on the composition of the atmosphere produced by the combustion of town gas, propane and butane.

hydrogen and water, as well as inert nitrogen. Furthermore, when the metal being sintered has a high affinity for carbon, as does iron, then decarburization–carburization equilibria must also be considered. Compositions of atmospheres derived from various hydrocarbons are shown in Fig. 37.

With a knowledge of equilibrium constants it is, in most cases, not difficult to specify an atmosphere which ought to provide reducing conditions for a particular metal. However, it was pointed out earlier that it is very likely that the conditions inside the pores of a compact differ greatly from those in the

Table 8. Dissociation Pressures of Oxides (mmO$_2$)

Compound	Temperature, °K					
	600	800	1000	1200	1400	1600
CuO	1.1×10^{-11}	1.9×10^{-5}	8.0×10^{-2}	19	—	—
Cu$_2$O	1.5×10^{-19}	2.5×10^{-12}	5.0×10^{-8}	3.3×10^{-5}	—	—
Fe$_2$O$_3$	1.4×10^{-24}	1.9×10^{-14}	3.3×10^{-8}	4.1×10^{-4}	3×10^{-1}	—
NiO	—	—	3.5×10^{-13}	4.9×10^{-9}	4.3×10^{-6}	6.8×10^{-4}
CoO	—	—	8.3×10^{-15}	1.4×10^{-10}	1.2×10^{-7}	2.1×10^{-5}
Cr$_2$O$_3$	—	—	2.5×10^{-28}	9.4×10^{-22}	4.5×10^{-17}	1.5×10^{-13}
Mn$_2$O$_3$	—	3.5×10^{-5}	1.6×10^{-1}	7.54	—	—

Table 9. Vapour Pressures of Some Common Metals

Vapour pressure torr ⟶	Temperature, °C						Melting point °C
	10^{-5}	10^{-4}	10^{-3}	10^{-2}	10^{-1}	1	
Aluminium				1210			660
Carbon		2100	2250	2430			3730
Chromium	1060	1160	1270				1875
Cobalt	1160	1260					1495
Copper		1030	1140	1270	1430	1620	1083
Iron	1110	1210	1320				1537
Lead	490	550	630	720	830	980	327
Manganese	700	770	850	950	1070	1230	1245
Molybdenum	1990	2170					2610
Nickel	1140	1250	1360				1455
Niobium	2190	2360	2500				2470
Silicon	1180	1280	1360	1550	1720	1930	1410
Silver	760	830	920	1030			960
Tantalum	2400	2590	2810				3000
Tin			1090	1230	1400		231
Tungsten	2550	2760	3010	3330	3650		3410
Vanadium	1430	1551					1900
Zinc		250	290	340			420

furnace. It is always necessary, therefore, to aim for atmospheres of much lower water-vapour content, etc. than that indicated by simple equilibrium calculations. Moreover, reactions between sintering atmospheres and the furnace should not be overlooked. When refractory materials are exposed to the sintering atmosphere then unwanted reactions may occur which will raise the water vapour content of the atmosphere. This complication is best avoided either by using high-purity refractories in the furnace construction or by employing a metallic muffle to contain the atmosphere.

One type of sintering 'atmosphere' not yet considered is vacuum. Vacuum sintering has a number of advantages over gaseous neutral and reducing atmospheres, of which the positive removal of air from interconnected porosity is very important. Most vacuum sintering of metal powders uses pressures in the range 1 to 1×10^{-4} torr. This cannot be regarded as complete removal of gas, as there are sufficient quantities of gas remaining in the atmosphere for chemical reactions to occur. Chemical reactions will occur according to the principles given above, since equilibrium constants depend only on the partial pressures of reactants. Two further factors which must often be taken into account when considering low-pressure reactions are: (i) that dissociation of compounds and evaporation of some metals can occur to an extent sufficient to affect the equilibrium and (ii) there will often be carbon compounds present due to back-streaming and cracking of pumping oils (or from reactions with graphite heating elements when these are employed). The dissociation pressure is of particular importance; consider the following, oxide RO can be represented as being in equilibrium

$$RO \rightleftharpoons R + O \qquad (29)$$

The reaction will proceed until the partial pressure of oxygen reaches a certain value (the dissociation pressure) and then equilibrium will be maintained. If the pumping capacity at the dissociation pressure is such that oxygen is being continuously removed from the system, dissociation will continue. Some values of the dissociation pressures of common oxides are given in Table 8, while Table 9 gives the vapour pressures of some common metals.

SINTERING PRACTICE

The discussion of sintering so far has been confined to the underlying principles. It has been shown that the process involves heating a metal-powder body to some appropriate temperature in a controlled atmosphere. The aims of sintering practice, therefore, are to regulate the temperature, the time of heating (and sometimes the heating rate) and the characteristics of the controlled atmosphere. It is necessary that the operation shall be achieved as cheaply as possible. Vacuum sintering, for instance, although frequently giving a technically superior product, is too costly for many competitive items.

There are two main items of plant involved in sintering, the furnace with its auxillary power and control equipment and the plant for generating the controlled atmosphere.

Sintering Furnaces

The choice of a sintering furnace for a particular sintering operation depends on a number of factors of which the most important are: (i) the temperature range, (ii) the type and purity of atmosphere, (iii) the maximum size of the compacts and (iv) the required throughput. It will be convenient to assess the various types of furnace in terms of these factors.

A distinction must also be made between continuous and batch-operated furnaces. Continuous furnaces are more expensive to install but give much greater outputs than do batch furnaces; overall they result in lower sintering costs if there is sufficient volume of work and this fact makes them essential for processes where minimum cost is important.

An important feature of the continuous furnace is the mechanism by which the charge is conveyed through the furnace. The preferred method of achieving this is by a moving belt. Mesh belts are normally employed and their load-carrying ability and maximum-operating temperature are of some importance to the powder-metal industry. At the present time mesh belts can be used, with reasonable work loads, at temperatures up to about 1150°C. If continuous furnaces working above 1150°C are required another, less reliable, more complex and more expensive conveying system becomes necessary. For low-cost production, therefore, the furnace conveyor system is one of a number of factors which imposes an economic upper limit on the sintering temperature. At temperatures of about 1300°C there are a number of alternative means of conveying work through a furnace. Roller-hearth and walking-beam arrangements have been tried but the most successful seems to be linking together the boats which contain the work and pulling and/or pushing these through the furnace. In this case the ability of the boat material to withstand the loads needed to overcome friction dictates the upper temperature limit, which seems to be about 1350°C for cheap metal boats (mild steel). For still higher temperatures a pusher system can be used which imposes only compressive stresses on the boats. At these high temperatures refractory metal, ceramic or graphite boats are necessary; in some designs the furnace is tilted so that gravity assists the travel of the charge. Continuous furnaces have been operated up to about 2000°C. In batch furnaces, Plate 5 (a), the charge is stationary and, therefore, the temperature limitations imposed by conveyor systems do not apply. Batch furnaces may therefore be designed for temperatures up to 3000°C.

Very large compacts are not produced in sufficiently large quantities to justify the use of expensive continuous furnaces. Continuous furnaces (Plate 5 (b)) are made in the form of tunnels and it is unusual to build these more than

18 in. wide for use at 1150°C; at higher temperatures 8–12 in. wide furnaces are more usual.

Batch furnaces show some advantages when high purity or critically controlled sintering atmospheres are needed. Vacuum furnaces are a special case; they are always batch operated, although semi-continuous furnaces are now being developed. If it is required to operate with a high-purity atmosphere in a batch furnace it is possible for the air inside the furnace to be removed, either by prolonged purging or by pre-evacuation. Subsequent ingress of air can be prevented by correct design of seals and by operating the furnaces at a slight positive pressure. Such methods are impracticable in continuous furnaces because the ends through which the work enters and is discharged cannot be sealed completely. To minimize the amount of air entering continuous furnaces, devices such as curtains of burning gas are often employed; when components are placed loosely on mesh-belts this is fairly effective in keeping the air out. Another method of minimizing air ingress when hydrogen atmospheres are used is to employ a hump-backed furnace (Plate 6 (a)). In this type of furnace the central (sintering) zone is at a higher level than the ends, and since the sintering atmosphere is much lighter than air the centre zone retains a 'pure' atmosphere. For high-temperature furnaces, where the work is packed in refractory powder in boats, a great deal of air may be carried into the furnace. A way of combating this is to incorporate a getter in the packing powder; chromium-steel powder or swarf, aluminium, titanium, etc. have been advocated for this purpose. In continuous furnaces operating below about 1200°C, reactions between the sintering atmosphere and the furnace refractories may be prevented by employing a metallic muffle (iron–chromium–nickel alloys are generally used).

Continuous furnaces give a somewhat more consistent product than do batch furnaces. This is due to a number of factors of which the most important are that in continuous furnaces (i) all the compacts pass through the same maximum-temperature zone and remain in it for the same time, and (ii) the heating and cooling rates are the same for all compacts. With batch furnaces the work nearest the heating elements has a significantly different heating and cooling rate from that in the centre and, even if a homogeneous temperature distribution is obtained, the whole of the work will not attain this temperature at the same time. Thus continuous furnaces have a technical advantage where sintering times and temperatures are very critical.

One final factor which can determine the type of sintering furnace chosen is the time of sintering (or the rate of heating). Long sintering times are normally impracticable in a continuous furnace since they would mean extremely long hot zones unless the speed of travel of the belt were very slow. In practice, continuous furnaces usually operate with sintering times of $\frac{1}{4}$–2 hours and may become uneconomical for longer times of sintering.

8

Summarizing the factors governing the choice of continuous or batch furnaces: continuous furnaces are preferred where large quantities are involved, because of their consistency and relatively low sintering cost per piece; batch furnaces are appropriate for small quantities of work and for extreme conditions, e.g. extremes of temperature, atmospheric purity and compact size.

Sintering furnaces are almost always electrically heated, although gas-fired furnaces have been used and attempts have been made to use the combustion products to provide the sintering atmosphere. The majority of electric furnaces are resistance heated, the choice of element material depending upon the required temperature range. Furnaces working in the range 800–1150°C, in which the bulk of copper and iron-base materials are sintered, normally use nickel–chromium alloy heaters; the iron–chromium–aluminium alloys are less often used. In vacuum furnaces the chromium-containing alloys have somewhat lower maximum-operating temperatures than those given above, because of the volatility of this element.

Molybdenum is the most common element material for sintering temperatures in the range 1300–1700°C. Because of the very low oxidation resistance of molybdenum a protective atmosphere must be provided around these elements; usually the sintering atmosphere performs this function, although atmospheres containing carbon are unsuitable since molybdenum carbide may form. For still higher temperatures the use of tungsten is possible, but wire and strip are not readily available in sufficient lengths to provide elements for large furnaces. Most sintering furnaces operating above 2000°C have graphite elements. Graphite heaters have to be made in forms which necessitate the use of low-voltage high-current power supplies. Molybdenum, tungsten, tantalum and graphite are all suitable for use in high-temperature vacuum furnaces, although graphite and molybdenum are not recommended for use above about 2000°C.

One form of resistance heating not previously mentioned is that in which the powder compact is also the resistance element, i.e. direct-resistance sintering. This technique is of particular value in the production of the refractory metals, because the very high temperatures (2500–3000°C) required can be easily obtained, and reaction between the compact and its support is completely avoided. The terminal connections are water cooled to prevent them welding to the compact, and because of this the compact ends are not fully sintered and must be discarded. This method is, therefore, only of value for materials to be used for secondary fabrication.

A feature of sintering which has not yet been referred to is dewaxing, i.e. the removal of lubricants. In commercial operations it is usual to add lubricants to the powders to improve pressing characteristics. The usual lubricants are paraffin wax, stearates, etc. If these were volatilized in the hot zone of the sintering furnace they could cause undesirable reactions. For instance, they might lead to alteration of atmosphere characteristics resulting in carburization of the work or the heating elements. Lubricants are therefore removed before sintering commences and it is usual to carry out the dewaxing operation at the lowest possible temperature in an oxidizing atmosphere so that evolution of carbon dioxide and water vapour occurs. To prevent these gases from contaminating the sintering atmosphere the dewaxing section of the furnace is often separated from the sintering portion. If any oxidation of the metal occurs this is usually easily reduced by the sintering atmosphere; such mild oxidation has, in fact, been recommended for iron parts as an aid to good bonding. In dewaxing, the temperature must be raised slowly so that violent gas evolution does not occur.

Sintering Atmospheres

It was noted previously that most sintering atmospheres are reducing, although inert atmospheres such as nitrogen, helium and argon also find some application.

Hydrogen, for many applications, would be the preferred sintering atmosphere but for its high cost. Even when cheap hydro-electric power is available for on-site production of electrolytic hydrogen the cost still limits its use to rather special applications. A cheaper source of hydrogen and one much more widely used, is dissociated (or 'cracked') ammonia. Catalytic decomposition of ammonia produces a gas which consists of 25% nitrogen and 75% hydrogen (by volume). Reference has already been made to the need for hydrogen atmospheres to have a low water content (low dew point). One of the important advantages of ammonia dissociation is that the liquid ammonia can be prepared virtually water-free; typically a dew point of $-60°C$ can be obtained directly from a correctly functioning cracker. In those cases where stable oxides need to be reduced, the use of metal hydrides, which dissociate to liberate highly reactive 'nascent' hydrogen, is recommended. A well-known example of this principle is the incorporation of titanium hydride in Alnico compacts to reduce the stable alumina films on the aluminium-rich master alloy.

The most important of the atmospheres used in commercial sintering are those which consist of carbon monoxide, carbon dioxide, hydrogen and nitrogen with traces of water vapour, etc. These atmospheres are obtained by combusting natural gas (methane), liquefied petroleum gases (propane or butane) or town gas, etc. The gas composition obtained from this combustion depends upon the air–gas ratio and, as is shown in Fig. 37, variations of this ratio can produce mixtures ranging from very reducing gases (which are rich in hydrogen and carbon monoxide) to a neutral gas in which carbon dioxide and nitrogen are the principal constituents. (Water vapour will also be formed during combustion, the amount being inversely proportional to the free hydrogen content; the water is removed before use.) Gases with high air–gas ratios are termed 'exothermic', because when they are produced the heat of combustion is sufficient to maintain the reaction. With lower air–gas ratios additional heat must be supplied to maintain the reaction (a catalyst is also used to assist this), and the gas is then termed 'endothermic' or more simply 'endogas'; it is strongly reducing and carburizing. Since a smaller volume of gas is obtained by producing endogas it is more expensive than exothermic gas. The cost (1959) of endothermic gas produced from liquefied petroleum gases was 3s per 1,000 ft³ for bulk production and about 4s 6d per 1,000 ft³ for small quantities, about the same as preparation from town gas.

Occasional use may be made of inert atmospheres for sintering, and of these nitrogen and carbon dioxide are the cheapest. Nitrogen may be obtained from cylinders where consumption is small. Larger quantities can be prepared by combusting dissociated ammonia and removing the water vapour. Carbon dioxide is also available in cylinders and cheap carbon dioxide–nitrogen mixtures are available from 'lean' exothermic gas. Argon and helium are completely inert gases but cost restricts their use.

As was shown earlier, it is essential to maintain a low water vapour content in sintering atmospheres. Since in many cases water is formed during the production of sintering atmosphere gases, methods of gas drying must often be provided. The dew point of a gas represents the amount of water required to saturate it at a given temperature and one method of removing water is to cool the gas to the required dew point temperature. Temperatures down to about 5°C may be obtained with normal water supplies which will reduce the water content of 'wet' gases to about 1%. Refrigeration can be used to obtain 'drier' gas, but it is normally too expensive to produce gas drier than about −10°C dew point. For dew points between −10°C and 60°C, the most important range for most sintering applications, the final drying is done with chemicals. The most important of these chemicals is 'activated' alumina, its great virtue being the ease with which it can be regenerated. For still drier gas, such as may be required in the laboratory, molecular sieves may be used down to about −100°C dew point, while for hydrogen gas, diffusion through palladium will remove substantially all impurities as well as water vapour. It is also usually necessary to remove free oxygen. This is often accomplished by catalytic oxidation with platinized asbestos to form water (adding hydrogen gas if necessary) and then removing the water by one of the drying methods given above. Oxygen may also be removed by gettering, i.e. passing the gas over a metal which has a high affinity for oxygen and whose oxide is not reduced by the dried gas. The getter may sometimes be sited within the furnace.

Mention has been made earlier of vacuum furnaces and vacuum sintering.

A mechanical (or rotary) pump is used to provide the 'rough' (or fore) vacuum. Mechanical pumps work most efficiently in the pressure range 760–0·05 torr; below this their pumping speed is very low. Higher vacua are usually obtained by oil-diffusion pumps. Diffusion pumps (which must be backed by suitable mechanical pumps to provide the fore pressure) have good pumping speeds, down to about 1×10^{-4} torr. Even faster pumping speeds may be obtained from vapour-booster pumps.

REFERENCES

1. Kuczynski, G. C. in *Powder Metallurgy*, Leszynski (ed.), 11, Interscience, New York (1961).
2. Frenkel, J. *J. Phys. (U.S.S.R.)*, Interscience, **9**, 5, 385 (1945).
3. Mackenzie, J. K. and Shuttleworth, R. *Proc. phys. Soc.*, B **62**, 12, 833 (1949).
4. Kingery, W. D. and Berg, M. *J. appl. Phys.*, **26**, 10, 1205 (1955).
5. Alexander, B. H. and Baluffi, R. W. *Acta met.*, **5**, 11, 666 (1957).
6. Arthur, G. *J. Inst. Met.*, **83**, 7, 329 (1955).
7. Eudier, M. Symposium on Powder Metallurgy, 1954 (*Special Rept. No. 58*), 59, 1956, London (Iron and Steel Institute).
8. Rhines, F. N., Birchenall, C. E. and Hughes, L. A. *Trans. Amer. Inst. min. Engrs.*, 188, 378 (1950).
9. Le Claire, A. D. in *Progress in Metal Physics*, Chalmers (ed.), **1**, 306, Pergamon Press (1949).
10. Brattain, W. H. and Becker, A. *Phys. Rev.*, **43**, 428 (1933).
11. Huttig, G. F. *Metallwirtschaft*, **23**, 367 (Oct., 1944).
12. Seith, W. and Schmeken, H. *Z. Elektrochem.*, **54**, 222 (1950).
13. Kingery, W. D. in *Kinetics of High-Temperature Processes*, Kingery (ed.), 187, M.I.T. and Wiley, New York (1959).
14. Price, C. H. S., Smithells, C. J. and Williams, S. V. *J. Inst. Met.*, **62**, 239 (1938).
15. Schwarzkopf, P. Symposium on Powder Metallurgy, 1954 (*Special Rept. No. 58*), 55, 1956, London (Iron and Steel Institute).
16. Trapnell, B. M. W. *Proc. roy. Soc.*, A. **218**, 1135, 566 (1953).
17. Tomkins, F. C. *Nature*, **186**, 4718, 3 (1960).
18. Williams, J. *J. Iron St. Inst.*, **172**, 1, 19 (1952).
19. Kubaschewski, O. and Evans, E. Ll. *Metallurgical Thermochemistry*, 3rd edn., Pergamon Press (1958).

CHAPTER 5

ENGINEERING COMPONENTS

In this and subsequent chapters the more important products of the powder-metallurgy industry are discussed. Most of these products, cemented carbides, porous filters, etc., could not reasonably be produced other than from powders, and therefore the range and combination of properties they possess are unique. In such cases the properties which the powder metallurgy products possess are so advantageous that their use is rarely much restricted by the lower cost of alternatives produced by more conventional methods. The possibly high cost of the metal-powder product is more than offset by the economics or performance resulting from its properties. An example of this is the use of cemented-carbide tools for high-speed machining where, if the cheaper alloy-steel tools were employed, the slower machining rates that would be necessary would more than outweigh the higher initial cost of carbide tools.

Cost Considerations

In the field of engineering components the situation is different; the products could almost always be produced by other methods and only rarely are the properties of the sintered material superior overall to those which could be attained by the alternative production methods. Indeed, some of the properties of the powder part are usually markedly inferior and ductility, for instance, is often near to the minimum acceptable level. In this situation it is the low cost of the powder product that justifies its use. Costs then are the essence of the production of engineering components from powders and, because of this preoccupation with cost, the manufacturing philosophy in this field often differs widely from that for other powder metallurgy products.

It is instructive at this stage to consider some of the more important factors that affect the costs of sintered engineering components. One of the most important factors is the properties that are required and so far as sintered steels are concerned the relationship between properties, composition and cost is critical to their competitive position. For example, improving properties by increasing the density beyond a certain point is usually extremely expensive. Powder of high purity (and therefore greater cost) may be necessary to give better compressibility, or greater compacting pressures may be needed which either demands better tools (carbide instead of steel dies for instance) or more frequent tool replacement. Repressing (coining) may also be used to increase density but this, an additional operation, demands extra handling and requires a further set of tools, etc. Another factor which can increase costs is the dimensional accuracy required. The actual tolerance which it is possible to maintain easily varies, not only with the type of component and the alloy used, but also can be different for various dimensions of one component. For instance, it is easier to hold radial tolerances that are formed by the substantially rigid die than the axial tolerances that are produced by moving punches. However, it is not only during pressing that difficulties in maintaining tolerances are encountered, significant dimensional changes also occur during sintering. The factors that control the amount of shrinkage or growth on sintering are complex and, perhaps more important, are difficult to control. Therefore, if tolerances closer than a certain level are demanded, these can only be achieved with certainty by a sizing operation on the sintered part, which adds to the cost.

Cost considerations also play an important part in the selection of sintering furnaces, and in the choice of sintering temperatures and controlled atmospheres. Continuous furnaces are, of course, necessary to achieve the desired low cost and the number of parts being produced easily justifies their use. Wherever possible, sintering temperatures are kept below 1150°C, because, as was discussed in Chapter 4, at such temperatures the economical mesh-belt furnaces with nickel-chromium alloy heaters may be used (Plate 6 (b)). Even in this 'low sintering temperature' range relatively small changes can alter costs; for example, the higher belt loadings (weight of compacts per unit area of belt) which are possible at 1100°C compared with 1150°C can lead to significantly lower sintering costs per piece. Unfortunately, in order to meet the demands for better mechanical properties, it is often necessary to employ sintering temperatures higher than 1150°C and mesh-belt furnaces are no longer usable. Instead pusher-type or walking-beam furnaces, heated by molybdenum resistance elements, must be used and these have smaller throughputs than the mesh-belt furnaces and also present problems of element protection. When nickel–chromium alloy heating elements are used the cheaper sintering atmospheres based on combusted hydrocarbons are often suitable, but with molybdenum resistors atmospheres containing carbon monoxide, methane, etc., must be avoided and resort is generally made to dissociated ammonia. Maintenance costs are also greater with molybdenum furnaces and such costs are sensitive to modest temperature changes (say from 1300°C to 1350°C); 1350°C, in fact, appears to be the maximum sintering temperature at which economic throughput and reasonable furnace life can be achieved.

It is apparent from the above that the fields in which powder metallurgy can compete with other manufacturing processes are limited to certain property levels and certain tolerance limits. These present limits are not such that the powder metallurgist cannot overcome them, but rather that the techniques necessary to overcome them would make the process uneconomic. It also follows that a purchaser looking for a product at the lowest possible cost must avoid specifying unduly high quality standards or dimensional accuracies. So far as accuracy is concerned it is rare that all dimensions on a part need to be held to the same tolerances; by specifying only the essential requirement substantial savings in cost may result.

Apart from the limitations to the fields of application for sintered engineering components, which are imposed by the property-cost and accuracy-cost considerations discussed above, there are also several factors which further limit the types of component made. There are obvious limits to the shape complexity that can be produced by high-speed die pressing. Many of the basic limitations have been discussed in Chapter 3. In some cases it is worthwhile machining sintered components in order to incorporate undercuts, transverse holes, screw-threads, etc., which cannot be directly moulded. Despite the machining operation many components are most cheaply produced by this combined process.

There are also definite limitations as to the size of component that can be produced. Rapid-acting presses larger than 100-tons capacity are still rare and since the usual range of compacting pressures for sintered engineering components is 20–35 tons/in², there is often a size limit of about 3–5 in² maximum cross-sectional area. The maximum length of component is also to some extent determined by the cross-sectional area and by the stroke of the available presses. Although presses of greater capacity than 100 tons are available, they are usually somewhat slower in operation than those preferred for producing engineering components. Rapid-acting presses are, of course, necessary to obtain economic utilization of floor area and to minimize labour and overhead costs.

Economic Quantities

One final factor that should be mentioned is the minimum number of components which it is economical to make of any one design. A few producers do not accept orders for quantities of less than 100,000 parts and 10,000 is often considered to be a reasonable lower limit. The principal reason for such minimum quantities is that unless very large quantities are produced the cost of the tooling cannot be spread sufficiently. There is also an appreciable cost accrued in setting up a press and again unless a large quantity of parts is involved the costs cannot be spread sufficiently to maintain the competitive position of the product. The high cost of producing a set of tools and setting into a press is also an embarrassment when preliminary samples are required. A practice often adopted is to machine samples from sintered blanks and only proceed with the manufacture of a tool set when a firm order is received. The practice of machining trial samples from 'blanks' must be used with caution because the local density variations present in a complex-shaped part will not be reproduced.

Because of the large contribution which tool costs make to total costs, it is almost always necessary to use the very best possible tool materials and construction, in order that the maximum possible number of components is obtained before replacement becomes necessary. Carbide-lined dies are now used on all except the rare short production runs; in general, quantities of up to 500,000 parts are expected from the best carbide dies. Carbide-faced punches are also becoming popular for both compacting and coining/sizing operations. These punches combine to some extent the toughness of the steel backing with the abrasion resistance and compressive strength of carbide. Owing to the high pressing loads used, punch lives are generally shorter than those of the die, 200,000 parts being considered a good performance.

The severe limitations under which the manufacturer of sintered engineering components works can be appreciated from the foregoing discussion. Quality targets are constantly being increased in order to meet competition from various sources, and yet the obvious means of achieving higher quality in powder metallurgy products often cannot be used because of the increased cost, etc. It is scarcely surprising that in order to meet the standards demanded powder metallurgists appeal for the opportunity to advise designers on how to take advantage of the potentially low-cost sintered materials. The desirability of consultations between the designer and the powder metallurgist cannot be too strongly emphasized; it is hardly possible for minimum cost to be achieved unless there is such consultation.

FERROUS MATERIALS

Just as wrought or cast steels are the most commonly used materials for general engineering, because of their properties, availability and low cost, so sintered ferrous materials predominate in the field of sintered engineering components. Iron powder is readily available at reasonable cost and a wide range of technically useful properties can be obtained with relatively simple (and thereby inexpensive) processing. The sintered ferrous alloys can be conveniently divided into three classes: those produced (i) by mixing elemental or master-alloy powders with iron, (ii) by infiltration of an iron skeleton and (iii) from pre-alloyed powders. The properties attainable in the various groups are discussed below.

Plain Iron

Iron without any alloying additions is rarely used, mainly because of its low strength. In certain cases, where strength is unimportant but appreciable ductility is needed, plain iron may be the preferred material. Probably the largest amount of sintered plain iron is used for parts where magnetic properties are required. (Further details of the use of sintered iron as a soft magnetic material are given in Chapter 10.) In general the magnetic properties which can be obtained (permeability, etc.) are lower than those of solid materials but their use is justified by the ease and low cost of producing complex shapes.

In those cases where the high ductility of sintered plain iron is needed, coupled with maximum attainable strength, then the highest possible density is necessary. Density may be considerably improved by coining but additionally much can be gained by employing the soft, high purity electrolytic iron powders; these are, however, considerably more expensive than reduced powders.

An indication of the properties of sintered iron of various densities is given in Fig. 38.

Sintering temperatures are commonly about 1150°C, although for best properties temperatures as high as 1300°C may be used. For maximum ductility fairly pure atmospheres are needed. Endogas is frequently used at the lower sintering temperatures, but it must be carefully controlled to prevent carburization. 'Cracked' ammonia is a satisfactory atmosphere for plain iron, although it is more costly than atmospheres derived fom hydrocarbons.

Iron–Carbon Alloys

The chief disadvantage of cheap plain iron is its low strength. A logical development has been, therefore, to follow established steel practice by adding carbon to the iron. It is essential that carbon is added as a separate powder, either as graphite or, less frequently, in the form of a carbon-rich alloy such as cast iron. Pre-alloyed iron–carbon is unsuitable because of its poor compressibility.

There have been a number of investigations of the properties of sintered iron–carbon alloys and it is clear that the principal factor in obtaining optimum properties is the selection of the raw materials. Practical experience shows that the carbon content can be varied over a fairly wide range without materially affecting the properties. Most commercial manufacturers, in fact, seem to aim for about the eutectoid composition. The oxide content of the iron powder is of some importance since this is reduced by the carbon at the sintering temperature with a consequent carbon loss. It is therefore customary to add more carbon than is desired in the final product to allow for this loss;

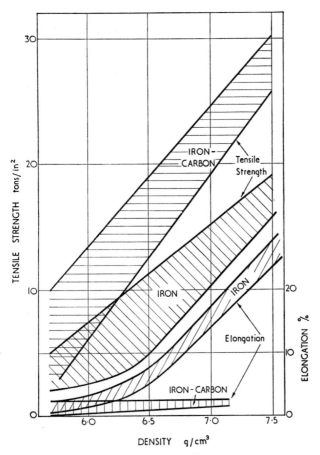

FIG. 38. The influence of density upon the strength and ductility of sintered iron and iron–carbon alloys.

typically 1·3% graphite might be mixed with the iron powder in order to obtain a 0·8% carbon alloy. To produce the most acceptable combination of strength and ductility it is essential that the carbon is taken into solid solution in the iron at the sintering temperature. The rate at which carbon dissolves in iron powder varies greatly according to the source of carbon employed. Natural graphite is reputed to be superior to the synthetic varieties. For maximum ductility carbon 'black' is sometimes used rather than a graphite; it has been suggested that the low ash content of carbon black is responsible for the better ductility. Fig. 38 shows the relationship between density, tensile strength and ductility for sintered iron–carbon alloys. Sintering conditions are generally similar to those used for plain iron, sintering temperatures of 1100–1150°C being the most usual. Ideally the carbon potential of the sintered atmosphere ought to be matched to the desired final carbon content throughout the furnace. In practice the delicate balance in the sintering atmosphere necessary to achieve this cannot be easily achieved throughout the whole length of the sintering furnace. Consequently it is more usual to aim for a non-decarburizing atmosphere, such as endogas, or even to use dissociated ammonia.

Iron–Copper Alloys

For many years the compositions produced from iron and copper occupied a dominant position in the field of sintered ferrous materials. Although these alloys have tended to lose their dominance during the last decade, particularly in Europe, they are still important to the powder metallurgy industry, and in the U.S.A. they probably remain the most widely employed of the sintered iron-base materials.

There are two distinct types of iron–copper materials, those produced by sintering mixtures of iron and copper powders and those produced by infiltrating copper into iron skeletons. Copper powder is an ideal additive to iron in many ways: its softness and ductility give good compressibility and high green strength; its surface oxide is easily reduced in the atmospheres commonly used for sintering iron; it forms a liquid phase well below 1150°C (a temperature of critical importance to sintering costs as discussed earlier); and finally, molten copper has only a limited solubility for iron (see Fig. 39). This is a remarkable list of advantages and it is not surprising that the iron–copper materials have been so popular.

Sintered iron–copper suffers from one grave disadvantage, the tendency for compacts to grow during sintering. Plain iron, like most metals, shrinks during sintering but the addition of $1-2\frac{1}{2}\%$ of copper eliminates shrinkage while greater amounts of copper cause definite dimensional increases. The growth of iron–copper compacts is generally considered to be due to the diffusion of copper into the iron particles at the sintering temperature. As the copper diffuses into the iron particles these expand giving a pronounced growth. The solubility of iron in copper is insufficient to compensate for the volume changes produced by copper diffusing into iron. Maximum growth is found with 8–10% copper, which corresponds to the solubility limit of copper in iron. Because of this growth a sizing operation is often necessary in order to maintain tolerances.

There have been many attempts to find additives which will inhibit the growth of iron–copper compacts.[1] Tungsten tri-oxide is reported to be very effective and it is claimed completely to eliminate growth. However, the oxide is rather expensive and is not often used. Phosphorus-rich compounds have been tried, but although successful in counteracting growth the volatile by-products which are formed cause rapid deterioration of the furnace. The amount of growth can also be decreased by using fine powders. In practice this solution to the problem cannot be employed, because not only do very fine powders give rise to flowability problems and other difficulties, but also

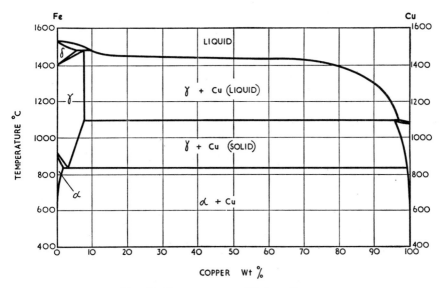

FIG. 39. Iron–copper equilibrium diagram.

the only powders which it is economical to use contain coarse particles (up to 100 mesh). Neither the heating nor cooling rate affects the growth, although the cooling rate does have some effect on the mechanical properties. Ductility is enhanced by slow cooling (which allows precipitation of a copper-rich phase), while fast cooling increases hardness and strength.

The most effective means of combating growth is to add carbon to the mix in the form of graphite. It is believed that a Fe–Cu–C eutectic forms, which melts at a temperature a little lower than the sintering temperature, thus allowing the iron skeleton to yield and shrink. About 1% graphite is usually added; this also increases the strength and acts as a useful lubricant during pressing. It is unfortunate that the growth-controlling effects of graphite seem to be very sensitive to the sintering-atmosphere composition.

In Figs. 40 and 41 some properties of various iron–copper materials are given, typical of current U.S.A., German and U.K. practice. Where the need for a sizing operation can be tolerated, or where dimensional tolerances are such that sizing is not necessary, the iron–copper alloys provide a useful

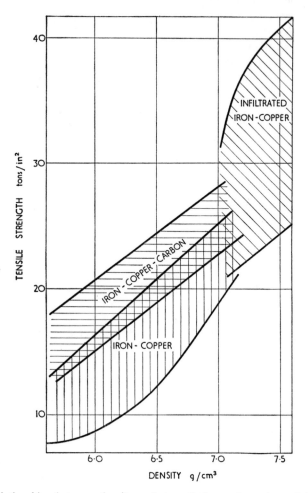

Fig. 40. Relationships between density and strength for various sintered iron–copper alloys.

combination of strength and ductility compared with other sintered iron-base materials. Where maximum wear resistance is needed iron–copper is not as good as some of the alternatives, because it is difficult to form a continuous hard surface by carburizing.

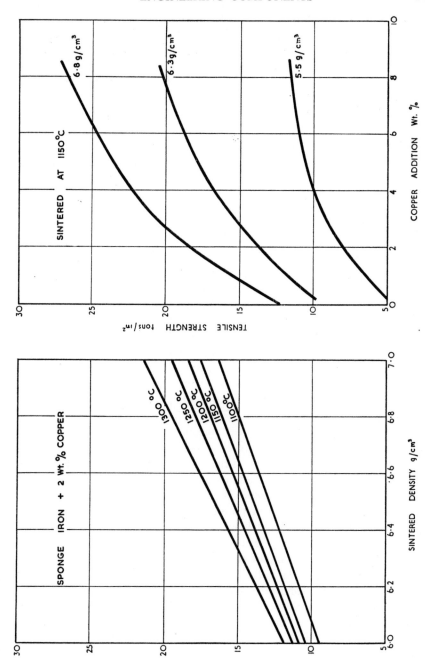

FIG. 41. The relationship between density, sintering temperature and copper content and their influence on tensile strength.

Iron infiltrated with copper is a very different material from that produced by mixing iron and copper powders. Unlike most other sintered materials used for engineering components, infiltrated iron is practically non-porous. The essential steps in the preparation of an infiltrated structure have been referred to in Chapter 4. The infiltration of iron by copper-rich alloys has been discussed by Elliot.[2]

Because of the significant solubility of iron in molten copper it is possible for the surface of iron parts to be badly eroded during infiltration. Formerly the 'bridge method' (see Chapter 4) was much used to overcome this erosion, but it is now more usual to use copper saturated with iron. Infiltration with a copper that is saturated with iron requires accurate temperature control. A slightly high infiltration temperature increases the solubility of copper for iron causing erosion, while infiltration is difficult just below the optimum temperature owing to the precipitation of iron. Infiltration temperatures are somewhat less critical when copper–iron–manganese alloys are used. A further advantage of these alloys is that the manganese acts as a getter for any oxygen present in the infiltrant or the furnace atmosphere and gives better infiltration. A powdery deposit of manganese-rich oxide is formed on the component surface which is easily removed. However, it has been found that when infiltrants containing manganese are used, up to 20% of the infiltrant weight remains on the surface as residue. Recently[3] it has been claimed that copper–cobalt alloy infiltrants are superior to copper–iron–manganese, as they give better strength and ductility properties without the formation of surface deposits. No erosion apparently occurs with copper–cobalt infiltrants, the cobalt decreasing the solubility of iron in copper.

As with the sintering of mixed iron–copper powders, infiltration causes a small growth which leads to difficulties in meeting precise tolerances, although Elliot[2] indicates that radial tolerances of 0·5% may be held on infiltrated parts. Dimensional correction of infiltrated iron by sizing is difficult, owing to the high strength and low porosity of the material.

Normally, infiltration with copper is carried out at 1100–1150°C. Equilibrium is complete within about 30 minutes, although the actual time allowed may be much less than this. Infiltration with manganese-containing alloys is also carried out in this temperature range. Infiltration can sometimes be combined with brazing; complex components which cannot be pressed in one piece have been built up in this way.

The properties of the infiltrated part depend to a surprisingly large extent upon the quality of the iron skeleton. Although a green skeleton can be successfully infiltrated, a pre-sintered skeleton produces better strength and very much higher ductility. Strength may also be increased by adding carbon or by increasing the density of the iron skeleton. Typical strength values for infiltrated iron are given in Fig. 40.

The infiltrated iron materials are among the strongest of the sintered materials used for engineering components. When the amount of infiltrant added is carefully controlled so that substantially all the pores are filled, good ductility accompanies the high strength.

Because of the properties obtainable, infiltrated iron has found widespread use, particularly in the U.S.A., for stressed components such as gears. The relatively high compression strength is also valuable where indentation is likely to occur. However, infiltration is an expensive process; not only must the component be heated twice, but three sets of tools may be needed and three pressing operations required to compact the skeleton and the infiltrant, and to size. Furthermore, about 20% of copper or copper-rich alloy, which is considerably more expensive than the iron, is required to fill the pores. Thus the use of infiltrated iron is essentially confined to those cases where high strength and good ductility are needed and where the manufacturer does not wish to exceed process temperatures of 1150°C.

Alloyed Irons

A serious drawback to the materials discussed so far is that appreciable ductility can only be obtained in rather weak (plain iron) or expensive (copper-infiltrated) materials. Because of this low ductility, in combination with the notch-effects of the pores, it is difficult for the full strength potential of the alloys to be developed and they therefore lack toughness. It is well known that, so far as wrought steels are concerned, the iron–carbon eutectoid alloy does not represent the optimum combination of strength and toughness. When high strength is required, together with appreciable ductility, it is usual to take advantage of the beneficial effects of alloying elements such as nickel, chromium, molybdenum, vanadium, etc. A fairly obvious development for sintered steels, therefore, has been to alloy in a similar manner.

The number of alloying elements which it is possible to use in practice is, however, very limited. One factor in particular which limits the possible additions is the great affinity for oxygen of elements such as chromium, vanadium, titanium, silicon, etc. In the protective atmospheres which are normally employed for sintering considerable amounts of oxide may be formed, and these oxides cause the product to be extremely brittle. Comparatively good properties can be obtained if special sintering atmospheres, such as very dry hydrogen or high vacuum, are employed, but these are much too expensive for widespread use. There are then only a few useful additions to iron powder and, of these, nickel is the most important. Nickel is not normally added alone but is usually employed in combination with carbon and sometimes also with copper. Another element which may be added is molybdenum (often as ferro–molybdenum), and occasionally certain of the highly oxidizable

9

elements (e.g. silicon and manganese) may be added when combined into master alloys with iron or nickel.

Relatively small additions of the various alloying elements are sufficient to achieve marked increases in strength. It might be thought therefore that many of the difficulties associated with the oxidizable elements could be avoided by using pre-alloyed powders. However, even if the pre-alloyed powders were of low carbon content (possible because a graphite addition would be made later) the high strength and rapid work-hardening characteristics of the alloy powders would result in very poor compacting properties and low green density. Hence, since shrinkage must be restricted to maintain dimensional accuracy, sintered density and therefore strength and ductility would also be low. Furthermore, the cost of pre-alloyed powders is still too high for many applications.

For sintered low-alloy steels, therefore, the only successful commercial approach is to mix elemental or master-alloy powders with iron powder. In practice, as noted earlier, nickel is the most important alloy addition but, unfortunately, the diffusion of nickel into iron is rather slow and it is impossible to get truly homogeneous alloys with practical sintering cycles. Maximum homogenization is achieved by using fine nickel powder (usually carbonyl powder of about 1μ particle size) and sintering temperatures of 1300°C or higher. The need to use sintering temperatures above the range of mesh-belt furnaces is an important characteristic of this type of alloy. Some European producers (including those in the United Kingdom) have preferred to achieve high strength in sintering alloys by using additions of nickel, molybdenum, etc., and employing sintering temperatures of about 1300°C, rather than adopt techniques such as infiltration, or the use of large copper additions with their attendant growth problems but which enable furnace temperatures below 1150°C to be used.

Some typical tensile strength and ductility properties of the most widely

Table 10. Properties of Alloyed Irons

Type	Density g/cm³	Tensile strength tons/in²	Elongation %	Ref.
Nickel-steels				
NS 5/20	7·0	26–32	6–10	4
NS 5/20	7·0	60	1	4
NS 5/80	7·0	38–44	2 min	4
SN 5	6·6–6·9	25–30	5	5
SN 10	6·6–6·9	35–47	3	5
SN 15	6·6–6·9	48–60	2	5
69 NS	6·9	26	3–7	6
Nickel-molybdenum steels				
MN 18/60	7·0	55–65	4 min	4

used types of sintered alloy steels are given in Table 10. The most important of the high-strength alloys are those containing 5% nickel or combined nickel plus molybdenum. Although tensile strengths up to 60 tons/in² can be obtained from high-nickel alloys they are rather expensive because of the high cost of nickel powders. In order to obtain the ductility necessary to take advantage of these high-strength alloys, densities in the region of 7·0 g/cm³ are normal; these are achieved by coining, or by using very high sintering temperatures.

The alloyed irons usually contain about 0·2% carbon after sintering; it is difficult to maintain higher carbon contents consistently at the high sintering temperatures employed. In order to increase wear resistance, parts made from alloyed iron are often carburized by one of the methods described later.

Pre-alloyed Steels

The most serious limitations to the use of pre-alloyed low-alloy steel powders are their high cost and poor compressibility. This compressibility limitation does not apply to all of the high-alloy steels; in particular the low-carbon austenitic alloys, such as the corrosion-resistant stainless steels, are readily compacted. These stainless-steel powders are produced by atomization and, whereas formerly it was found necessary to add up to 3% silicon in order to control particle shape, pre-alloyed stainless-steel powders of low silicon content (0·5%) are now available with excellent compacting characteristics. The influence of alloy composition upon the compacting properties of austenitic stainless steels has been discussed by Sands and Watkinson.[7] The preferred compositions are shown in Table 11. It will be seen that nickel contents are somewhat higher than those normally specified for wrought products.

Table 11. Compositions of Stainless Steels suitable for producing Sintered Engineering Components[7]

Type	Composition wt %					
	C	Si	Cr	Ni	Mo	Nb
Cosint* 410L	0·1	0·5	13	—	—	—
Cosint 304L	0·05	0·5	18	10	—	—
Cosint 316L	0·05	0·5	18	12	2	—
Cosint 347L	0·05	0·5	18	12	—	0·5

* 'Cosint' is a trade name of B.S.A. Metal Powders Ltd.

Stainless-steel powders are sintered at either 1150 or 1300°C, usually in cracked ammonia. In a few cases the use of very dry hydrogen atmospheres or even vacuum is justified, giving improved ductility and corrosion resistance.

Heat Treatment

Almost all of the sintered ferrous materials will respond to heat treatment, exceptions being plain iron and some of the stainless steels. All of the iron alloys which contain carbon are capable of being hardened by conventional heat treatment. Alloys of iron and copper can be strengthened by a precipitation hardening heat treatment.

Although the heat treatment of sintered steels is based on the same well-established principles used for cast and wrought steels, many differences in the method of and response to heat treatment are evident. The presence of extensive porosity is the main cause of these differences, although in alloy steels heterogeneity may also have important effects. It is well known that with solid steels there exists, for any composition, a critical cooling rate for 'through' hardening; if this cooling rate is not attained or exceeded complete hardening does not occur. One of the important effects of porosity on response to heat treatment is the reduction of thermal conductivity and thus for a given quenching medium a porous steel may cool at a slower rate than does a solid one. Therefore, for certain compositions, section sizes and heat-transfer rates, sintered steels may have poorer hardenability than solid ones. However, in very porous steels the effect may be reversed, owing to the quenching medium penetrating the pores so that heat transfer is no longer confined to the outer surface.

A further distinction between the sintered and wrought steels is the purpose of heat treatment. For solid steels the most usual reason for hardening is to increase strength. Although the ductility of solid steel is reduced by hardening, its inherent ductility is such that, after hardening, advantage can be taken of the enhanced strength. The ductility of sintered steels is, as has been shown, always low and after through-hardening the steel may be so brittle that in practice advantage cannot be taken of the increased strength. Thus the prime reason for hardening sintered steels is to increase wear resistance, and increased strength is often of much less importance. Since it is a wear-resistant surface which is most often needed the relatively poor hardenability of sintered steels is not always of great importance. Indeed, surface hardening, rather than 'through' hardening, is usually a better method of achieving wear resistance since it does not lower the core toughness.

Of the various methods of surface hardening, gas carburizing and salt-bath carburizing are the most widely used for sintered steels. Pack carburizing is less often used because an additional heat treatment is required, whereas it is possible to harden directly from the gas and salt-bath processes. Gas carburizing has the disadvantage that internal surfaces (pore surfaces) are also carburized with consequent embrittlement of the core. As shown in Fig. 42, the problem of restricting the carburizing action to the surface layer is particularly difficult with low-density materials (the greater the porosity the easier the

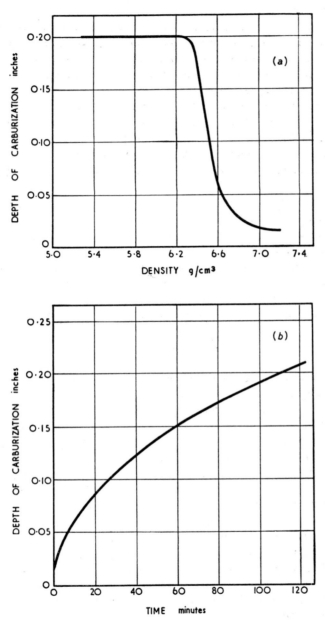

FIG. 42. Factors controlling the depth of case in carburized sintered iron. (*a*) Carburized 850°C, for 80 min and oil quenched. (*b*) Sintered iron, density 7·0 g/cm³, carburized at 850°C.

(Courtesy of Höganäs Billesholms AB)

access for the carburizing gas to the internal surfaces). An interesting method of overcoming this difficulty has been proposed by Bockstiegel[8] who used sulphur additions (0·25–0·5%) to encourage the formation of closed spherical pores, thus preventing the access of carburizing gas to the internal pores.

The problems of restricting the depth of the carburized layer are much less severe when salt-bath carburizing is used. Unfortunately some salt is usually entrained within the pores and its removal is extremely difficult. If the salt is allowed to remain within the pores it slowly absorbs moisture which leads to corrosion. The cyanide salts which are used for salt-bath carburizing are extremely poisonous, so that their complete removal is desirable for this reason also. In general, alloys containing copper are less amenable to case hardening than the simple iron–carbon alloys, owing to the slow rate of diffusion of carbon into the copper-rich regions and to the difficulty in obtaining a transformation to martensite.

Precipitation hardening of iron–copper alloys, which has been mentioned, is possible because the solubility of copper in iron decreases markedly with decreasing temperature (Fig. 39). The alloys are heated to a temperature near to the maximum solubility, quenched and then aged; this gives a precipitate which results in appreciable strengthening. Fig. 43 compares the strength of 'as-sintered' and heat-treated iron–copper alloys. It will be seen that the strength is increased and the ductility lowered by this form of heat treatment.

Finishing Operations

Sintered iron parts may be given certain finishing treatments in addition to the optional heat treatments discussed in the previous section. In some cases a machining operation is necessary to obtain features such as undercuts or screw threads which cannot be formed during compacting. Only very rarely is machining needed to improve tolerances or surface finish. Care must be exercised in the selection of coolants; water and certain oils must be avoided because they cause corrosion if retained in the pores. Taylor[9] states that sintered parts should be machined dry whenever possible, using an air blast to remove chips and cool the tool. The use of a volatile coolant is another way of overcoming the corrosion problem.

A finishing operation often applied to sintered parts is barrelling. This is necessary to remove unwanted sharp corners and the flash formed when the pressing tools wear. Barrelling is usually arranged so that in addition to the removal of flash, some burnishing occurs which improves the general appearance of the components. Since barrelling normally takes place in water there is again a corrosion problem if water is retained in the pores. The most acceptable solution is to impregnate the parts with oil prior to barrelling.

The origins of the frequently occurring corrosion problem in sintered iron alloys are: (i) the large surface area of porous parts, (ii) the possibility of electrolytic cells being formed within the pores, and (iii) the active nature of the metal surface after it has been subjected to reducing conditions at a high temperature. Many means of overcoming corrosion have been suggested but only three are now of practical importance, oxidizing, electroplating and oil impregnation. A protective oxide surface film can be achieved by immersing the parts in certain hot oxidizing solutions, such as sodium hydroxide–sodium nitrate mixtures, but a better method, which avoids entrainment of the oxidizing solutions within the pores, involves the use of superheated steam. The object

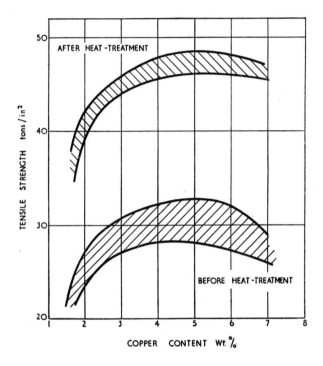

FIG .43. The effect of heat treatment on the strength of sintered iron–copper alloys.

of these treatments is to form a dense layer of corrosion-resistant magnetite (Fe_3O_4) which, because of the presence of extensive porosity, is well keyed to the surface and provides a fair degree of protection.

A more sophisticated method of obtaining a corrosion-resistant coating is electroplating. A satisfactory coating cannot be electroplated directly on to porous parts and thus electrodeposition has to be preceded by a treatment designed to reduce the effect of the pores. (Such treatments are not necessary for the substantially non-porous copper-infiltrated iron.) The pre-treatment is also necessary to stop electrolyte being trapped within the pores. Currently the most popular pre-treatments are oxidation with steam, which both blocks the pores and gives a surface coating of oxide, and impregnation with water-repellent compounds. The relative merits of these pre-treatments have been discussed by Arbstedt[10] who favours steam oxidation. Electrodeposited coatings are most often nickel, sometimes with an overlay of chromium for additional corrosion resistance or decorative appearance. Apart from improving corrosion resistance, electroplating of sintered parts is sometimes carried out for decorative purposes, although this is rather unusual at the present time as the process is expensive and does not fit into the minimum-cost pattern.

Of the three methods for protecting sintered parts against corrosion, oil impregnation is probably the most usual. The process is comparatively inexpensive and, most important, the oil which is retained within the pores also serves to provide a measure of self-lubrication. Oil impregnation is best carried out by immersing the part in hot oil and then either to allow the oil to cool or to transfer the part to a bath of cold oil. By this treatment the air in the pores is largely displaced by oil. An alternative way of displacing the air is to use vacuum impregnation. However, the oils commonly used for impregnation contain volatile constituents which may be lost during the vacuum treatment.

NON-FERROUS MATERIALS

Earlier the reasons for the production of certain engineering components by powder metallurgy were outlined. It was shown that for certain types of rather complex shape not exceeding a certain size, and where the application does not require very high values of ductility, toughness, fatigue strength, etc., parts can be produced more cheaply by powder metallurgy than by other processes. In the discussion of the iron-base alloys it was seen that there exists a definite and critical relationship between cost, composition and processing conditions necessary to obtain the various strength and ductility classes. The general objective of producing components at minimum cost is as true for the non-ferrous sintered materials as it is for the sintered steels. Since invariably the cost of the raw non-ferrous powders is somewhat greater than that of iron powder it is also obvious that very cogent reasons must exist for a part to be made in a non-ferrous alloy instead of a sintered steel.

In general engineering the term 'non-ferrous alloys' covers a very wide range of materials, including the aluminium and magnesium light alloys, the innumerable copper-base alloys, the corrosion and creep-resistant nickel-base alloys and refractory-metal alloys. However, so far as engineering components produced by powder metallurgy are concerned, only a tiny fraction of these alloys need be considered. This can readily be appreciated by a consideration of the attributes that a material must possess in order to be used in this class of product. For instance, the cost of the raw materials must be low, which favours the pure metal powders and those alloys which can be produced by mixing elemental powders, and also the useful properties must be developed by economically feasible compacting and sintering methods. This limitation effectively rules out those alloys which only attain useful properties when porosity is eliminated, or alloys which react with impurities present in the sintering atmospheres (for instance oxide formation by aluminium and magnesium alloys), and also those materials which need sintering temperatures in excess of about 1350°C. The last condition, that the sintering temperature is not greater than 1350°C, although substantially true at the present time may have to be modified in the future if the increasing tendency to use components made from the refractory metals continues. Since refractory metals are extracted in powder form it is possible that, for some types of component, the method of compacting to shape and sintering may be the most economic. This would, however, involve sintering temperatures higher than 1350°C.

The limitations outlined above have confined the use of non-ferrous materials used for sintered engineering components to copper and a few copper-base alloys, notably copper–zinc (brass), tin–bronze and nickel–silver, as well as some nickel–copper alloys. The choice of these alloys, instead of sintered steels, usually depends on the need for better electrical or thermal conductivity, greater corrosion resistance, superior decorative appearance (for domestic appliances) or bearing properties, etc.

Copper

Unalloyed copper finds occasional use for those sintered parts where maximum electrical conductivity is needed. There are few problems in processing copper parts and high ductility is readily obtained. The principal disadvantage of sintered copper is its low strength. As will be seen in Fig. 44, the strength does not exceed about 5 tons/in² until the density is greater than 7·0 g/cm³ (20% porosity). Copper powder has excellent compressibility and is readily compacted to high density without the need for excessive pressures. It can be sintered in any of the common reducing atmospheres.

Tin–Bronze

The tin–bronzes are one of the two most important groups of non-ferrous alloys used for engineering components. The principal virtue of the alloys is their excellent bearing properties, and sintered bronzes having a wide range of properties are available. High-density bronzes produced by double pressing have high strength and also excellent bearing properties, while high-porosity bronzes, which can be impregnated with a lubricant to give self-lubricating properties (see Chapter 7), are used in less heavily stressed applications. The high-density sintered bronzes always need additional lubrication when used as heavy-duty bearings. The presence of some residual porosity does, however, lead to superior retention of the lubricant compared with cast bronze bearings. The basic composition employed for tin–bronze is 90% copper

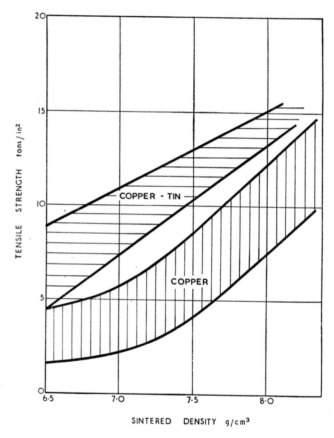

FIG. 44. Strength-density relationships for sintered copper and sintered bronze.

10% tin, to which may be added small quantities of graphite and, less often, lead. Graphite and lead both improve bearing properties but they also reduce the overall strength. When lead is added about 2% is usual; the graphite content is normally about $1\frac{1}{2}$%.

The processing conditions for the bronzes are generally similar to those

given later (Chapter 7) for the oil-impregnated bearings, except that the compacting pressures are necessarily greater in order to get higher densities, and also less attention need be paid to particle-size distribution of powders. The alloy is produced by mixing copper and tin powders and, if required, graphite and lead. The graphite is a useful lubricant during compacting; if it is not added then a stearate lubricant is employed. Compacting pressures are often as high as 30 tons/in², while pressures up to 50 tons/in² are used in special cases. Coining pressures can also be in the same range. The sintering temperature is about 800°C.

In Fig. 44 the typical strength–density relationship for tin–bronze is shown. Elongation values are in the range 2–20% depending upon the density.

Brasses

The other important non-ferrous material employed for engineering components is brass. Only two compositions find much use in practice, 90% copper 10% zinc and 80% copper 20% zinc; the 70–30 alloy, which formerly was widely used, now appears to be less popular. Almost invariably a small amount of lead (1 to 2%) is added to the sintered brasses.

Unlike the bronzes and most of the sintered steels, brass parts are produced from pre-alloyed powder. The use of pre-alloyed powders is dictated by the high volatility of zinc. If zinc powder and copper were mixed together and sintered much of the zinc would be lost (and the furnace might be damaged by the zinc vapour). Even with pre-alloyed powder 'dezincification' occurs unless special precautions are taken and for this reason brass parts are often sintered in sealed boxes. A partial pressure of zinc is formed inside the boxes which restricts further zinc loss. Since it appears that zinc loss is also reduced by eliminating oxidation, carbonaceous materials may be put inside the sintering boxes to achieve this result.

Generally the compacting pressures and sintering temperatures for brasses are similar to those used for tin–bronzes. There has been some controversy over the best pressing lubricant for brass powder. Zinc stearate is usually preferred but lithium stearate has been claimed to give improved properties. The strength–density relationships for the 90–10 and 80–20 alloys are shown in Fig. 45. Ductility values are usually much higher than those of the sintered steels, 10–20% being quite common.

Nickel–Silver

The alloys of copper, zinc and nickel, known as nickel-silvers, are finding increasing application in powder metallurgy. Because of the relatively high price of nickel the alloys are rather more costly than the other non-ferrous alloys discussed so far. The most important reason for their use is their corrosion resistance and the fact that they can easily be given a lasting attractive lustre. The pre-alloyed powder most commonly used contains 64% copper, 18% zinc and 18% nickel; processing is similar to that used for brass. Fig. 45 includes strength data for sintered nickel–silver as a function of its density.

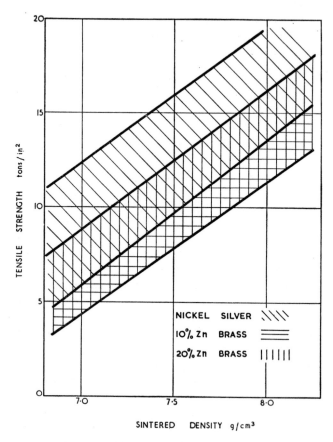

FIG. 45. Strength density relationships for sintered brass and sintered nickel–silver.

Nickel–Copper Alloys

The nickel–copper alloys (approximately 65% nickel 35% copper) at present find only a limited use for sintered engineering components. They can be produced by mixing elemental powders or from pre-alloyed powders, and in both cases the high cost of nickel is a deterrent to their wider use. Excellent strength and ductility (30 tons/in², 10% elongation) can be obtained by sintering the pre-alloyed powder at 1150–1300°C in cracked ammonia.

It seems that sintered nickel–copper alloys may find increasing use in the future, particularly in corrosive environments where they may be an alternative to sintered stainless-steel. These alloys have practically the same corrosion-resisting properties as the solid alloys.

Finishing Operations

Some of the finishing operations applied to iron-base parts are also used for sintered non-ferrous engineering components. The sintered non-ferrous alloys do not respond to heat treatment, and increased wear resistance cannot be easily achieved. Barrelling to remove sharp edges and pressing flash is quite common and some of the bronzes are impregnated with oil. Parts requiring an attractive appearance may be burnished. This treatment is often applied to the nickel–silvers. Electroplating of sintered non-ferrous alloys is possible but rarely carried out, the alloys generally having sufficient corrosion resistance without this treatment.

APPLICATIONS

The fields of application for sintered engineering components can be defined in various ways. For instance, as was mentioned earlier in this chapter, there are definite limitations as to size, shape and minimum number of components required, which lead to the rather arbitrary definition of 'small, costly-to-machine components, in minimum quantities of 10,000'. There are also strict limitations as to the mechanical properties (in particular toughness) which can be economically achieved. To attain even moderate increases in tensile strength and elongation usually results in a marked increase in the cost of the component. There is thus an understandable tendency to limit the use of powder metallurgy to lightly stressed parts. However, it is fairly easy to obtain high (true) hardness in sintered steels which thereby possess excellent resistance to wear. Hence the most important field of application for sintered steels is lightly stressed parts subject to wear. The excellent wear-resisting characteristics can often be further improved by impregnating the pores with oil, somewhat in the manner of a porous bearing. It is a general characteristic of this group of materials that there is a virtually continuous transition in properties and performance from high-density high-strength parts, through parts needing strength but with propensity for impregnation and marginal bearing properties, to the true high-porosity low-strength oil-impregnated bearing. The combination of wear resistance and good strength with bearing properties, together with the ability to produce components of complex form, has allowed single sintered parts to replace assemblies previously built up from two or more materials.

A general indication of the wide use of sintered engineering components is given by Table 12. Some typical parts are shown in Plates 7 and 8.

Table 12. Typical Sintered Engineering Components
(*after Hards*[11])

Machinery	Bearings, gear wheels, hand-wheels, levers, cranks.
Motor vehicles	Oil-pump gears, gear wheels, valve guides, plain bearings, shock absorber pistons.
Bicycles and light motor cycles	Sprockets, clutch-plates, glands, special bearings, hubs and keys.
Sewing machines	Levers, pressure feet, bearings, eccentrics.
Office machines	Counting wheels, levers, bushes, profile plates, cams.
Weapons and projectiles	Feeders, triggers, magazine and firing mechanism parts, shell driving bands.
Electrical equipment	Switch parts, armatures, pole-pieces, cores.
Domestic machinery	Spur and bevel gear wheels, levers, mincer discs and knives.
Precision tools	Micrometer frames, clamps, tripod parts, calipers.
Fine mechanics and optics	Racks, gear wheels, guide winding knobs.
Ball and roller bearings	Cages and cage segments.
Chemical apparatus	Nozzles and similar parts.

The automobile and domestic appliance industries both make increasing use of sintered ferrous parts. Both are mass production industries and one way in which they seek to achieve minimum cost is by using the smallest amount of raw material, if necessary accepting the need for complex shapes provided these can be produced cheaply. The advantages which powder metallurgy can offer in this situation have been appreciated by automobile engineers, particularly in the U.S.A., where one single model uses 100 powder-metal components. Typical applications are door-lock parts and oil pumps. Self-lubricating bearings are also of major importance in the automobile industry. Extensive trials with sintered high-duty parts, such as gears, have also been made, a development which holds hope for even greater exploitation of powder metallurgy products in the future. In this connection the recent development of a compacting technique for producing helical gears is of interest. Sintered steels find many applications in textile and accounting machines, and again these are generally lightly-stressed components, often very small and complex, which need good wear resistance. Apart from the use of sintered high-density bronze in bearing applications, the non-ferrous alloys find increasing use in domestic appliances and business machines. One highly successful use of stainless-steel powder is the manufacture of small nuts by pressing and sintering hollow hexagons, followed by a screwing operation.

In those industries where sintered parts have been successfully applied, close co-operation between the designers and producer has been virtually essential. Although sintered materials are frequently much weaker than those they replace it has been found that careful design can overcome this deficiency. Frequently the changes in design are such that they would not be considered unless the part were to be made by powder metallurgy. Some of the design modifications necessary when changing to sintered components have been reviewed by Robinson.[12]–[15] In the case of sprockets, Robinson notes that the vast majority are used in light-duty applications, for instance, in farm equipment, lawn mowers, chain saws, ciné projectors, etc., and that sintered sprockets, of the same design as those they replace, can be used. However, where the tooth loading is normally high, design changes become necessary to decrease the tooth loading; this can be achieved by increasing the number of teeth, increasing the sprocket diameter or incorporating an idler sprocket to increase the number of teeth carrying the load. Somewhat similar considerations apply to straight spur gears. Powder-metal gears for light and medium-load transmission present few problems. Sintered gears should not be used where there is shock loading and for heavy-load transmission copper-infiltrated iron is needed to withstand the compression loads without indentation. A modified tooth form (true involute), which has better load-carrying capacity than the form specified for machined gears, may be readily produced by powder metallurgy.

Gears made by powder metallurgy generally have better dimensional accuracy than machined gears (except when very precise shaving has been carried out), and have no machining marks. They also have certain self-damping qualities and the resulting noise reduction is often an advantage. An important feature of cams is that the surface generating the motion is under compression and therefore the ease with which porous metals become indented is a disadvantage in this application. Infiltration is indicated where surface loads are high. In general metal-powder cams are not suitable where impact loading occurs. Edge cams are only produced more cheaply by powder metallurgy when the contour is complex, whereas face and internal cams are almost invariably produced more cheaply and more accurately by powder metallurgy.

In all of these components, sprockets, gears and cams, non-circular holes for attaching to the driving shaft are readily provided, and frequently a single part may perform more than one function. Examples are combinations of gear and dog-clutch, and multiple sprockets. The use of sintered components in domestic appliances and ciné cameras reflects the potential of powder metallurgy in the situation where large numbers of appliances can be sold when the cost is lowered. Since this situation of large sales at low cost shows every sign of dominating the consumer market for many years, the future for sintered engineering components is very bright indeed. It is in these applications where appearance and freedom from corrosion are important that the sintered non-ferrous alloys are becoming increasingly important.

REFERENCES

1. Hulthén, S. I. *Höganäs Handbook, 1957*. Section C, Chap. 30, 1.
2. Elliot, J. E. *Höganäs Handbook, 1962*. Section E, Chap. 30, 17.
3. Rennhack, E. H. *Metal Progress*, **83**, 4, 93 (April, 1963).

4. *Powder Metallurgy Production*. B.S.A. Sintered Components Ltd. (Sept., 1959).
5. 'Durasint'. Sintered Products Ltd. (1961).
6. 'Ferrocite'. Sintered Products Ltd. (1961).
7. Sands, R. L. and Watkinson, J. F. *Powder Metallurgy*, No. 5, 85 (1960).
8. Bockstiegel, G. ibid., No. 10, 171 (1962).
9. Taylor, H. G. *Höganäs Handbook, 1962*. Section G, Chap. 20, 1.
10. Arbstedt, P. G. ibid., Section G, Chap. 40, 1.
11. Hards, K. W. *Metalworking Production*, **107**, 14, 47 (April, 1962).
12. Robinson, T. L. *Precision Metal Moulding*, 56 (May, 1961).
13. Robinson, T. L. ibid., 24 (June, 1961).
14. Robinson, T. L. ibid., 36 (August, 1961).
15. Robinson, T. L. ibid., 69 (October, 1961).

CHAPTER 6

TOOL MATERIALS

The tools with which this chapter is concerned are those which are used to cut, abrade or form other materials and which therefore require high hardness and high abrasion resistance. Probably the greatest single contribution of powder metallurgy to production engineering has been to make usable tools from the hardest known materials. Cemented carbides, to which the bulk of this chapter is devoted, are the most important of these materials. Diamond tools are also widely used and recently tool materials based on oxides and borides have been introduced.

CEMENTED CARBIDES

The carbides of many metals possess great hardness and hence would be eminently suitable as tool materials were it not for their inherent brittleness. An outstanding achievement of powder metallurgy has been to produce cemented carbides in which the great hardness of the carbide is retained and a measure of toughness is introduced; such materials are commonly termed 'hard-metals'.

The historical development of the hard-metals makes interesting reading and a good account of this work is given by Swarzkopf and Kieffer.[1] During the early years of this century much work was carried out on the fusing and sintering of pure carbides for use as drawing dies for tungsten wire, but the products found few applications owing to their extreme brittleness. The idea of using a binder metal in order to reduce this brittleness is generally attributed to Schröter[2] who suggested the use of metals of the iron group, and in particular cobalt, for this purpose. Schröter's technique of blending the carbide with a metal binder and sintering in the presence of a liquid phase is the

135

basis of modern cemented-carbide technology. The original tungsten carbide–cobalt compositions have remained the most important, but for certain applications these have been modified by substituting other carbides for part of the tungsten carbide. These multi-carbide compositions have proved particularly successful in the high-speed machining of steel.

Apart from their use as cutting tools, cemented carbides have been widely applied as wear-resistant materials and where great compressive strength is required.

Production of Cemented Carbides

The basic cemented-carbide production technique is a typical powder-metallurgical process. However, unlike the manufacturer of structural parts and bearings, a producer of cemented carbide parts will often make his own metal and carbide powders, although in the United States the tendency is to purchase the metal powder. Because the production of these powders is peculiar to the hard-metal industry, their manufacture is discussed in this chapter instead of Chapter 2. Particle sizes of both carbide and binder metal are required to be in the sub-sieve range. They are blended by ball milling and this is one of the most critical operations in the whole process.

The blended powders may be cold pressed and sintered, or hot pressed. In many cases machining is carried out after a presintering operation. A flow sheet indicating the sequence of operations in the production of cemented-carbide parts is shown in Fig. 46.

Raw Materials

The preferred method for the production of carbide powder is direct reaction of the metal with carbon, the strictest control of composition being most easily achieved by this technique. In many cases, however, the metal powder is comparatively expensive (for example, titanium and tantalum) and therefore it is often preferred to react the oxide with carbon. When reduction and carburization are carried out in one operation accurate control of the final carbon content is difficult and it often becomes necessary to crush and recarburize. At the present time, of the carbides commonly used in the hard-metal industry, only those of tungsten and molybdenum are produced by direct metal–carbon reaction. However, if titanium and tantalum powders become available at more economic prices this situation may change.

Carbide producers obtain their tungsten from the chemical industry in the form of the trioxide (WO_3), tungstic acid (H_2WO_4) or ammonium paratungstate; all these compounds are readily reduced by hydrogen. The particle size of the resulting tungsten powder depends on a number of factors, including (i) reduction temperature, (ii) particle size of the original oxide (or other compound), (iii) water content of the hydrogen, (iv) time of reduction, (v) rate of hydrogen flow, (vi) rate of passage of oxide through the furnace and (vii) thickness of the oxide bed.

Reduction is carried out in continuous furnaces. Two types are in common

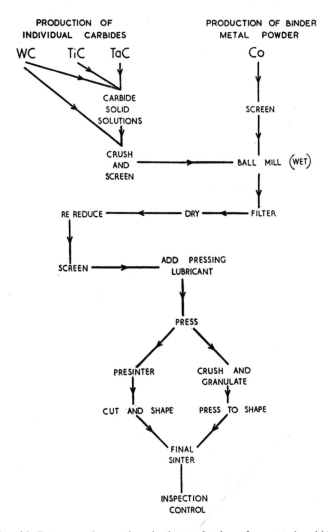

Fig. 46. Sequence of operations in the production of cemented carbides.

use, namely, the rotary furnace and the muffle type. The rotary furnace employs an inclined rotating tube so that oxide fed in at the higher end moves through the heated zone aided by the rotary motion. Muffle furnaces are widely used, in which oxide, paratungstate or tungstic acid, loaded into shallow trays, is stoked through the furnace. Finer tungsten particles are obtained if the reduction is carried out in two stages; the first at a temperature of about 550°C reduces the oxide to a sub-oxide, W_4O_{11}, the second stage at about 800–1000°C completes the reduction to metallic tungsten. A typical two-stage muffle furnace for the production of tungsten powder is shown in Plate 9 (a).

To produce tungsten carbide the metal powder is first blended with lamp black. To avoid under-carburization, which leads to the formation of brittle W_2C, an excess of carbon over that required to produce stoichiometric WC is used. The tungsten–carbon mixture is packed into graphite boats and pushed through a continuous carburizing furnace. These furnaces may be molybdenum-wound, carbon-tube or of the high-frequency induction type. Carburization is carried out in a hydrogen atmosphere at temperatures between 1370 and 1650°C. The particle size of the resultant carbide depends on the particle size of the starting materials and also on the temperature.

After carburizing, the agglomerated lumps are crushed, ball milled and sieved. If the material is undercarburized, i.e. the carbon content is below about 6·1%, then further carbon is added and the carburization operation is repeated.

Molybdenum carbide (Mo_2C) has been used in experimental hard-metal compositions as a replacement for tungsten carbide. The production methods used for molybdenum carbide follow closely those used for tungsten carbide. Direct reaction of molybdenum metal powder and carbon is carried out at slightly lower temperatures than those employed for tungsten carbide production.

Titanium carbide (TiC) is included in almost all steel-cutting compositions and ranks second in importance to tungsten carbide in the hard-metal field. Titanium carbide is produced by reacting the oxide with carbon. Titania, TiO_2, which is extracted from the ores rutile or ilmenite, is used in large quantities by the paint industry from which most carbide manufacturers obtain oxide of adequate purity at reasonable cost. The oxide is blended with lamp black and, after drying, the mixture is briquetted and carburized. The temperatures required for carburization are in the range 2100–2300°C. Carbon-tube or high-frequency induction furnaces must therefore be used.

It is difficult to control accurately the carbon content in the mass-production of titanium carbide and most commercial material is deficient in carbon and contains residual oxygen and nitrogen. As titanium carbide is generally used in the form of solid solutions with other carbides, final purification can be achieved during the formation of solid solutions.

Like titanium carbide, tantalum carbide is widely used in steel-cutting hard metals. Tantalum powder is expensive and therefore the technique for the production of carbide is similar to that outlined above for titanium carbide, i.e. reaction of tantalum pentoxide with carbon. The reaction is carried out at about 1550°C and recarburization is often necessary to achieve the desired carbon content. An alternative method often used is to carburize ferro–tantalum–niobium which is cheaper than tantalum pentoxide; after an acid treatment the TaC–NbC solid solution is obtained. The presence of niobium carbide is not detrimental.

Many other carbides have been used for experimental compositions including zirconium carbide (ZrC), niobium carbide (NbC), vanadium carbide (VC), chromium carbide (Cr_3C_2) and hafnium carbide (HfC). Reaction of the respective oxides with carbon is almost invariably adopted in their production. As with titanium carbide it is difficult to control the carbon content.

It was demonstrated early in the history of cemented carbides that solid solutions of more than one carbide produce superior materials to those based on mixed individual carbides. Since at the usual sintering temperatures interdiffusion is very limited it is preferable to produce such solid solutions by a high-temperature treatment prior to the addition of the binder metal. It is usual to produce the individual carbides separately, blend and ball mill (wet) and finally to heat to temperatures in excess of 2000°C in furnaces similar to those used in carbide production.

Most hard-metal manufacturers produce their own cobalt powder. Reduction of the oxide or oxalate is carried out in hydrogen at a temperature of 600–700°C using furnaces similar to those employed for the reduction of tungstic oxide. Variables such as temperature and hydrogen flow rate control particle size; finer powders are obtained at low reduction temperatures.

Milling

The properties of cemented carbides are very dependent upon the nature of the carbide-binder metal dispersion. A very fine, uniform dispersion is required and this is invariably achieved by ball milling. Vibratory mills have become very popular in Europe in recent years but most British and American hard-metal producers still seem to prefer rotary mills. A typical rotary mill for the blending of carbide-binder mixtures is shown in Plate 9 (b). Advantages usually claimed for the vibratory mill are that the same degree of blending is achieved in a much shorter milling time and the wear on mills and balls is less, so that contamination of the charge is reduced.

Although steel milling balls may be used these lead to iron pick-up in the charge, particularly if water is used as the milling liquid. Most manufacturers prefer carbide balls which they make themselves by hot pressing; tungsten carbide with 6–8% cobalt is the usual composition. Mill pots are usually of stainless steel, although carbide-lined mills are also widely used. Milling techniques vary from one manufacturer to another; typically for 1 kg of carbide-binder metal mixture, 1–3 kg of milling balls and 300–400 ml of liquid are used. The milling liquid can be distilled water or alcohol, acetone, benzene, paraffin or any of a number of other organic liquids.

Milling times are relatively long, varying between two and five days and are determined by the experience of the individual manufacturer. The exact function of this extended milling time is a subject of some controversy. An argument frequently advanced is that it enables a coating of cobalt on the carbide particles to be obtained. Recent work,[3] using the electron microscope, seems to bear out this hypothesis to some extent, although the results indicate that the main feature is an embedding of the smaller carbide particles in flakes of cobalt. The larger particles of carbide are not so readily coated with binder metal, but it seems that cobalt does tend to settle in the surface irregularities of these particles.

The mixture is dried by separating the balls, filtering off excess liquid and heating the powder in an oven. The last operation may be combined with a second reduction to eliminate any oxygen picked up during milling. Vacuum drying is also very popular. The mill pots may be connected to a vacuum line and heated gently, organic liquids being condensed and collected for re-use.

Shaping

The classical method of preparing cemented-carbide shapes is to cold press a blank and presinter to produce a material which may be machined to shape and sintered. Because of the brittle nature of the powders, particularly those low in cobalt, substances which act as both lubricants and binders are added prior to pressing. Paraffin wax and camphor are the most widely used additives, usually as a solution in an organic liquid. Such solutions contain 5–15% of lubricant and sufficient is added to give 0·5–2·5% residual lubricant after volatilization of the solvent. Larger amounts of lubricant may be necessary in certain cases, especially when the cobalt content is low.

Large blanks are compacted on hydraulic presses. Pressures used range from 5 to 30 tons/in², although 10 tons/in² is most usual. Split dies are used and filled by hand with pre-weighed charges; side rams are often necessary to keep the die closed.

Presintering is carried out in hydrogen at temperatures between 900 and 1150°C, the actual temperature employed depending primarily on the cobalt content. During sintering no liquid phase formation or sintering of carbide particles occurs but sintering of the binder metal takes place. A material of 'chalky' consistency is produced and this can be machined with cemented-carbide tools or ground with silicon carbide or metal-bonded diamond wheels; allowance must be made for the high shrinkage (12–25% linear) which occurs during final sintering.

With the increasing use of standard forms, particularly tool tips, the practice of compacting direct to shape is becoming widely used. Since carbides themselves are relatively expensive the number required to justify the cost of a die is much less than for the iron-base materials.

The very poor flow properties of milled carbide–cobalt mixtures make them unsuitable for automatic pressing where dies are filled by volume. Agglomeration, by compacting and controlled crushing, is used to improve the flow characteristics. Briquettes, pressed at 3 to 5 tons/in² from powder containing about 2% lubricant, are crushed through a granulator, screened and tumbled in rotating drums to spheroidize the granules. The powders are sieved and the fines returned for re-cycling. It is important that the granules are sufficiently hard to resist breakdown under their own weight during storage, but granules which are too hard will not crush under pressing loads and will cause voids in the final compact. The hardness of the granules is a function of lubricant content and initial compacting pressure.

The agglomerated powders have good flow properties and high apparent density and thus they are suitable for use with any of the types of automatic press described in Chapter 3. Although steel dies may be used for small numbers of parts, carbide-lined dies and carbide-tipped punches are usually necessary owing to the abrasive nature of the powder. Most manufacturers make their own punch-tips and die-inserts. A typical selection is shown in Plate 10 (a). These are often produced by hot pressing.

Carbide powders flow very poorly during pressing, thus limiting the intricacy of shape which may be produced. Complex shapes, therefore, are more often produced by the presinter/machine process. Where quantities warrant it, however, a partly-formed blank may be produced by automatic pressing, the blank being then presintered, machined to final shape and sintered. In special cases, such as the production of carbide balls and bushes, isostatic compacting may be used. Relatively high pressures can be employed without the formation of pressing cracks, and the high green density reduces the sintering shrinkage.

The extrusion of powders containing binders and plasticizers, described in Chapter 3, has been used for cemented carbides. It is particularly useful for shapes with high length to cross-section ratios, such as rods and tubes which are difficult to make by other means. The major disadvantage of the method is that the amount of binders and plasticizers required is so high that after removal a very porous product is left and sintering shrinkage is consequently very high.

Hot pressing is widely used for the production of wear-resistant parts such as dies and milling balls, and has the advantage that the material produced is virtually free of residual porosity. Graphite dies are necessary because of the temperatures involved (1300–1600°C, depending primarily on cobalt content). Pressures, which are usually applied hydraulically, are limited to 0·5 to 2 tons/in², with external, direct resistance, or induction heating.

Sintering

Densification during the sintering of cemented carbides relies upon the formation of a liquid phase. The reactions taking place during the sintering of tungsten carbide–cobalt mixtures have been widely studied and much of this work has been reviewed by Swarzkopf and Kieffer.[1] Sintering temperatures vary with cobalt content between 1350–1500°C. Most often the temperature is below the melting point of cobalt (1495°C). However, cobalt dissolves tungsten carbide in the solid state and its melting point is thereby reduced as shown in Fig. 47. Eventually the cobalt has dissolved sufficient tungsten carbide to become liquid (point *a*, Fig. 47) and the liquid continues to dissolve carbide until it achieves its equilibrium composition (point *b*). The horizontal broken line at 1400°C in Fig. 47 represents a typical sintering temperature for a 94WC–6Co composition; at equilibrium the compact would contain about 11% liquid phase.

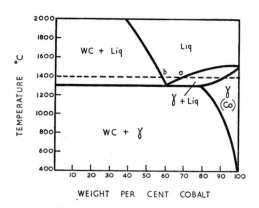

Fig. 47. Pseudo-binary equilibrium system, tungsten carbide–cobalt.

The mechanisms causing shrinkage during liquid-phase sintering are the subject of some controversy, as discussed in Chapter 4. The early heavy metal theory[4] of solution and reprecipitation has been challenged in more recent years by a liquid-flow theory.[5, 6] Possibly both types of mechanism operate in the sintering of cemented carbides.

Eutectic structures are not normally found in sintered tungsten carbide–cobalt; the carbide precipitated by the eutectic reaction grows preferentially on the existing carbide particles. If large cobalt flakes are formed during milling, however, they may result in the formation of areas of the undesirable eutectic structure.

The solubility of tungsten carbide in cobalt at room temperature is less than 1%. Therefore, unlike nickel and iron in which tungsten carbide is

PLATE 9

(*a*) Two-stage muffle furnaces for the reduction of tungstic oxide.
(*Courtesy of Edgar Allen & Co. Ltd.*)

(*b*) Nine-pot ball mill stand for blending carbide-binder mixtures.

(*Courtesy of Edgar Allen & Co. Ltd.*)

PLATE 10

(*a*) Pressing dies and punches for the production of carbide parts.
(*Courtesy of Edgar Allen & Co. Ltd.*)

(*b*) Vacuum furnace employed for sintering cemented carbides.
(*Courtesy of Edgar Allen & Co. Ltd.*)

PLATE 11

(*a*) Selection of throwaway carbide tips and toolholders.
(*Courtesy of Edgar Allen & Co. Ltd.*)

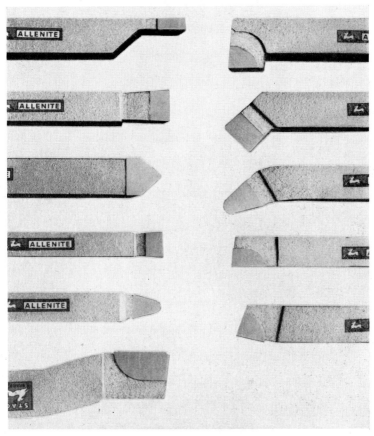

(*b*) Selection of carbide turning tools with brazed tips.
(*Courtesy of Edgar Allen & Co. Ltd.*)

PLATE 12

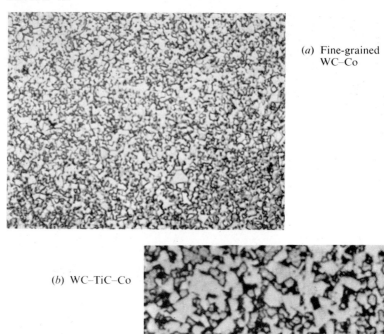

(*a*) Fine-grained
WC–Co

(*b*) WC–TiC–Co

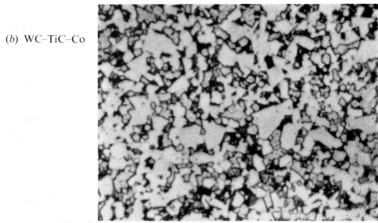

(*c*) WC–TiC–TaC–Co

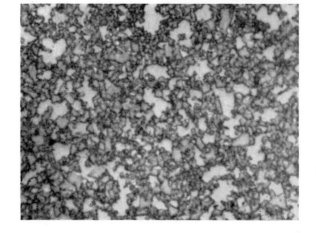

Microstructures of various
cemented carbides
(×2000).

PLATE 13

(a)

(b)

Use of cemented-carbide tools for heavy-duty turning;

(a) continuous cutting, 5 in. diam. bar of En 9 steel (0·55% carbon) at a speed of 470 ft/min, with a feed of 0·017 in. per revolution and a depth of cut of 0·160 in.

(b) intermittent cutting, mild-steel plate 6 in. × 1 in. section at a speed of 546 ft/min, with a feed of 0·013 in. per revolution and a depth of cut of 0·160 in.

(Courtesy of Edgar Allen & Co. Ltd.)

PLATE 14

(*a*) Brick moulding die. (*Courtesy of Jessop-Saville Small Tools Ltd.*)

(*b*) *Wire-drawing dies.*
(*Courtesy of Jessop-Saville Small Tools Ltd.*)

Illustrations of the wide range of wear-resisting applications of cemented carbides. (See also Plate 15.)

PLATE 15

(c) Cemented carbide percussion drill bits. (*Courtesy of Edgar Allen & Co. Ltd.*)

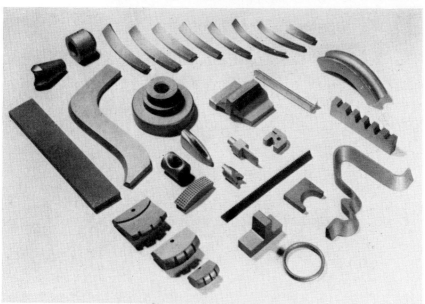

(d) Miscellaneous cemented carbide parts.
(*Courtesy of Jessop-Saville Small Tools Ltd.*)

PLATE 16

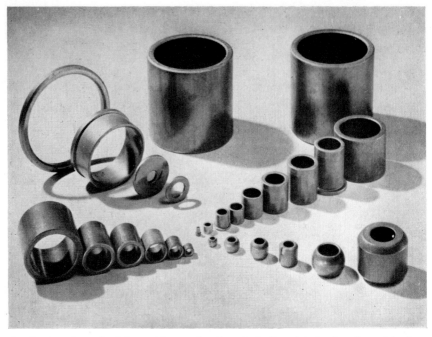

A selection of standard sintered bronze bearings, including plain bushes, flanged bushes, thrust washers and self-aligning bearings.

(*Courtesy of Bound Brook Ltd.*)

more soluble, cobalt remains fairly ductile and acts as a barrier to crack propagation.

Carbon deficiency in the tungsten carbide powder leads to the formation of brittle compounds such as η-phase (Co_3W_3C), θ-phase ($Co_3W_6C_2$) and K-phase ($Co_3W_{10}C_4$) during sintering. Graphite may be present in the final product if the original tungsten carbide powder contained an excess of carbon. Moreover, the carbon content may change during sintering; a carbon-tube furnace with a dry hydrogen atmosphere will be carburizing, whereas high vacuum sintering tends to be slightly decarburizing.

The sintering of compositions other than tungsten carbide–cobalt has been less widely studied. Although the interfacial energies and mutual solubilities are altered by the substitution of other carbides for tungsten carbide the basic sintering characteristics remain unchanged. For pure titanium carbide or tantalum carbide, or for multi-carbide compositions based on these, nickel or nickel plus chromium, iron, etc., are better binder metals than cobalt.

Cemented-carbide parts are usually sintered in hydrogen or vacuum, but in some instances cheaper atmospheres such as cracked ammonia may be used. Furnaces employing a hydrogen atmosphere are usually of the continuous type, which are heated by means of carbon tube or molybdenum resistance elements and are similar to those employed for the production of carbide powders. The compacts are contained in graphite boats and may be embedded in graphite powder if carburization is desired. Vacuum furnaces may operate under a medium vacuum (10–100 μHg) or a high vacuum (less than 1 μHg). While medium-vacuum conditions may be slightly carburizing (owing to the presence of carbon monoxide) a high vacuum is virtually neutral or slightly decarburizing. Although high vacuum effectively removes impurities some loss of cobalt by volatilization also occurs. Metallic heating elements are rarely used in these vacuum furnaces, graphite resistors being more common and high-frequency heating being also widely employed. A typical installation is shown in Plate 10 (b). Compacts are loaded into the furnace on graphite supports.

Better properties are obtained in tungsten carbide–cobalt materials if sintered in hydrogen but multi-carbide materials, particularly those containing titanium carbide, are preferably sintered in vacuum.

Sintering temperatures decrease with increasing cobalt content, while temperatures are higher for multi-carbide materials than for 'straight' tungsten carbide–cobalt compositions. Time of sintering is governed mainly by the section size of the part, although fine-grained materials require shorter times than coarse-grained.

Cemented-carbide materials can also be produced by infiltration of a porous-carbide skeleton. Infiltration may be accomplished by immersing the carbide skeleton in the liquid binder or by placing a piece of binder metal on top of the carbide skeleton and heating in a reducing atmosphere. In the latter case it is not necessary to heat to above the melting point of the binder. A normal sintering temperature may be employed at which alloying at the surface occurs to give a liquid phase as shown in Fig. 47.

Although not widely used, infiltration has some advantages in the preparation of compositions very high in binder content which tend to be porous when produced by the standard sintering technique.

Machining, Grinding and Polishing of Sintered Carbides

It is difficult to maintain close dimensional tolerances by either the sintering route (because of the large shrinkage) or hot pressing (the graphite dies wear rapidly). Some machining is therefore usually necessary, and grinding with silicon carbide or metal-bonded diamond wheels is the preferred method. In special cases single-point diamond tools may be used for turning, while carbides with a high binder content may be machined with a hard, fine-grained material such as 94–6 tungsten carbide–cobalt.

In recent years spark machining and ultrasonic machining have found application in the hard-metal industry. Spark machining is particularly useful in the preparation of complex dies and blanking tools; the ultrasonic process is finding similar applications.

For many applications cemented-carbide parts are required to have a high degree of surface finish, which reduces friction and, in the case of dies, provides a good finish on the part being shaped or drawn. A high polish may be obtained on cemented-carbide materials by lapping and polishing with fine diamond powders or pastes.

Tipped Tools

Complete tools are rarely made from cemented carbide because of its high cost and brittleness. Small milling cutters are occasionally made completely from cemented carbide, but in larger tools usually only the cutting edge is carbide, the rest of the tool being steel. The type of steel used for this purpose depends on the application of the tool, but steels with a tensile strength of at least 45 tons/in² are usually required to withstand the stresses involved. Carbide tips are either brazed or mechanically clamped to the steel shank. Common practice has been to use brazing for small tips and mechanical attachment for large pieces, but mechanical clamping is becoming increasingly popular for small tips, particularly for lathe-turning tools. One of the reasons for the increased popularity of mechanical attachment is that 'throw-away' tips can be used, i.e. tips which are discarded when all the cutting edges (six for triangular and eight for square tips) have been used. A selection of typical mechanically-clamped tools is shown in Plate 11 (a). The successful use of such tools is very dependent upon the design of the tool holder. Early tool holders often failed to provide adequate support for the tip, but this problem has been largely overcome and several successful designs are available. Most tool holders also incorporate a variable chip breaker.

For brazed tools copper is the most common brazing material, although silver solders are also widely used and, where service temperatures are likely to be high, copper–nickel alloys are employed. Tips are placed in position on the shank and if likely to move during brazing are bound to the shank with iron or nickel–chromium wire. To ensure a good brazed joint across the whole interface, the face of the shank receiving the tip is usually larger than the tip itself and after brazing the shank is ground back. The brazing alloy is used in the form of sheet or wire, and heating is effected by gas torch, furnace, direct-resistance or high-frequency heating. The last two methods have the advantages of speed and very localized heating. Some form of protection against oxidation is usually required.

When brazing large tips the difference in the thermal-expansion coefficient between tip and shank can lead to cracking of the tip on cooling. A method often used to overcome this fault is to employ a 'sandwich' braze material incorporating a fine mesh of iron or steel wire to accommodate the difference in contraction on cooling. An alternative method, suggested by Zimmer[7] is to interpose between tip and shank a material whose composition and coefficient of thermal expansion vary from one face to the other. Such 'transition pieces' have been prepared by powder metallurgy (see Chapter 12).

After brazing and cleaning, the shank and tip are ground to the correct size and angles using silicon carbide or diamond-impregnated wheels. A selection of brazed carbide-tipped lathe tools is shown in Plate 11 (b).

Properties of Cemented Carbides and Methods of Testing

The general methods of testing employed in powder metallurgy have been described in Chapter 2. As the properties of cemented carbides differ markedly from other powder metallurgy products certain specialized testing methods are required and these are discussed here.

The usual tests to which cemented carbides are subjected are density, hardness, transverse-rupture measurement and metallographic examination, which are supplemented by service evaluation such as cutting or wear-resistance tests. Routine chemical analysis is usually restricted to determination of free and combined carbon, although a check on cobalt may be made occasionally (particularly if vacuum sintering is employed), while nitrogen and oxygen contents may be determined on materials containing titanium carbide.

X-ray diffraction and magnetic testing methods have also been adopted by certain manufacturers as non-destructive tests in general production work. Other properties which are of interest in certain applications are thermal conductivity, thermal expansion, hot hardness, compressive strength, impact strength, electrical conductivity, modulus of elasticity and resistance to oxidation and corrosion; these properties are not determined for routine production control.

Performance Evaluation. Samples from production batches of cutting tools usually undergo some form of performance test. Specimens are subjected to turning, milling, drilling or shaping operations under very arduous conditions so that service life is short (compared with life under normal conditions) and an indication of expected performance is quickly obtained. A test often carried out is to plot what are called T-V curves. In this test the tool life T is plotted against cutting speed V. Unless the tool fails in some catastrophic manner, T is the time taken to develop a certain width of wear mark on the end clearance face of the tool. When both T and V are plotted on logarithmic scales the results give a straight line which characterizes the material.

Density. For maximum performance a cemented carbide must have minimum porosity; a density determination is therefore a useful control test. The density of non-porous cemented carbides is dependent upon the composition. With tungsten carbide–cobalt the density decreases with increasing cobalt content (tungsten carbide 15·6 g/cm³, cobalt 8·9 g/cm³). The addition of titanium carbide (4·9 g/cm³) also reduces the density. Density is therefore a convenient sorting test for cemented-carbide grades and a rough, though speedy, method is to use mercury (13·6 g/cm³) as a buoyancy medium; tungsten carbide–cobalt compositions will sink whereas multi-carbide compositions containing titanium carbide will float.

Hardness. The Rockwell 'A' test is usually adopted for production control, but for more exact determinations the Vickers test with a 50-kg load is used. Increasing cobalt content (Fig. 48) lowers the hardness, whilst the addition of titanium carbide increases hardness. Tantalum carbide is a relatively soft carbide so that it tends to lower hardness, but it also has the effect of restricting carbide grain growth which may lead to an increase in hardness. The increase in hardness with decreasing grain size is shown by the following example: a 94–6 WC–Co material with tungsten carbide grain size of about 2 μ has a hardness of about 92 R_A, while the same composition with a tungsten–carbide grain size of 6 μ has a hardness of only 89 R_A.

Hot Hardness. The retention of tool hardness to high temperatures is of great importance in high-speed machining where tool temperatures may rise well above red heat. At temperatures above about 600°C, high-speed steels rapidly lose their hardness because of over-tempering, while cemented carbides show no such sudden drop in hardness. A 6% cobalt grade has a hardness of 1,000 V.P.N. at a temperature of 750°C, compared with the room temperature value of 1,500 V.P.N. Titanium carbide increases hot hardness, whereas cobalt has the opposite effect.

Transverse-rupture-strength. Transverse-rupture-strength, being a good indication of toughness, is usually determined on all production batches. The test involves three-point loading using cemented-carbide supports.

The strength of tungsten carbide–cobalt materials increases with increasing cobalt content (Fig. 48). Values of 450,000 lb/in² have been obtained with a 20% cobalt composition compared with 50,000 lb/in² for the sintered carbide with no cobalt, but it is obvious that this trend must be reversed at some point since pure cobalt exhibits a strength of only about 40,000 lb/in². The exact composition which gives maximum transverse-rupture-strength is a matter of some controversy. Most authorities place this point at between 16 and 25%

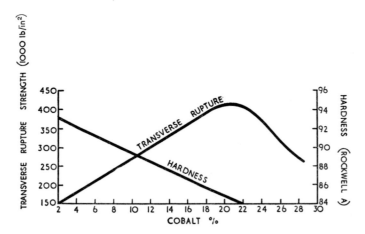

FIG. 48. Relationship between cobalt content and hardness and transverse-rupture-strength of cemented tungsten carbide.

cobalt, but recent work by Hinnüber and Rüdiger[8] indicates that there is no fall in traverse-rupture-strength up to 30% cobalt. Cemented carbides fail by transgranular fracture, and therefore carbide grain-size has a significant effect on transverse-rupture-strength. For a given cobalt content, carbide grain-size controls the mean free path between carbide grains through which the fracture must propagate; since the cobalt is ductile, the greater the mean free path (larger grain size) the higher is the strength. Gurland and Bardzil[9] have established that at 6% cobalt transverse-rupture-strength increases with increasing carbide grain-size and that this tendency is reversed in high-cobalt materials (about 25% Co), while at intermediate-cobalt contents the transverse-rupture-strength apparently shows a pronounced maximum at a grain size of about 3 μ.

The presence of free graphite or of intermediate phases lowers the toughness of tungsten carbide–cobalt compositions. Titanium carbide additions give a similar effect which can be overcome by the introduction of some tantalum carbide.

Impact Strength. Impact strength is a measure of the toughness of a material, a property particularly important in the case of cutting tools used for intermittent cutting. The impact strength of tungsten carbide–cobalt materials increases with increasing cobalt content, rising from about 6 ft-lb at 6% cobalt to about 13 ft-lb at 20% cobalt; titanium carbide additions lower impact strength.

Compressive Strength. The compressive strength of cemented carbides is very high and that of tungsten carbide–cobalt may exceed 600,000 lb/in². However, the maximum compressive strength occurs at a relatively low cobalt content (about 4%), above which compressive strength decreases until at about 25% cobalt it is about 300,000 lb/in².

Metallographic Examination. Although density measurements serve to indicate the degree of porosity a more accurate determination requires metallographic examination. Such examination also reveals the type and distribution of porosity. The procedure recommended by the American Society for Testing Materials,[10] requires an examination at a magnification of 200 and comparison with standard photomicrographs. Diamond polishing is essential in the preparation of cemented carbide micro-specimens because of their hardness.

Much higher magnifications, in the region of 2000 times, are required to reveal the actual microstructure. Detailed examination of features such as carbide grain-size, the presence of secondary carbide phases, the distribution of carbide and binder phase, etc., will indicate probable service performance.

The microstructure of tungsten carbide–cobalt compositions contains only the two phases, WC and γ (cobalt with WC in solid solution). The WC grains usually appear as regular shapes such as triangles or trapeziums and are usually referred to as α phase. Where TiC is present it leads to the formation of a second carbide phase, the TiC–WC solid solution (β phase), which is distinguished from α by electrolytic etching in a nitric–hydrofluoric acid mixture or by a heat-tinting technique, both of which darken the β phase. In general the β grains are more rounded than α. When TaC is also present it tends to go into solid solution in the β phase, although in some cases a TaC-rich solid solution may form. Some typical cemented-carbide structures are shown in Plate 12.

Thermal Conductivity. The thermal conductivity of a cutting tool should be as high as possible since much of the heat resulting from the cutting action must be dissipated by conduction through the tool, otherwise very high temperatures will develop at the cutting edge leading to rapid tool failure. Cemented carbides generally have higher thermal conductivities than the tool steels. Tungsten carbide–cobalt has a particularly high thermal conductivity which is lowered somewhat with increasing cobalt. The addition of titanium carbide results in a pronounced lowering of thermal conductivity (see Table 13).

Thermal Expansion. The coefficient of thermal expansion has an important effect on tool performance; it determines to some extent the magnitude of the stresses set up due to heating at the cutting edge and the thermal shock resistance in intermittent cutting operations. The relationship between the expansion coefficient of the carbide tip and that of the shank also determines the stresses set up during cooling after brazing. Cobalt and titanium carbide both increase the coefficient of thermal expansion of cemented carbides, but their effect is small and compositions of commercial importance have expansion coefficients in the range $5-6 \times 10^{-6}/\text{degC}$.

Oxidation and Corrosion Resistance. Tungsten carbide has a relatively poor oxidation resistance which is improved by the addition of titanium carbide. Several materials based on titanium carbide have been developed for high-temperature applications and these generally have a nickel, or nickel alloy, binder. The corrosion resistance of cobalt-bonded carbides is also relatively poor, but for application in corrosive environments tungsten carbide bonded with corrosion-resistant nickel–chromium alloys has been used with success. Chromium carbide bonded with nickel has much better corrosion and oxidation resistance than the other cemented carbides and has been widely applied where these properties are important.

Some of the properties of a number of typical commercial cemented-carbide materials are given in Table 13.

Applications of Cemented Carbides

Cutting Tools. Tools for metal cutting and machining of abrasive materials is the major application of cemented carbides and indeed most of the development of new compositions has been undertaken with this end in view. Early workers found that while the tungsten carbide–cobalt grades were excellent for machining cast iron, non-ferrous metals and austenitic steels they were not suitable for the fast cutting of ferritic steels; this was a very serious drawback since these steels are by far the most common structural materials.

The failure of tungsten carbide–cobalt when machining ferritic steels is almost invariably due to 'cratering'. Unlike cast irons, ferritic steels form long, continuous chips during machining because of their high ductility. This chip, which is very hot due to friction and deformation during cutting, is guided back across the rake face of the tool, its actual path being determined by the tool geometry. There is considerable pressure between chip and tool causing a tendency for the hot chip to weld to the tool; in the case of tungsten carbide–cobalt such welding takes place fairly readily. Breakaway immediately occurs,

Table 13. Typical Properties of a Number of Commercial Cemented-carbide Materials

Composition (weight per cent)					Density (g/cm³)	Hardness (R_A)	Transverse rupture strength (lb/in^2)	Thermal conductivity (cal/cm sec deg C.)
WC	TiC	TaC(NbC)	Co	Others				
97			3		15·2	92	155,000	0·21
94			6*		15·0	90·5	240,000	0·19
94			6†		15·0	91·5	215,000	0·19
89			11		14·2	89	260,000	0·17
75			25		12·9	83	350,000	0·16
94	1		5		14·6	90·5	212,000	0·19
86	5		9		13·3	90	220,000	0·15
75	16		9		11·0	90·5	180,000	0·07
61	32		7		8·9	92·5	130,000	0·04
91·5			7	0·5VC	14·6	92	208,000	—
81		10	9		14·4	89	240,000	—
85	4	1	10		13·3	90	250,000	0·13
76	7·5	6·5	10		12·1	91·5	265,000	0·11
62	12	18	8		11·8	91·5	185,000	—
50·5	38	5	6·5		8·6	89·0	145,000	—
	75	1	5	15 Ni 5 Cr	6·0	87·5	180,000	—
	15			15 Ni 70 Cr$_3$C$_2$	6·5		100,000	—

* Coarse grained.   † Fine grained.

owing to the rapid motion of the chip, but the chip often carries with it some of the tool material, so that as the process continues a 'crater' is formed on the rake face at the point where welding tends to take place.

The problem of cratering has been overcome by the substitution of titanium carbide for some of the tungsten carbide. Various theories have been proposed to explain the effect of titanium carbide and it seems likely that its success is due to (i) a higher temperature being needed to weld a ferritic steel to a titanium-carbide-bearing tool and (ii) the addition of titanium carbide lowers the coefficient of friction between the chip and the tool, resulting in a somewhat cooler chip. Both effects are probably due to the presence of a more stable oxide film on the materials containing titanium carbide.

The toughness of the tool, as indicated by its transverse-rupture-strength, is markedly reduced by the addition of titanium carbide. Although toughness may be improved by the addition of tantalum carbide and also by a slight increase in binder content, the steel-cutting compositions are, in general, more brittle than the 'straight' tungsten carbide–cobalt grades. Thus they are less suitable for intermittent cutting and extra care is necessary in the avoidance of vibration or chatter during machining.

Another cause of failure of cutting tools is what is termed 'built-up edge'. This is the building up of a layer of the work material at the cutting edge of the tool which breaks away periodically and usually leads to crumbling of the cutting edge. The phenomenon occurs most readily at low cutting speeds on continuous-chipping materials and at these low speeds multicarbide compositions seem to be more prone to built-up edge than 'straight' tungsten carbide. For this reason tungsten carbide grades may often be preferred for steel cutting where speeds are low, particularly where heavy intermittent cutting is required since their extra toughness is a further asset.

Other modes of failure of cemented-carbide tools are simple breakage (due to low impact resistance, incorrect tool geometry or insufficient machine tool rigidity), oxidation, thermal shock or simple abrasive wear.

The factors, described above, which control the cutting performance of cemented carbides in turning operations also apply, with minor modifications, to other forms of machining. In operations such as planing, shaping and milling, intermittent cutting is always involved so that extra toughness is required in the tool. A particular feature of milling is the thermal cycle imposed on each blade every revolution as it cuts over a small arc and then cools. This can lead to failure of the cemented carbide by thermal shock and indeed cracks due to this mechanism are the major cause of failure of milling tools. The cracks are usually found on the rake and clearance faces and, by electron microscopy, Hinnüber and Rüdiger[8] have shown that they develop mainly in the binder phase. Drilling is a particularly arduous operation because the tool is buried in the hot workpiece and it is difficult efficiently to feed the

11

cutting tip with coolant. Oxidation, therefore, is the chief cause of failure of carbide-tipped drills.

To obtain the most efficient performance from cemented-carbide cutting tools the following general points should be borne in mind: (i) the machine tool should be in good condition to avoid excessive vibration and chatter, (ii) the tool must be rigidly supported, (iii) correct tool geometry must be employed and, (iv) the correct grade of carbide material should be used. Points (i) and (ii), although obviously good workshop practice, are of particular importance when cutting with cemented carbides. An old and somewhat worn machine may give satisfactory results when cutting with high-speed steel, but in order to use carbide materials to full advantage much more power is consumed and any slackness or lack of rigidity will give rise to vibration and chatter and lead to early failure of a carbide tool. Tool geometry is determined by the machining conditions, the workpiece material, the tool material and, probably most of all, by experience. However, since cemented carbides are much more brittle than high-speed steels, narrow lip angles should be avoided. Negative-rake angles may have to be employed and this will increase the power consumption and the pressure on the tool, a feature only possible with cemented carbides because of their high compressive strength. The choice of carbide grade depends primarily on the material being machined and the type of machining operation. For light, high-speed finishing cuts low-cobalt compositions are employed because of their extreme hardness, while the tougher, high-cobalt compositions are necessary for roughing operations. 'Straight' tungsten carbide grades are suitable for machining plastics and other abrasive non-metallic materials as well as cast iron, non-ferrous metals, super-

Table 14. Typical Applications of Various Cemented Carbide Grades

Composition wt–%				Typical uses as cutting tools
WC	TiC	TaC	Co	
93–97			3–7	Finishing to medium-roughing cuts on cast iron, non-ferrous metals, austenitic alloys, plastics, etc.
85–93			7–15	Rough cuts on cast iron, etc.
48–77	20–40	0–5	3–7	Light high-speed finishing cuts on ferritic steel.
63–80	10–20	3–7	7–10	Medium cuts on ferritic steel at medium speeds.
70–83	5–12	2–6	10–12	Roughing cuts on ferritic steel.
66–79	3–7	10–17	8–10	General purpose and heavy cutting of ferritic steel, particularly where resistance to abrasion by scale is required.

alloys and other austenitic compositions. For high-speed cutting of ferritic steels it is necessary to use multi-carbide compositions. For light, high-speed finishing of ferritic steel the titanium-carbide content is usually high (about 30–40%), while tantalum carbide is present in only small amounts (perhaps 0–5%) and cobalt is low (3–7%). Tantalum carbide is increased somewhat at the expense of titanium carbide where resistance to abrasion by scale is required; like cobalt it also increases toughness.

Table 14 summarizes the applications of various cemented-carbide grades as cutting-tool materials. Examples of the type of cutting that may be achieved with cemented-carbide tools are shown in Plate 13.

Other Applications. Reference has already been made to the widespread use of cemented carbides as wear-resistant materials. For most of these applications 'straight' tungsten carbide–cobalt compositions may be used, cobalt content depending on the toughness required. A selection of typical wear-resistant parts is shown in Plates 14 and 15.

Cemented-carbide dies are very widely used for the drawing of wire, rod, tube and other sections between 0·04 and 0·4 in. For sections below 0·04 in. diamond dies are mandatory, while for sections above 0·4 in. steel dies are usual, although even at these larger sizes carbide dies find quite wide application. Small dies are manufactured in very low (about 3%) cobalt material of high hardness, but as the section size increases toughness becomes more important and cobalt is increased. Very large dies may be made from materials with as much as 15% cobalt. When drawing steel and certain other materials such as the refractory metals tungsten and molybdenum, a type of wear similar to 'cratering' in metal cutting may occur. For these applications die materials containing additions of titanium carbide or tantalum carbide (up to 15%) are necessary. Cemented carbides are rarely used for the complete die, but usually take the form of inserts or nibs which are contained in a strong, supporting metallic-casing. Carbide-lined dies for the compacting of metal and ceramic powders have been described in Chapter 3.

In the mining industry cemented carbides have proved a very economic proposition as drill tips and are used in the drilling of all types of rock, coal, salt, etc. They are used for both rotary and percussion drilling, the latter requiring a tough grade of material (8–15% cobalt) owing to the high compressive and impact stresses involved.

Although tungsten carbide compositions are adequate for most wear-resistant applications there are cases, particularly in the chemical industry, where corrosion and oxidation resistance are required in addition to wear resistance. In such cases it is necessary to use nickel-bonded chromium carbide, or titanium carbide bonded with nickel–chromium alloys.

The sheet-metal industry uses large amounts of cemented carbide as inserts, etc., in blanking dies. Carbide-lined dies are economically advantageous for long production runs and have proved their worth, particularly when blanking abrasive materials such as high-silicon transformer sheet.

OXIDE AND BORIDE CUTTING TOOLS

A number of oxide and boride cutting tool materials have been developed and these compete with cemented carbides in certain applications.

The so-called 'oxide' or 'ceramic' cutting tools are all, at present, based on alumina, Al_2O_3. The advantages of alumina as a cutting tool are very good hot hardness, extremely good oxidation resistance and very low wettability by metals with consequently little tendency to weld to the metal chip. Alumina tools, therefore, rarely suffer from cratering or built-up edge, although occasionally there may be some tendency for badly oxidized material to adhere.

Ceramic tools are more brittle than the cemented carbides and they also have less thermal-shock resistance. They are therefore generally unsuitable for intermittent cutting and require sturdy, vibration-free machine tools. It is in the field of high-speed finishing that oxide tools rival the very hard carbide grades. Oxide tools are cheaper than carbides because of the low cost of the raw material.

At present ceramic tools fall into three groups: (i) basically alumina with minor additions (less than 1%) of metals such as silicon and chromium, (ii) at least 90% alumina with additions of other oxides such as Cr_2O_3, SiO_2, MgO, etc., and (iii) at least 60% alumina with additions of carbides WC, Mo_2C, TiC, TaC, etc., or occasionally borides or silicides.

Tips in these materials are prepared by the standard methods employed for the cemented carbides, i.e. cold pressing and sintering or hot pressing, and are usually fired in air, although compositions containing carbides must be sintered under a protective atmosphere. Carbide additions increase thermal conductivity and transverse-rupture-strength and such materials are particularly suited to the high-speed cutting of steel. Although ceramic tips may be brazed to shanks, using special techniques, they are more often used as 'throwaway' tips in mechanical holders.

Since borides generally exhibit very high hardness, in some cases (e.g. TiB_2) higher than most of the carbides it seemed likely that they might make useful cutting-tool materials, with the particular advantage that they would conserve strategic materials such as tungsten and cobalt in times of emergency. Several boride tool compositions have been developed based mainly on the borides of titanium, zirconium and molybdenum with various additions. However, although these materials have proved themselves equal to cemented carbides under certain conditions they have not yet been used in general production work.

DIAMOND TOOLS

Diamond is the hardest known mineral and is therefore a very desirable tool material. Unfortunately diamond is extremely expensive and is only found, or produced, as relatively small pieces, the larger of which, being in great demand as gems, are the most expensive. Diamond is also extremely brittle and this, together with its high cost, dictates the method of its use. Although 'single-point' diamond tools are occasionally used for precision machining, the most usual way of overcoming the high cost and brittleness is to incorporate fine diamond particles in a softer matrix to form an abrasive tool. Several types of material, plastics, ceramics, metal and cemented carbides, are used as the matrices in which the diamond is held. The last two only will be discussed here.

Because of the very high cost of diamond, the cost of fabricating the tool is a relatively minor one compared with the raw material cost. Consequently the techniques employed in the production of diamond tools, such as individual weighing of charges, hand loading of dies and hot pressing, are justified.

The characteristics of a diamond tool, besides being dependent upon the production technique are also affected by the following variables: (i) diamond grit size, (ii) concentration (proportion of diamonds in matrix), (iii) content (total amount of diamonds in tool) and (iv) matrix or binder material. Each of these factors must be varied according to the application of the tool, so that the maximum amount of useful work is obtained from the diamonds.

Diamond grit size is the factor which, more than any other, determines the surface finish obtained on the component. The range of diamond grit sizes generally used in the manufacture of various diamond tools lies between 60 and 400 mesh. The coarser sizes are used mainly for cutting discs, medium sizes for grinding wheels and the finer sizes for finishing operations such as honing and lapping.

The concentration or proportion of diamond to binder is usually expressed as a code number. There is no standard coding system, so that a concentration of 100 may mean, perhaps, 20 volume per cent of diamond to one manufacturer and 10 to another. However, a widely used system is to designate 25 volume per cent diamond (equivalent to 72 carats per cubic inch) as 100 concentration; other concentrations are then proportional to this. The grinding performance of a tool increases with concentration up to an optimum figure, beyond which the diamonds are released from the matrix before doing their maximum work. A further factor to be considered when choosing a concentration for a particular application is the fact that diamond particles act in the same way as voids and weaken the matrix. The strength of a diamond composite therefore decreases with increasing concentration.

The diamond content of a tool is determined by the concentration and the thickness of the diamond-bearing layer. The thickness of this layer determines the total life of the tool, other factors being equal, but it cannot be made too thick since a certain amount of back-up material is necessary to provide the tool with adequate strength. Furthermore, since the cost of fabricating the tool is more or less constant, the total cost increases in direct relationship with 'content' and consequently failure by breakage of high-content tools entails a large capital loss. Total diamond content, therefore, is governed by tool geometry, conditions of service and economics.

The major function of the matrix is to hold the diamonds in position while they do their job of cutting. However, it is also very important that the matrix should wear away at such a rate that diamond particles are released progressively as they wear and are no longer cutting efficiently.

Diamond is thought by many to wear away by burning due to the frictional heat, although another school considers that small pieces are chipped away. The rate of wear of the diamond, whilst depending on the workpiece material, is also related to such factors as rotational speed and tool pressure. The rate of wear of the matrix is governed by the abrasive properties of the debris produced during service which is not entirely dependent upon the macro-hardness of the material being worked. Many of the so-called soft rocks, for example, consist of loosely bonded hard particles. The choice of matrix material is determined mainly by the material being worked and by the method of working. Other factors that must also be considered are strength (which is affected by diamond concentration) and the properties of the matrix which affect its suitability for the techniques of powder metallurgy (availability in suitable powder form, compressibility, etc.). The materials in common use as binders for diamond tools are copper, various bronzes and brasses, cupro-nickels, cobalt, iron and various steels, also 'heavy metal' compositions and cemented carbides. Solid lubricants, such as molybdenum disulphide and boron nitride, are occasionally added to the powder mix to reduce friction during service; the use of ceramic 'fillers' such as mica and alumina is also quite common.

Production of Diamond Tools.

Three basic methods are used for the production of metal-bonded diamond tools, namely, cold pressing and sintering, hot pressing, and electro-plating. The last method is outside the scope of this book and will not be considered.

Cold pressing and sintering is generally not as satisfactory as hot pressing, because it results in higher residual porosity. Such porosity is likely to occur particularly around diamond particles so that they tend to fall out more easily in service. However, the sintering method is particularly useful for matrix compositions such as 'heavy-metal' where the liquid phase present at sinter-ing temperatures would tend to be squeezed out during hot pressing. Furthermore, cold pressing and sintering is cheaper than hot pressing, so that it is often used for tools of low-diamond content produced in large numbers.

Hot pressing, however, is the preferred method for the production of high-quality diamond tools. Most of the matrix compositions may be hot pressed at temperatures where heat-resistant metal dies can be used, although graphite dies are necessary for cemented-carbide-bonded tools.

Dies are filled by hand with pre-weighed charges in individual layers, i.e. diamond-bearing and back-up layers. The loaded dies are then usually pre-compacted at about 10 tons/in² at room temperature, heated under a protective atmosphere and, after temperature equalization, removed from the furnace and placed in a press for final compaction. In some cases dies are then re-heated to a higher temperature and pressure applied again. Some typical hot pressing temperatures and pressures for various matrix compositions are shown in Table 15.

Table 15. Hot Pressing Pressures (tons/in²) at Various Temperatures for Metal-bonded Diamond Tools

Matrix material	Temperature (°C)							
	400	660	700	750	850	875	900	1300
Copper	—	—	—	10	—	—	—	—
Bronze— 5% Tin	—	—	—	10	—	—	—	—
10% Tin	—	—	10	—	—	—	—	—
15% Tin	—	10	—	—	—	—	—	—
20% Tin	—	10	—	—	—	—	—	—
40% Tin	10	—	—	—	—	—	—	—
Brass	—	—	—	10	—	—	—	—
70/30 Copper/Nickel	—	10	—	—	—	—	—	—
Cobalt	—	—	—	10	10	—	—	—
Iron and Steel	—	—	—	10	—	6·7	0	—
Tungsten Carbide —10% Cobalt	—	—	—	—	—	—	—	1·5

In many instances only the working face of a diamond tool is made by powder metallurgy, and then attached to a solid metal backing in a variety of ways, such as mechanical fixing, brazing, soldering, sinter-brazing (during sintering or hot pressing), or by means of adhesives.

Diamond tools of various types are widely used for the drilling, cutting and sawing of all manner of hard materials such as rocks, quartz, glass, concrete and cemented carbides, and are also used for the grinding, lapping and polishing of hard metals, stone and glass (particularly in the generation of optical surfaces). Germanium and other semiconductor materials may also be sliced economically with diamond-cutting discs.

Metal-bonded diamond tools are best used wet to reduce frictional heat at the high speeds (6,000–12,000 surface ft/min) used in practice. Various coolant-lubricants are in use, including water, various aqueous solutions and mineral cutting oils. The coolant also serves to remove the abrasive dust resulting from the grinding action. In the mining industry diamond tools are generally restricted to deep drilling, cemented carbide and steel being adequate for most other operations. The optimum matrix material is determined by the rock being drilled; for example, diamonds bonded with iron have been found suitable for Portland stone, while granite needs a softer matrix. However, in deep drilling a hole may pass through several types of rock so that a compromise must be reached.

Diamond tools with an iron or steel matrix are generally suitable for the grinding of cemented carbides, while copper and various bronze matrices are usually employed for glass grinding. Many different types and shapes of diamond wheels, saws, hones and other tools are produced for industries ranging from mining to dentistry.

REFERENCES

1. Swarzkopf, P. and Kieffer, R. *Cemented Carbides*, Macmillan, New York (1960).
2. *German Patents* 420,689 and 434,527, *U.S. Patents* 1,549,615 and 1,721,416.
3. Hinnüber, J., Rüdiger, O and Kinna, W. *Powder Metallurgy*, No. 8, 1 (1961).
4. Price, G. H. S., Smithells, C. J. and Williams, S. V. *J. Inst. Met.*, **62**, 239 (1938).
5. Cannon, H. S. and Lenel, F. V. *Proc. First Plansee Seminar*, 106 (1953).
6. Parikh, N. M. and Humenik Jr., M. *J. Amer. ceram. Soc.*, **40**, 9, 315 (Sept., 1957).
7. Zimmer, F. *Metal Progress*, 101 (Jan., 1963).
8. Hinnüber, J. and Rüdiger, O. *Cobalt*, **19**, 57 (June, 1963).
9. Gurland, J. and Bardzil, P. *J. Metals*, **7**, 311 (1955).
10. *A.S.T.M.*, B 276–54.

CHAPTER 7

BEARING MATERIALS

Some of the most important applications of powder metallurgy occur in the field of bearings. The various types of bearing produced by powder metallurgy account for a considerable, and increasing, proportion of total bearing usage. According to Jones,[1] the tonnage of metal powders used in the production of porous bearings, the most important of the bearing types produced by powder metallurgy, may well exceed that used for any other type of sintered component. The annual United Kingdom production (1960)[2] of porous bearings has been estimated to exceed 100,000,000, while the world production (1961)[3] may be greater than 10,000,000 per day. The great success of powder-metal bearings is due to the ease with which 'duplex' materials, (metal–metal, metal–plastics, metal–liquid lubricant), having controlled characteristics, can be produced at low cost. It is possible that, as the fundamentals of bearing behaviour become even better understood, this unique ability to produce 'duplex' materials will increase the importance of powder metallurgy in this field.

The friction loss of a bearing is largely dependent upon the presence of a lubricant, usually a liquid. The characteristics of the lubricant, together with the geometry, speed and load of the machine, determine the degree of friction; in general the nature of the bearing material exerts little influence upon the friction value of well-lubricated systems. There are two mechanisms whereby lubricants operate, hydrodynamic and boundary-film lubrication. Hydrodynamic lubrication is the most desirable condition since the load is sustained by the hydrodynamic pressure generated by relative motion of the bearing and journal. Under hydrodynamic lubrication conditions the load-carrying ability is determined by the hydrodynamic pressure, which is itself a function of the relative motions. Unless a pump is used, hydrodynamic lubrication does not occur during starting.

It is, however, usual for part or all of the load to be carried by sliding contact between the bearing and journal surfaces separated only by a thin film of lubricant. This condition is known as 'boundary film lubrication'. With boundary film lubrication the performance of the bearing is thus dependent upon the ability of the lubricant to maintain a continuous film under load. Since direct bearing-journal contact does not normally occur the bearing material has only a minor influence upon friction losses.

A low friction-loss is not, however, the only criterion for a good bearing and the bearing material does have an important influence on the overall bearing performance. Indeed, the superiority of 'white-metal' and phosphor-bronze, etc., in certain applications is well known. The chief requirements of a good bearing material are that the rate of wear of both journal and bearing should be a minimum and that seizure, distortion and mechanical failure should not occur under the chosen load/speed conditions. Some of these properties are needed as an insurance against inadequate lubrication. To avoid distortion and mechanical failure adequate compression and fatigue strengths are needed, requirements which are best met by hard materials of high compressive strength. Unfortunately, hard materials do not conform well to the journal, nor do they allow abrasive particles (which in practice are frequently present) to become embedded in them. Soft materials are better able to accommodate hard particles by allowing them to embed, but are, of course, relatively weak. Thus the structure of an ideal bearing is a mixture of hard and soft phases.

A criterion often applied in judging bearing performance is what is called the PV factor. P is the pressure (lb/in^2) on the projected area (the projected area is the diameter times the length of the radial bearing area) and V is the peripheral speed of the shaft (ft/min); the units of PV are therefore lb/in^2 ft/min. PV is known to be an unreliable guide to the performance of liquid-lubricated bearings, although, as will be shown later, it is of value in assessing bearings having a solid lubricant. In oil-lubricated bearings it has been found that the maximum value of P increases with increasing V because of the ability of the oil film to carry greater loads.

OIL-IMPREGNATED BEARINGS

The most important bearing produced by powder metallurgy is the porous oil-impregnated type. This consists of a porous metal within which a lubricant is held by capillary forces. Loss of lubricant from the bearing is small and additional lubrication is usually unnecessary. The elimination of periodic lubrication has been particularly valuable in the field of fractional horse-power electric motors and associated devices such as are found in domestic equipment. Their use in industry has led to substantial savings in maintenance costs.

Method of Production

Porous bearings are made in bronze, aluminium or iron alloys. The four basic steps involved in producing a porous bearing are: compacting, sintering, sizing and impregnation.

Bronze bearings have tin contents in the range 6–12%, the 9% tin alloy being the most widely used. Additions of graphite and lead may also be made, the former being the more common. As well as providing an increased degree of self-lubrication these additions improve the pressing characteristics. Graphite reduces strength, and additions are therefore usually limited to less than $1\frac{1}{2}\%$, although, where strength is not important, up to 5% graphite has been used. Lead additions are kept below 10% since this also reduces strength. The presence of solid-lubricant additions is particularly valuable where the loads are oscillating or reciprocating and where a load-carrying oil film is not built-up; leaded-bronze is preferred in those cases where a soft journal is used.

Elemental copper and tin are preferred to alloy powders for the production of bronze bearings. Improved pressing characteristics are obtained from the elemental powders and it is also possible to get higher sintered strengths because of the tin-rich liquid-phase formed during sintering. High-purity annealed powders are necessary for the best compacting performance; for highest green densities fine tin powder is used.[4] Bearings are pressed on high-speed presses; the flow properties of the powders are therefore important and vibration of the powder feed is usually necessary. Production rates of 2,000 compacts per hour are typical and even higher rates have been obtained on small presses (about 2-tons capacity). Compacting pressures are normally about 15 tons/in², but may reach 35 tons/in² where maximum strength is needed. Presses of 50-tons capacity are adequate for the production of most bearings.

The high production rates necessitate the use of mesh-belt sintering furnaces, usually with hydrocarbon atmospheres. A typical sintering cycle is to hold the compact at 400–450°C to expel the lubricant and allow the molten tin to diffuse into the copper, followed by further heating to 800°C for as little as 5 minutes. At this higher temperature a tin-rich liquid-phase is again formed and is absorbed by the copper. Temperatures much above 800°C must be avoided, otherwise the pores may become isolated.

Certain dimensions of a bearing need to be held to close tolerances; not only is there an optimum fit on to the moving shaft but an accurate fit into the bearing housing is also necessary. Growth occurs during sintering and, since this cannot be accurately controlled, sizing is necessary. This operation also serves to improve surface finish. Where the pore size is small, sizing may close the surface pores, in which case careful machining is preferable. The sizing operation is used to control the inside and outside diameters as well as the height. Size reductions of 0·01–0·02 in. may be obtained by this operation.

Impregnation with oil is the final process; it is usually carried out by the bearing producer, although porous bearings are also sold 'dry' and impregnated by the user. Bearings are impregnated in hot oil ($\sim 110°C$) and this operation is often carried out under reduced pressure to remove air from within the pores.

Porous iron bearings are manufactured by similar methods to those used for bronze, but compacting pressures tend to be somewhat higher and the sintering temperature is about 1100°C. Iron–copper compositions are used, frequently with additions of graphite, the copper content being within the range 2–10%. (Much higher copper contents were formerly used but these have been superseded.)

The production of aluminium bearings follows along similar lines to those employed for iron and bronze. Great care has to be exercised in the selection of a pressing lubricant in order that 'galling' of the die is prevented. Storcheim[5] gives the range of compacting pressures as 5–40 tons/in², and the sintering temperature as 600–650°C.

Properties

The simple concept of the oil-impregnated bearing as being a metal-lubricant mixture where only that lubricant near the bearing surface acts to reduce the frictional loss, has been shown to be inadequate. Lubricants only perform efficiently within a restricted temperature range; if they are overheated chemical or physical changes will occur which rob the lubricant of its properties. Heat is always generated at bearing surfaces; such heat may be dissipated by conduction through the shaft or through the bearing housing, although in continuously lubricated systems much of it will be removed by circulation of the lubricant.

The thermal conductivity of a porous metal is low and unless the lubricant within the bearing is circulated the surface layer will overheat. It has been shown that circulation of the lubricant within a porous metal bearing does indeed occur. Fig. 49, due to Morgan and Cameron,[6] demonstrates this fact. Fig. 49 was obtained from experiments in which a bearing was impregnated with a dyed oil and surrounded by a felt ring containing uncoloured oil. The explanation of these effects is that the hydrodynamic pressure causes an oil pressure within the bearing in the direction of the load line and, since the pressure in the unloaded area is less, the oil circulates. The rate of circulation is determined by the permeability of the porous metal and the viscosity of the oil. Permeability is controlled by the choice of particle-size distribution and

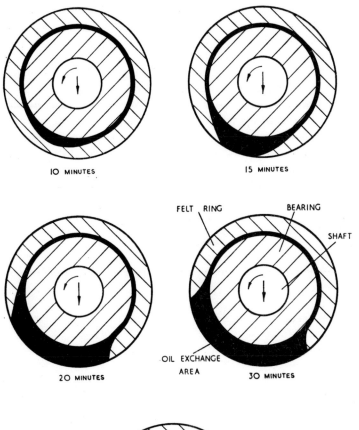

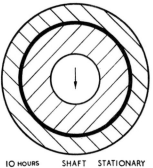

FIG. 49. Oil-pressure distribution within a porous bearing. Dark area denotes region of high pressure.
(*Morgan and Cameron*[6])

compacting pressure, while viscosity depends upon selection of the correct oil. To some extent, circulation is automatically regulated, since an increase in the temperature of the oil decreases its viscosity, which leads to faster circulation. Where relatively heavy loads are likely to be encountered a 'heavy' oil (SAE 60) is preferred with a coarse pore size; for light loads and high speeds a thinner oil (SAE 20) is used with a fine pore size.

During service the surface pores may be closed somewhat, and this is accentuated by overloading. Pore closure reduces circulation and thereby leads to overheating of the lubricant. The ultimate life of a bearing has been shown to be dependent upon the running temperature of the oil and, since the heat produced is related to $PV\mu$ (μ being the friction coefficient), PV can be used as an approximate design parameter for porous bearings.

As discussed earlier, the ability of a fluid film to carry the load determines the performance of the bearing. Morgan and Cameron[6] have shown that, for porous bearings, higher values of speed and viscosity are necessary to develop the required fluid film than is the case with solid bearings, the film pressure presumably leaking away through the pores. With solid bearings,

Table 16. Typical Properties of Porous Bearings

		Bronze	Iron	Iron–Copper
Density	g/cm³	5·7–6·7	5·7–6·2	5·0–6·3
Ultimate tensile strength	lb/in²	12,000–14,000	—	12,000–30,000
Ultimate compressive strength	lb/in²	69,000	—	—
Limit of proportionality in compression	lb/in²	10,500	12,200	17,500
Compression, 0·001 in. deformation	lb/in²	12,500	15,000	23,000
Compression 0·003 in. deformation	lb/in²	14,500	18,500	31,000
K factor*	lb/in²	17,500–22,500	—	22,500–40,000
Hardness	B.H.N.	30–40	40–50	—
Maximum static loading	lb/in²	7,500–10,000	8,000–10,000	15,000–20,000
Maximum slow moving loading	lb/in²	4,000–5,000	—	7,500–12,000
Maximum speed	ft/min	1,500	800	—
Maximum PV	lb/in² ft/min	50,000–60,000	40,000–50,000	35,000–60,000
Maximum running temperature	°C	65	65	—
Thermal conductivity	cal/cm/s/deg C	0·1	0·1	—
Coefficient of linear expansion	in/in/deg C	15×10^{-6}	10×10^{-6}	—

* Note: the K factor enables the radial crushing strength P to be determined from the formula:

$$P = \frac{KLT^2}{D-T}$$

where D is the outside diameter (in.), T the wall thickness (in.) and L the bush length (in.).

the load carrying ability of the film can be improved by using lubricants containing additives, but these may not be used in porous bearings since the additive would interfere with circulation.

The pressure which causes the lubricant to circulate throughout the bearing also tends to cause loss of lubricant from the free surfaces. In a cylindrical bearing, losses from the ends are the most important. Since it is surface tension forces which hold the lubricant within a porous bearing and which tend to cause reabsorption of exuded oil, losses are smaller the finer the pore size. Although it is obviously desirable that the amount of oil held by the bearing (20–35% by volume) shall be sufficient to last the life of the bearing, in some cases it is necessary to supplement the supply of lubricant. Fig. 50 shows some ways of achieving this. Tait[7] suggests that at medium to high speeds, where PV is greater than 25,000 lb/in² ft/min, supplementary lubrication is needed. The PV limit for long running without additional lubrication is given by Booser[3] as 20,000 lb/in² ft/min.

Typical properties of bronze and iron oil-impregnated bearings are summarized in Table 16. Maximum values of PV for the three types are similar, but the iron alloys, being stronger, are more suitable for high loads. Bronze bearings, by far the most common type, are preferable for higher speeds.

Forms of Porous Bearings

Most porous bearings are made to a variation of one of a few standard shapes. The principal manufacturers of bearings maintain large stocks of these

Table. 17. Size Range covered by Standard Bearings
(*Dimensions in inches*)

Type	Minimum	Maximum
Plain cylindrical		
Inside diameter	0·08	3·5
Outside diameter	0·2	4·5
Length	0·08	4·0
Flanged		
Inside diameter	0·18	1·5
Outside diameter	0·3	1·8
Length	0·25	2·0
Flange diameter	0·38	2·5
Flange thickness	0·06	0·18
Thrust washers		
Inside diameter	0·18	2·3
Outside diameter	0·5	3·5
Thickness	0·06	0·3
Self-aligning		
Inside diameter	0·06	0·5
Spherical diameter	0·2	1·0
Length	0·15	0·75

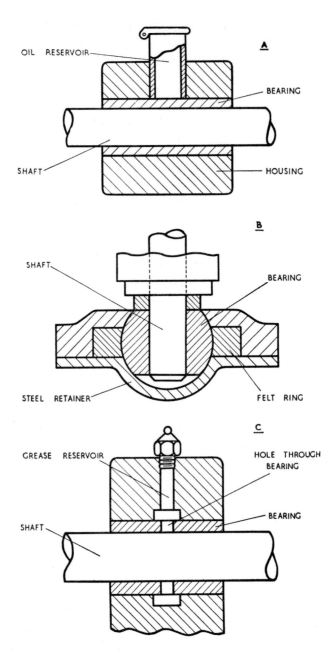

FIG. 50. Some methods of providing supplementary lubrication for porous bearings.

in various standard sizes. The common shapes are plain cylinders, flanged cylinders, thrust washers and self-aligning bearings. Examples are shown in Plate 16. The size range within which items have sufficiently large application to justify manufacturers holding substantial stocks is indicated in Table 17. There are many variations to the basic forms, and keyways, slots, profiles and fixing lugs may all be incorporated; in fact, bearings may be produced in shapes almost as complex as those achieved in the higher-density structural components. The restrictions in shape are essentially those outlined earlier (Chapter 3) and there is also the usual proviso that the quantity must justify the die costs.

The limitations to shape and size have been discussed by Booser[3] who gives the following rules for the form of bronze bearings: (i) counterbores may be formed at each end, and at a flanged end the counterbores must not be more than 30% of the flange depth (only 20% for iron or high-density bronze), (ii) full-length ribs, splines or grooves may be formed on outside or inside diameters (if of only partial length they must reach to one end) and (iii) the limiting length-to-diameter ratio is 5:1 for standard bronze and 3·5:1 for high-density bronze and iron.

Booser also gives the following size limits for plain bearings. They can be made up to 9 in. long, with length preferably not exceeding four times the outside diameter and never more than twenty-five times the wall thickness (which must be at least $\frac{1}{32}$ in.). For flanged bearings the overhang should be less than three times the flange thickness, and the body length not more than twelve times the wall thickness. Thrust washers have been made up to 30 in. in diameter.

The dimensional accuracy of porous bearings is particularly important. This arises because bearings are held in their housings by means of an interference fit, i.e. the outside diameter of the bearing is slightly larger than the bore in the housing. Forcing the bearing into the housing deforms the bearing and the unrelieved elastic strain serves to hold it rigid; the security with which the bearing is held depends on the degree of deformation. The deformation of the outside diameter of the bearing also reduces the bore size. The 'close-in' of the bore due to fitting into the housing is often calculated on the assumption that the housing is perfectly rigid. In fact, the housing does stretch to some extent. Fig. 51 shows, for various sizes of bearing, a relationship between the actual and calculated close-in.

The optimum shaft clearance depends upon a number of factors; light-duty bearings can have a small clearance, whereas for high PV values a large clearance is required. The shaft clearances recommended by one manufacturer are shown in Fig. 52. Since the bearing and the housing will usually be of materials with different coefficients of expansion, a change in temperature will alter the elastic strain in the bearing causing a change in the shaft

12

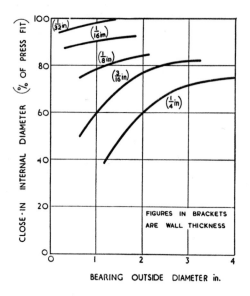

FIG. 51. Relationship between actual and calculated close-in of the internal diameter of a porous-bronze bearing.

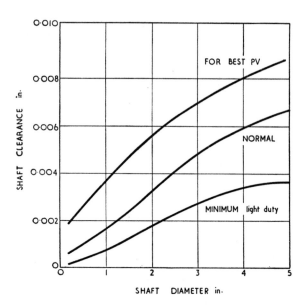

FIG. 52. Recommended shaft clearances for porous-bronze bearings.

clearance. In the frequently-occurring case of a steel shaft running in a bronze bearing held in an aluminium housing, the shaft clearance will increase with increasing temperature.

The best way of fitting a bearing into a housing is by means of a shouldered

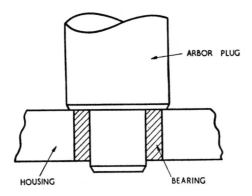

FIG. 53. Use of an arbor plug for fitting a bearing into its housing.

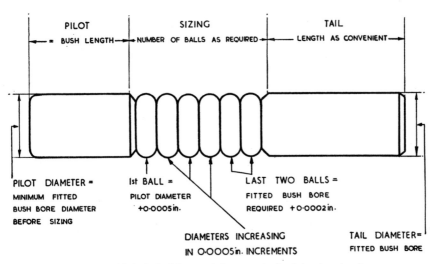

FIG. 54. Multiple-ball sizing tool for accurately sizing bearing bores.
(*Courtesy of Manganese Bronze Ltd.*)

punch of the type shown in Fig. 53. The diameter of the pilot should be about 0·0005 in. greater than the bottom limit of the desired bore. A multiple-ball sizing tool, which can be used for particularly accurate sizing, is shown in Fig. 54.

COPPER–LEAD BEARINGS

Earlier in this chapter the merits of a two-phase structure as a bearing material were mentioned. Some of the soft metals, such as lead, tin and cadmium, have excellent bearing properties because, in deforming easily, they compensate for irregularities in a moving shaft and remove hard particles by allowing them to become embedded. Additionally these metals have very low solubility in steel (the most common shaft material), a characteristic which reduces the tendency for cold welding. Moreover, because of their low shear strength, if cold welding does take place the weld is easily broken. Unfortunately, because these soft metals deform easily under load and have poor fatigue strengths, they have very limited use, in the pure form, as bearing materials.

The use of two-phase structures, where the soft 'bearing' metal is embedded in a strong 'load-carrying' matrix has proved to be a means of utilizing the desirable characteristics of soft metals at high bearing loads. Powder metallurgy is the preferred method of producing these duplex materials, because the distribution of the phases can be controlled.

The fatigue strength of bearing materials can often be improved by bonding a relatively thin shell of the bearing to a strong support, to steel for instance. This approach is often used for this type of bearing, bonding on to the support being combined with producing the two-phase structure.

Undoubtedly the most important bearing in this 'two-phase' class is that which comprises copper–lead bonded to steel. These bearings are very widely used, particularly in automobile engines, and they have often successfully replaced the traditional solid phosphor-bronze bushes. Copper and lead exhibit negligible solubility in each other in the solid state, so that the alloys formed consist of two separate phases. The properties of the alloy depend upon the amounts and distribution of the two-phases. In cast alloys more than 30% lead gives a continuous lead-phase with discontinuous copper, providing a mechanically weak, and therefore undesirable, structure. Sintered alloys, because of the different method of production, can accommodate up to 45% lead before the copper-phase becomes discrete particles in a weak lead matrix. In sintered alloys containing less than 45% lead, interlocking copper and lead networks are formed. This interlocking structure is very desirable since the copper provides structural stability together with a maximum amount of lead for lubrication.

In automobile engine applications the 25–30% lead alloy is generally preferred. A stronger alloy containing 20–25% lead and 2–4% tin is more suitable for higher loads. Tin is a frequent addition to these alloys; it modifies the structure due to its effect on the surface tension of liquid lead, increases the strength and has been reported to improve seizure resistance.

The production of steel-backed copper–lead is usually carried out on a continuous basis. Copper–lead powder is spread on to a steel sheet, previously prepared by degreasing and copper plating to ensure a better bond. The sheet is then passed through a furnace, after which it is rolled to compact the 'loose sintered' powder, and then resintered. The sintering temperature in each case is in the range 800–850°C.

Steel-backed copper–lead strip is usually pressed or 'wrapped' to form semi-cylindrical half-shell bearings. According to Forrester[8] the use of this type of bearing is increasing rapidly.

A problem often associated with the use of copper–lead bearings is oil corrosion, but to some extent this has now been overcome by careful formulation and selection of the lubricant. Forrester suggests that it was this corrosion problem which provided the impetus for the introduction of the overlay-bearing, i.e. a normal copper–lead bearing with a thin electrodeposited layer of lead or tin-base alloy on the bearing surface. Practically all heavy-duty engines now use overlay bearings. Apart from reducing corrosion, the soft electrodeposited layer assists initial bedding-in.

DRY-LUBRICATED BEARINGS

The so-called 'dry'-lubricated bearings contain solids which themselves have very low coefficients of friction, and therefore the presence of a liquid lubricant is not essential. Two such solid lubricants are commonly used, graphite and polytetrafluoroethylene (p.t.f.e.). In general these bearings are used where periodic lubrication is difficult or undesirable. Examples of applications where a liquid lubricant cannot be tolerated are found in the pharmaceutical, textile and food-processing fields.

Graphite

Graphite was the earliest of the solid 'self-lubricating' additions to be widely employed. It is frequently added to porous oil-impregnated bearings, and logical developments were copper–graphite and bronze–graphite. These materials have many similarities to certain of the sliding electrical-contact materials (Chapter 10), some of which also need to have the characteristics of a good bearing.

To attain optimum performance the materials need to have the maximum amount of graphite consistent with adequate strength. In order to achieve this aim the porosity must be as low as possible. Graphite tends to coat the metal particles during mixing, thus reducing metal-to-metal contact and lowering the sintered strength. This problem can be alleviated by careful selection of the graphite powder, although Jones[1] suggests that it may be necessary to use hot working techniques in order to get the best product.

There is a dearth of published information on the properties of bearings containing large amounts of graphite, and such bearings are little used at the present time. Some data on one type are given in Table 18.

Table. 18. Properties of Bronze–Graphite Bearings

Amount of graphite vol. %	Radial crushing strength lb/in²	PV max* lb/in² ft/min	Coefficient of friction
25	45,400	100,000	0·3–0·4
35	28,700	100,000	0·3–0·4

* With additional liquid lubrication the maximum value of PV is increased by 3 to 5 times.

P.T.F.E. Bearings

Polytetrafluoroethylene has a very low coefficient of friction. Values of less than 0·02 have been reported. It is produced as a powder which can be consolidated into large pieces by the powder-metallurgy techniques of cold pressing and sintering, or hot pressing. Apart from its extremely low coefficient of friction, p.t.f.e. possesses another important attribute, its chemical stability: it is stable from $-200°C$ up to about $300°C$ in the presence of most corrosive agents. Howver, p.t.f.e. has certain properties, low shear strength, low thermal conductivity and a high coefficient of thermal expansion ($20 \times 10^{-5}/°C$ in the range 20–200°C), which are undesirable in a bearing material. In order to take advantage of its remarkably low coefficient of friction, metal/p.t.f.e. mixtures have been developed, the metal providing the strength and raising thermal conductivity. There are two distinct types of p.t.f.e./metal bearing materials, those having a continuous skeleton of metal and those consisting of metal powder dispersed within a p.t.f.e. matrix. The type with a metallic matrix is probably the more important.

Impregnation of metallic matrices with p.t.f.e. has been discussed by Blainey,[9] who describes two methods, hot pressing and aqueous impregnation. For the hot pressing method a sheet of p.t.f.e. is placed on the porous metal and the plastic extrudes into the pores under the action of both heat and pressure; penetration depths much greater than 0·01 in. are difficult to obtain. This process is also limited to flat sheets, and substantial losses of p.t.f.e. may occur by extrusion around the edges of porous metal plate.

The alternative process, aqueous impregnation with a suspension of p.t.f.e. in water followed by sintering, is more suited to the production of cylindrical bearings, thrust washers, etc. Fairly complete penetration is possible, although it is difficult to obtain completely filled pores. The impregnation process is applied to the production of steel-backed material which is manufactured in semi-continuous lengths. Such solid-backed material is used in a similar manner to the analogous copper–lead alloys to produce 'wrapped' bushes.

Mitchell[10] has examined the factors which control the performance of p.t.f.e./metal matrix bearings, and some of his results are shown in Fig. 55. It will be seen from (a) that performance increases as the volume fraction of p.t.f.e. is increased, at least up to a p.t.f.e. content of about one third. The bearing performance is also dependent upon the thickness of the surface layer of p.t.f.e. From the data given in Fig. 55 a layer 0·002 in. thick seems to be the optimum for thrust washers.

Mitchell also gives data for the effect of load and speed on the time-to-failure (Fig. 55 (c)). The plot of PV against time-to-failure shows two linear relationships, one representing the performance above about $PV = 9,000$ lb/in^2 ft/min and the other for lower PV values. At high PV values, where the load rotates around the bearing, approximately twice the life is obtained compared with the case of unidirectional loads, presumably owing to the greater bearing area which is involved in the first case. At low PV values the bearing life increases greatly and Mitchell suggested that this may be due to back transfer of p.t.f.e. from the journal which reduces the rate of p.t.f.e. loss.

The performance of p.t.f.e. bearings is greatly affected by the journal material. Table 19 gives the results of tests involving various sleeve materials running against p.t.f.e.-impregnated thrust washers.

Table 19. Effect of Sleeve Material on the Performance of P.T.F.E.-Impregnated Thrust Washers

Sleeve material	Hours to failure	
	$PV = 20,000$	$PV = 40,000$
Mild steel	50	25
Lead-plated steel	396+	98
p.t.f.e.-coated steel	322	50
MoSi$_2$-coated steel	150	73
Chromium-plated steel	67	29
Phosphated steel	55	35
Anodized aluminium	62	10
Cadmium-plated steel	26	19
Tin-plated steel	20	5
Sintered copper–lead	10	3
Copper	4	3
White metal	1	1
Aluminium	$\frac{1}{2}$	$\frac{1}{2}$

It has been shown that improved performances can be obtained by incorporating certain fillers into the p.t.f.e. According to Morgan[11] about 25% of lead or molybdenum disulphide greatly increases the bearing life.

The p.t.f.e.-impregnated bearing material produced by The Glacier Metal

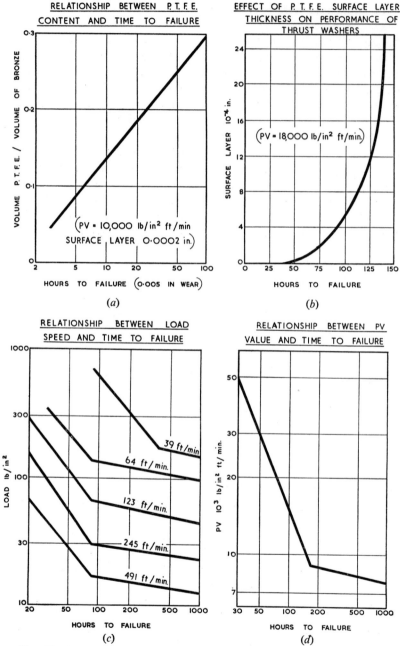

FIG. 55. Factors affecting the performance of p.t.f.e./metal matrix bearings.
(*Mitchell* [10])

Co., Ltd. is a good example of how the various factors affecting the performance have been balanced. A backing strip of steel, tin-plated to protect it from atmospheric corrosion, is used to provide additional structural strength. A layer of spherical bronze powder is sintered on to the backing strip and impregnated with a mixture of p.t.f.e. and fine lead powder. An overlay 0·001 in. thick of p.t.f.e.-lead powder is produced on top of the impregnated layer.

The alternative method of increasing the strength of p.t.f.e. is to disperse metal powder within it. Such a material consists of a continuous p.t.f.e. maxtrix, instead of the continuous metallic skeleton which characterizes the impregnated bearings discussed above. The additive which shows the greatest advantage is bronze, and again additions of lead powder may improve performance. A material of this type shows a thousandfold improvement in wear resistance compared with pure p.t.f.e. Some properties of a Glacier Metal Co., Ltd. product (Glacier D.Q.) are shown in Table 20.

Table 20. Properties of Glacier D.Q.

Density		3·4 g/cm³
Ultimate tensile strength, 20°C		875 lb/in²
Shear strength, 20°C		2000 lb/in²
Yield strength in compression,	−196°C	8,300 lb/in²
	20°C	2,700 lb/in²
	100°C	1,900 lb/in²
Modulus in compression,	20°C	50,000 lb/in²
Coefficient of expansion,	20−80°C*	8×10^{-5} per °C
Thermal conductivity,	100°C	$2·3 \times 10^{-3}$ cal/cm/s/deg C.
Electrical resistivity,	20°C	140 ohms cm
Water absorption		0·1% wt

* At 20°C there is a 0·2% increase in length associated with a phase change in the p.t.f.e.

OTHER TYPES OF BEARING

There have been several attempts to produce other types of bearing by powder-metallurgy techniques. The published literature up to 1948 is reviewed by Goetzel.[12] Currently the only powder-metallurgy bearing material, other than those already discussed, which is of commercial importance is high-density bronze. This is intended for use in applications similar to those for which phosphor-bronze is employed.

The typical properties of high-duty bronze bearings are: density 6·7–7·2 g/cm³, porosity 15–22%, PV factor 375,000 lb/in² ft/min. These high-duty bearings are not sufficiently porous for them to retain large amounts of oil and, therefore, it is necessary for them to be lubricated. Their use depends upon the ability of powder metallurgy to produce fairly complex shapes at relatively low cost. The factors which dictate the selection of a powder product rather than the machined version are similar to those discussed in Chapters 3 and 5.

REFERENCES

1. Jones, W. D. *Fundamental Principles of Powder Metallurgy*, 752, Edward Arnold, London (1960).
2. Pound, M. A., Rowley, A. E. S. and Elliott, J. E. *Powder Metallurgy*, No. 6, 129 (1960).
3. Booser, E. R. in *The Bearings Book*, Machinery Design, Chap. 4, 20 (1961).
4. Drapeau, J. E. in *Powder Metallurgy*, Wulff (ed.), 332, A.S.M., Cleveland (1942).
5. Storcheim, S. *Progress in Powder Metallurgy*, **18**, 124, M.P.I.F. (1962).
6. Morgan, V. T. and Cameron, A. *Proc. Conference on Lubrication and Wear*, 151, Inst. Mech. Eng. (1957).
7. Tait, W. H. *J. Instn. Auto. Engrs.*, **15**, 3 101 (Dec., 1946).
8. Forrester, P. G. *Metallurgical Reviews*, **5**, 507 (1960).
9. Blainey, A. Symposium on Powder Metallurgy, 1954 (*Special Rept. No. 58*), 223, 1956; London (Iron and Steel Institute).
10. Mitchell, D. C. *Proc. Conference on Lubrication and Wear*, 396, Inst. Mech. Eng. (1957).
11. Morgan, V. T. ibid., 775.
12. Goetzel, C. G. *Treatise on Powder Metallurgy*, Vol. 2, 503, Interscience, New York (1949).

CHAPTER 8

PERMEABLE METALS

Almost all powder metallurgy products are to some extent porous. Even Alnico magnets, cemented carbides and certain infiltrated compositions, which are produced in such a manner that porosity is minimized, usually contain some residual porosity. In the great majority of sintered materials the presence of appreciable porosity has important effects on the properties; in sintered engineering components porosity limits the strength and toughness which can be attained, while in porous bearings it is the porosity which allows impregnation with a lubricant. Thus, while the porosity of sintered materials may be detrimental it can also be used to advantage.

The class of materials which is to be discussed in this chapter depends for its usefulness on the presence of interconnected porosity. Such porosity makes these materials permeable and gives them the ability to filter particles from liquids and gases; they also possess such properties as large surface area, and low thermal and electrical conductivities.

CHARACTERISTICS OF PERMEABLE METALS

Permeable materials may usually be specified by the three parameters, porosity, pore size and permeability. To a first approximation, specifying any two of these parameters defines the third. For instance, a body with a high degree of porosity and a large pore size will have a high permeability, whereas a low permeability is obtained from a body of low porosity and a small pore size.

Porosity

Total porosity may be determined from a knowledge of the apparent and theoretical densities, while a measurement of the amount of a liquid which is required to saturate a porous body gives the interconnected porosity. Interconnected porosity can never be greater than total porosity and will frequently be much less. The relationship between total and interconnected porosity is determined by the character of the starting material and by the processing technique used to produce the porous metal. If the body is produced from a powder containing closed pores then the total porosity may be much greater than the interconnected porosity. In order completely to eliminate closed porosity, sintering to densities in excess of 95% of the theoretical density is required.[1] To obtain interconnected rather than unconnected porosity, the sintering shrinkage must be limited. The use of spherical rather than irregular powder also maximizes interconnected porosity.

The above simple treatment of the interrelationship between total and interconnected porosity ignores the fact that the determination of the latter by impregnation is dependent to some extent on the liquid used. It is likely that in porous metals there may often exist many fine fissures, the width of which is less than the size of the molecule of the impregnation liquid. Kopelman[2] has shown that the apparent density of tungsten decreases as the molecular volume of the liquid used for the determination increases, indicating the presence of fine pores within tungsten powder. It would seem, therefore, that the value obtained by liquid impregnation might well be termed 'apparent interconnected porosity'. Clearly it is difficult to obtain a true value of interconnected porosity which includes the fine pores and fissures. Measurement of surface area by gas absorption offers one method of assessing the fine structure, but here again the size of the adsorbed gas molecule must be taken into consideration.

The way in which the porosity is specified must obviously be most carefully considered. In applications where thermal conductivity is important and where the porous body is to be used as a light-weight 'space filling' material, it seems appropriate to characterize the material by its total porosity. For applications involving fluid transmission, as in filtering, the apparent interconnected porosity is perhaps the more important parameter. In catalysis, and other applications involving surface reactions, surface-area values are more relevant than porosity.

As will be seen later, when the methods of manufacturing permeable bodies are considered, porosity is largely determined by the way in which the powder particles are packed. During processing, compacting is either omitted or the pressures are low and the sintering temperature so chosen that very little shrinkage occurs. Thus it is the initial packing that largely determines the porosity. In general, powder metallurgists have preferred to approach the problem of pore-size control by using fairly narrow size-distributions of spherical particles. It is appropriate, therefore, to consider the packing of such powders. Morgan[3] lists five basic ways in which uniform spherical powders may be packed. Plate 17 shows the five systems. In practice it is not practicable to use uniform-sized spheres and some finite size-distribution must be chosen. The choice inevitably represents a compromise between the conflicting needs of a narrow size-distribution, desirable for strict control, and the lower cost of a wider size-distribution. A typical size distribution used is one in which the largest spheres are twice the diameter of the smallest. In general, it seems that such size distributions, when used commercially, give about 35% porosity.

Pore Size

The size of a pore is difficult to specify because of the complex shapes which are attained. Even in the simplest system comprised of uniform spheres regularly packed, there is no single dimension which will characterize the cross-section of the pore. Since porous bodies may also be made from irregular powders, having a finite size distribution in which there is irregular packing, the difficulty becomes obvious.

The pore size of a filter is related to the size of particles which it will remove from a fluid. Since this is one of the most important uses of permeable metals it is often necessary to measure pore size in some way, in order to determine the efficiency of the body as a filter and to measure the constancy of pore-size distribution throughout the body. The best approach to measuring pore size is by means of tests related to the end application. In practice two tests have been applied: (i) passing a fluid containing particles through the permeable metal and measuring the particle-size distribution before and after filtration, and (ii) forcing air through the permeable metal while it is immersed in a liquid of known surface tension and measuring the air pressure that just causes bubbles to break away. The first of these tests is intended to measure the 'cut-off', i.e. the size above which particles do not pass through the filter. This is a lengthy determination and the results of such measurements have been related to those of the more convenient 'bubble test'. Some indication of the homogeneity of pore-size distribution can also be obtained from the bubble test.

A relationship exists between the particle size of the powder from which the filter is made and the apparent pore size as determined by either of the tests referred to above. Taking as a model a porous body made from closely-packed uniform spheres, then the largest spherical particle which could pass through ought to have the same size as the inscribed diameter of the three-sided pore; this inscribed diameter is 15·6% of the diameter of the spheres which form the pore walls. It would seem that particles larger than 15·6% could only pass through if irregularities were present in the particle arrangement. However, it was pointed out earlier that, in practice, a porous body cannot be made from mono-sized spheres. Instead some finite size-range must be used, and one with the diameter of the smallest spheres being about one half that of the largest sphere (i.e. $d = D/2$) is usual. Atomized powder will generally have a normal frequency distribution of particle sizes (Fig. 56). If a powder is separated, by sieving for instance, such that the weight of particles of diameter D is the same as the weight of that of diameter $D/2$ (i.e. d) then there will be eight times as many particles of diameter d as there are particles of diameter D; with such a ratio the effective pore size will be

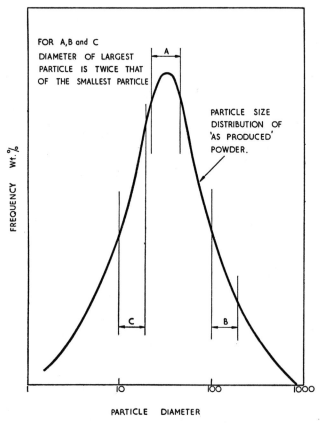

FOR A, B and C
DIAMETER OF LARGEST
PARTICLE IS TWICE THAT
OF THE SMALLEST PARTICLE

PARTICLE SIZE
DISTRIBUTION OF
'AS PRODUCED'
POWDER.

FREQUENCY Wt. %

PARTICLE DIAMETER

FIG. 56. Distribution of particle sizes.

related to d rather than D. There is, however, no reason why the weight of particles d diameter should be equal to those of diameter D, except in the special case of A shown in Fig. 56. For particle size distributions such as B, the proportion of small to large particles will be greater than 8:1, and thus the effective pore size will be close to 15·6% of d. On the other hand, if the size range chosen is much finer than A, such as C, then the weight of D

particles will be greater than that of d particles. The average pore size may then be considerably greater than 15·6% of d and, further, the spread of pore sizes is likely to be greater than for A or B.

The diameter of the inscribed circle which is formed by packing spheres in this size range in various ways has been examined by Morgan.[3] He shows that the average of seven plausible packing systems is 19·3% of D. Practical tests are also reported by Morgan and his results are reproduced in Table 21.

Table 21. Relationship between Pore Size (Determined by various Methods) and Powder Particle Size

Mean size of spheres μ	Pore size (μ)				Filtration results ÷ sphere size
	Bubble test		Filtration test	Bubble-test results ÷ filtration results	
	Water	CCl₄			
354	142		58	2·4	0·163
216	90	84	38	2·3	0·176
100	43	42	18	2·4	0·180
51·5	24·7	24	10	2·4	0·194
20		9·6	4	2·4	0·200

The relation between filtration and particle size shows a variation of 16·3 to 20·0%, in excellent agreement with the inscribed circle concept.

The pore size, as determined by the bubble pressure test, differs from that determined by filtration and obviously direct measurement of the effective pore size by the bubble test is not possible. A constant relationship seems to exist however between the two tests: a factor of 2·4 in Morgan's results for spherical particles and 3 according to Bishop and Collins[4] for irregular particles. The use of the convenient bubble test for routine testing has therefore some justification.

Permeability

Permeability is a measure of the ability of a porous body to allow passage of a fluid. Clearly permeability is related to the properties of the fluid and to both porosity and pore size. The greater the porosity the greater is the cross-sectional area through which the fluid can pass, and the larger the pore size the less is the frictional resistance to fluid flow. Permeability is usually specified by means of the well-known Darcy equation:

$$Q = \frac{\alpha A \rho \, \Delta P}{\eta t}$$

where Q is the mass flow rate of the fluid (lb/s or g/s), A the filter area (in² or cm²), ρ the fluid density (lb/in³ or g/cm³), η the absolute viscosity (lb/in² or poise), ΔP the pressure drop across the filter (lb/in² or dyne/cm²), t the thickness of the filter (in. or cm) and α the permeability coefficient. The permeability coefficient has the units of area (in² or cm²).

The flow of a fluid through a porous metal is accurately described by Darcy's equation up to a critical Reynolds number (Re_c). Above Re_c, increasing pressure produces less flow than predicted from the Darcy relationship. Reynolds number is a parameter used to define flow conditions, it represents

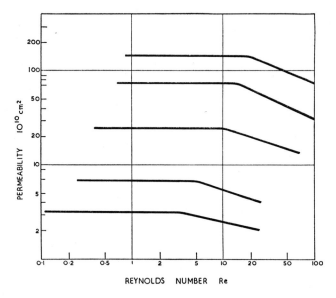

REYNOLDS NUMBER Re

Fig. 57. Relationship between critical Reynolds number and permeability for various grades of porous-metal filter plate.
(*Morgan*[3]).

the ratio of inertial to viscous forces. The following expression defines Reynolds number:

$$Re = \frac{V \rho L}{\eta}$$

where V is velocity and L a length characteristic of the system's geometry. The relationship between permeability and Reynolds number for various grades of porous metal filters is shown in Fig. 57. It will be seen that the point at which the curves deviate from lines parallel with the abscissa (Darcy's law) varies with permeability. The coarser the filter the higher the Reynolds number at which departure from the Darcy relationship occurs.

PRODUCTION OF PERMEABLE METALS

In the manufacture of permeable metals it is necessary to control one or more of the three properties—permeability, pore size and porosity—discussed in the previous section. The particular method of manufacture chosen will depend upon which of the properties is specified and also upon the importance of other properties such as strength and ductility. The combinations of properties most often desired are maximum permeability for a given pore size, or maximum strength with a given permeability.

It is clear from the earlier discussion that pore size can best be controlled by selection of powder particle size and that, for a given particle size, varying the porosity will control permeability. Strength is more difficult to control, and basically it will be related to the number and quality of the individual interparticle bonds.

Two general methods are used for producing permeable metals: (i) 'loose sintering', based on sintering uncompacted powders (or powders compacted under very low pressures) and (ii) those techniques in which higher compacting pressures are employed. In the latter group pore-forming additives may be used.

Loose Sintering

The loose sintering method is based upon controlling pore size and porosity by means of loosely packing the powder. It is most successful when spherical or almost spherical powders are employed, and an important limitation to the process is that for best results the metal or alloy must be available as spherical powder at reasonable cost. The alloys may occasionally be produced by mixing together elemental powders, and in this case it is important that the powder of the major component of the alloy is spherical.

Not all of the alloys required for the manufacture of permeable products are commercially produced in spherical form. The production of spherical copper-alloy powders by atomization is relatively easy but higher-melting-point alloys, notably some nickel-base alloys and the corrosion-resistant steels, are considerably more difficult. So far as coarse nickel- and iron-base alloy powders are concerned most of the production difficulties have been overcome and spherical powders are now available at a somewhat greater cost than the irregular types. The production of fine spherical powders in these alloys requires a secondary treatment of an irregular powder and the product is rather costly (see Chapter 2).

When spherical particles are used, compacting at low pressures has little effect on the density if the powder is well packed. Since the powders are usually vibrated it is rarely worthwhile compacting, certainly it is rare for the low compacting pressure to produce a green product with sufficient strength for handling and transporting to the sintering furnace.

13

Instead of compacting in a die it is more usual to pack the powders into a suitably shaped mould and pass the mould plus powder through the sintering furnace. The requirements of the mould are that it does not distort at the sintering temperatures, does not react with powder to be sintered (nor the sintering atmosphere), and has sufficient resistance to thermal shock to withstand the thermal cycling; additionally it should be cheap and readily machined. For the copper-base alloys, which form the majority of the products processed by this technique and which are loose sintered in the range 700–900°C, mild-steel moulds are usually suitable. Mild steel may require a refractory 'wash' (a thin surface coating applied by spraying or dipping) to prevent reaction with the powder. The heat-resisting Nimonic* alloys are also well suited as mould materials, although they are rather expensive and more difficult to machine. Moulds made of alloys which contain appreciable quantities of chromium, such as the Nimonic alloys, do not need mould washes since these form stable surface oxides which minimize mould/powder reactions. Ceramic moulds have been used, particularly when sintering temperatures above about 1200°C are employed, but as they are prone to thermal shock rapid changes in temperatures must be avoided. Graphite is a useful mould material in those cases where reaction with the powder is unlikely; it is cheap, readily machined and can be used up to very high temperatures.

The use of a mould restricts to some extent the variety of shapes which can be produced, as is discussed in Chapter 3. One problem which often proves troublesome is that during sintering shrinkage may cause cracking or hot tearing of the powder body, or distortion of the mould, if free contraction is restricted. Because of these limitations most porous products produced by loose sintering are in the form of flat sheets and discs or simple cylinders and cups, such as those shown in Plate 18. Further difficulties arise when relatively thin wall sections are required in cylinders and cups. Control of pore size by selecting the appropriate particle size means that in some cases coarse powders must be used and these are difficult to pack uniformly into thin walled cylinders, the proximity of the inner and outer walls preventing uniform packing.

Although there are a number of limitations to the use of loose sintering, it is probably the least costly of the various methods of producing permeable metals; it gives accurate control of the basic properties and is, therefore, used whenever possible. As will be shown later, there are certain limitations to the size of product which can be produced by the techniques which involve compacting. Loose sintering has therefore been applied to the production of large porous pieces, even in alloys whose powders can only be obtained with an irregular particle shape. Control of pore size is again achieved by selection

* Nimonic is a trade name of Henry Wiggin & Co. Ltd.

of the powder particle size, although inevitably the range of pore sizes obtained is greater, and control of permeability more difficult, than when spherical powders are used.

Oliver and Sands[5] have shown how the porosity, pore size and permeability are related to the powder particle size when using irregular powders. In their work they also investigated the effect of coining, i.e. pressing after sintering. The relationships are shown in Fig. 58. It should be noted that although Oliver and Sands favoured loose sintering for large objects because presses sufficient to compact these are both rare and expensive, they felt that the same limitation did not apply to the coining operation since on sheets this could be achieved by rolling.

The production of highly porous bodies from irregular powder has also been discussed by Tracey and Perks.[6] In this case fine (about 3 μ) carbonyl nickel powder of low apparent density was used to produce porous electrodes for nickel–cadmium batteries. Porosities of the order of 80% can be achieved with these powders and the maximum pore size may be as high as 50 μ.

Other methods of producing porous materials without compacting the powder have been described by Mowen and Fruda[7] including slip casting and spraying. It is possible by slip casting to produce shapes which cannot be made by loose sintering in moulds; for instance, those where the inner mould could not be removed. Since in a satisfactory slip the powder must be suspended in a liquid, it is generally limited to relatively fine powders and consequently to the production of fine pore-size material.

Permeable articles may be produced by spraying powder on to a substrate. The substrate is either removed afterwards or is itself permeable. Mowen and Fruda describe the use of a metal-gauze substrate on to which the powder is first sprayed and then sintered. The spraying is usually carried out cold using a binder to hold the powder. The binder must not lose its effectiveness prior to sintering nor react with the powder or substrate. Hot-spraying processes are also feasible, but care is necessary to maintain a compromise between the need for good interparticle adhesion and the avoidance of temperature and particle velocity conditions such that a body of low permeability is formed. Certain alloy powders, such as the stainless steels, are not suited to spraying through conventional oxy-acetylene guns because of excessive oxidation, etc. It seems possible that these powders might be sprayed with plasma spray equipment using controlled atmosphere boxes, if necessary.

Compacting Methods

The methods of producing permeable materials by processes which involve compacting are essentially applied to irregular powders. For many metals and alloys the only powders available at low cost have an irregular particle shape, and for these compacting processes are more convenient. Clearly,

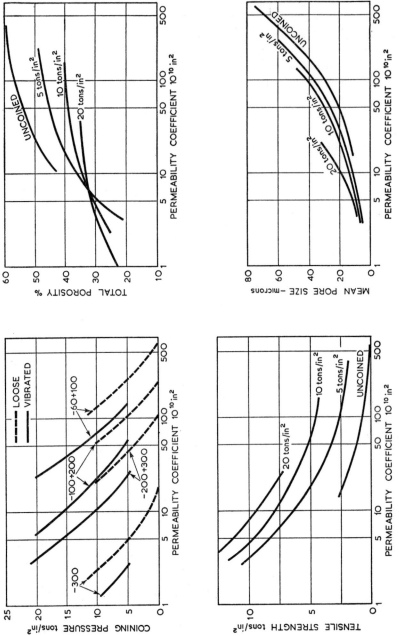

Fig. 58. Influence of the production method on the properties of sintered stainless-steel. (*Oliver and Sands*[5])

control of pore size is more difficult with irregular powders and it is particularly difficult to obtain the very desirable conditions of a narrow pore size distribution. The degree of porosity is not difficult to control in the majority of the compacting processes.

Since compacting will reduce porosity it is evident that for a given particle size the compacting processes will tend to produce lower permeabilities than will the loose-sintering methods. Lenel and Reen[8] have studied the porosity and permeability of compacted stainless-steel powders. Their results are summarized in Fig. 59. It is apparent that the range of porosities and permeabilities that can be obtained is severely limited. If the compact has to be sufficiently strong to be handled then it seems that more than about 35% porosity cannot be tolerated; at this porosity, with the coarsest grade of powder used by Lenel and Reen, permeability was less than about 30×10^{10} in². Because of this limitation the process finds little commercial application.

A method by which permeability may be increased in compacted powders was proposed by Duwez and Martens.[9] Powders of substances (fillers) which are volatile below the sintering temperature are mixed with the metal powder, and on sintering the pores formed by the filler increase the porosity and the permeability. The characteristics of a suitable filler material have been defined by Duwez and Martens as: (i) it should not be hygroscopic, (ii) it should be stable at room temperature, (iii) it should not react with the metal powder during the mixing operation, (iv) it should decompose well below the sintering temperature and (v) after decomposition it should not leave any solid or liquid residue that may be detrimental. A number of compounds were investigated by Duwez and Martens who concluded that ammonium bicarbonate was the most satisfactory for iron, nickel and copper powders. The technique consists of milling 80-mesh ammonium bicarbonate with the metal powder, followed by compacting in the usual manner. The compacts have sufficient green strength to be handled. The pore size of materials produced in this way is related to the particle size of the ammonium bicarbonate and therefore the milling operation is of the greatest importance in comminuting the filler. One of the most important applications of the filler method is the production of 'porous' stainless steel. Sugarman[10] has discussed some of the factors in the production of porous stainless steel by this method, and has shown that material with permeabilities in the range 5–250, 10^{10} in² can readily be produced.

In general the methods of producing porous metals by compacting are confined to discs, small sheets and simple cylinders. The methods are unsuited to the production of long cylinders because of the way porosity varies along the length.

Several other methods of forming special permeable products have been suggested and some of these find limited commercial application. Two

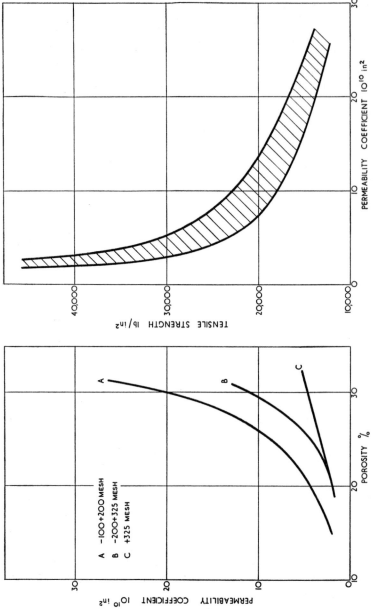

FIG. 59. Relationship between permeability, porosity and tensile strength of sintered stainless-steel produced by the method of Lenel and Reen.[9]

techniques of some importance are extrusion and roll compacting. Extrusion is a very useful method of producing long cylinders. Recently this process has been used to produce corrugated cylinders, a very desirable shape for filtration because it provides a large surface area within a small volume. As with the other compacting processes, extrusion of permeable articles requires the addition of a pre-forming filler to give a handleable product with a usefully high permeability.

Rolling is, in theory, an attractive method of making porous metals because of the high rate of output, and also because many permeable metals are required in the form of sheets and discs. In general the roll loads necessary to give a coherent strip are such that the product has limited interconnected porosity and it is therefore difficult to obtain useful permeability values. The addition of pore-forming fillers in this case does not seem to lead to an appreciable increase in the permeability. A method of overcoming this limitation consists of limiting the supply of powder to the roll gap, so that porosity is obtained in thin strip. For powders which were difficult to compact into coherent strip by this process Semenov used a plastic binder to give added green strength. By modification of the process it was possible to incorporate supports, such as wire mesh or perforated strip, into the product.

APPLICATIONS AND PROPERTIES

The applications of permeable metals are many and diverse. Some of the more important are described in this section together with the characteristic properties.

Filtration

Filters are probably the most important application of porous metals, self-lubricating bearings excepted (see Chapter 7). In the field of filtration permeable metals are required to compete with a number of other filtration materials, notably paper, woven fibre, glass and ceramics. Such materials as woven-wire and loose powder beds are required for filtration applications which lie outside the scope of permeable metals.

Usually a filter serves to remove solid particles from a stream of liquid or gas which passes through the filter but, as will be seen later, it is also possible to separate non-solid matter; two immiscible liquids, for instance, or a liquid from a gas. Filtration is used for a variety of purposes; the operation may often be a purification process in which an unwanted solid is removed from the fluid. Sometimes it is the solid particles which are of value and filtration serves to collect these. Examples of the latter case occur frequently in mineral dressing where filtration is often essentially a concentration process.

The advantages which permeable metal filters possess over their competitors are chiefly associated with their strength, ductility, heat resistance and amenability to fabrication into complex forms. The ability of porous metals to withstand use at elevated temperatures is often a decisive factor in their selection since materials like paper and cloth cannot be used much above ambient temperatures, whilst glass and ceramics are susceptible to early failure by thermal shock.

Clearly, metal filters must possess other attributes, such as resistance to corrosion and oxidation. For instance, if rapid corrosion occurred it would destroy the bonds between the particles and the whole filter might ultimately disintegrate. Milder forms of corrosion or oxidation in which a voluminous product were formed could block the pores of the filter and this form of attack must also be avoided. Because of these considerations the choice of filter material is most important. Metals such as copper and iron, although available as low-cost powders, are obviously ruled out for many applications. Most important of the various alloys used as porous-metal filters are the tin–bronzes, which are produced readily in spherical (or irregular) form and are used wherever possible. For more exacting requirements the austenitic stainless steels (18% chromium, 8% nickel or 18% chromium, 10% nickel, 2% molybdenum, etc.) are preferred, although the powders of these alloys are more expensive and processing costs are also higher. For certain special applications precious and semi-precious metals are necessary.

Strength is often an important consideration in the choice of a suitable filter. One of the factors that limits the rate of filtration is the pressure drop that the filter can withstand without rupture. This is particularly important when there is a large quantity of solid to be removed which may form a dense filter 'cake'; this decreases the permeability of the system and thereby raises the pressure drop necessary to maintain a given throughput. A similar situation exists when filtering aids are employed. Permeable metals, having greater strength than other filter materials, are able to withstand larger pressure drops and hence give higher throughputs. If conditions are such that fluctuating loads occur then the fatigue strength might be the controlling factor. Such conditions may occur where the filter is cleared by reversing the direction of flow. Where filters are employed at high temperatures the hot strength is important and in certain cases it may be necessary to consider the creep strength of the filter.

Metal filters also have greater ductility than most of their competitors. While it is often true that ductility of permeable metals is not of the same order as their solid counterparts, their ductility is at least of an order of magnitude greater than that of porous ceramics, glass, etc. Ductility is not always of great importance in the operation of a filter, but may be important in fabrication. The relative ease and precision with which permeable metals may be fabricated into complex forms can be an important reason for their

PLATE 17

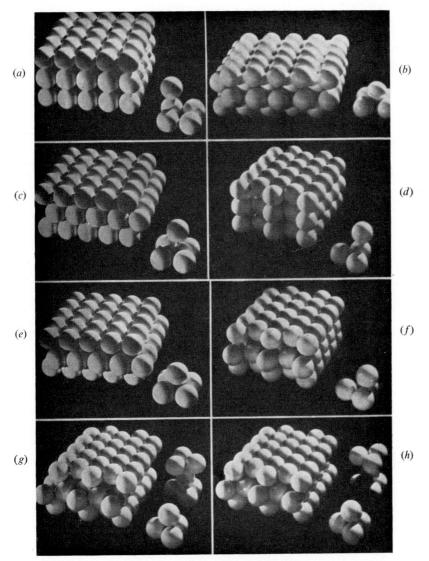

Packing systems for spherical particles:
(a) cubic; (b) body-centred cubic; (c) orthorhombic (from cubic base); (d) orthorhombic (from rhombic base); (e) rhombohedral (from cubic base), face-centred cubic; (f) tetragonal; (g) rhombohedral (from rhombic base), face-centred cubic; (h) rhombohedral (from rhombic base), close-packed hexagonal.

[*Reproduced by courtesy of the Iron and Steel Institute.*
(*See Chapter 8, p.* 178).]

PLATE 18

Selection of sintered bronze filters.
(*Courtesy of Sintered Products Ltd.*)

PLATE 19

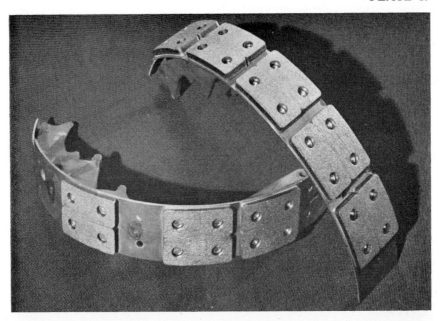

Two typical applications of sintered friction materials:
(*upper*) brake lining, (*lower*) clutch plates.

(*Courtesy of Sintered Products Ltd.*)

PLATE 20

Electron micrograph of a thoria dispersion in nickel (T.D. Nickel) ($\times$ 7500).
(*Courtesy of E. I. du Pont de Nemours & Co. (Inc.).*)

selection since, in practice, it implies a larger filter area for a given plant volume. A good example of the importance of ductility is the production of cylindrical filters by bending flat plates.

Permeable metals may be joined to each other or to solid metals in a number of ways. Processes such as soldering and brazing are sometimes difficult to control because of the ease with which the low-melting-point alloys are absorbed by the porous mass. However, soldering is often used for joining porous bronze. Joining by plastics is also possible, an admirable key being obtained by arranging that the plastic penetrates a small distance into the porous metal. Welding is widely used for the joining of porous stainless steels, and the tungsten electrode, inert-gas shielded-arc process is most commonly employed. A particular advantage of autogenous welding is that cathodic corrosion is eliminated, an important point in the corrosive environments in which these filters find use. Another method of joining, mentioned by Bishop and Collins[4] is metal spraying. This process does not now seem to be widely applied.

Care is necessary when machining permeable metals to avoid crushing and it may be necessary to provide some after-treatment to reopen surface pores that have been blocked during the machining operation. An example of such a finishing treatment for porous stainless steel is electrolytic etching with oxalic acid. For machining, Bishop and Collins recommend the use of carbide tools at low cutting speeds and cuts of 0·01 to 0·02 in. With larger cuts there is danger of particles being torn out, while finer cuts encourage smearing and glazing of the surface.

A further important characteristic of a filter is its ability to be cleared. Although the majority of the filtered particles will be retained as a filter cake, some particles will invariably become entrapped within the filter plate and reduce its permeability. Simple reversed-flow cleaning, while adequate to remove the filter cake, may not dislodge these embedded particles. One advantage of metal filters is that they may often be effectively cleaned by immersion in acids or alkalis or may be heated under oxidizing conditions.

The selection of the filter material for a particular application will depend upon some of the considerations discussed above. The size and shape of the filter will be determined by other factors, primarily by the required rate of throughput of the liquid, the maximum pressure (or pressure-drop) available, and the largest size of solid particle that is acceptable in the filtrate. In most cases the maximum size of the particles which may be allowed to pass through the filter will first be specified by comparison with data such as given in Fig. 60. This will determine the maximum permeability which can be employed. It should be noted that invariably the maximum permeability grade is required, consistent with adequate particle-size removal, since it impels maximum flow for a given pressure drop.

Having determined the grade of permeable metal that is to be used, then the area of filter plate needed to accommodate the flow rate at the specified pressure can be calculated. In most cases the permeability decreases as particles form either a surface filter cake or become entrapped within the filter. Allowance must be made for this factor unless rapid cycling (i.e. frequently reversing the fluid flow to remove the filter cake) is permissible. It is difficult to generalize as to the amount by which permeability decreases as filtration proceeds; usually practical trials are preferred to determine this, but an

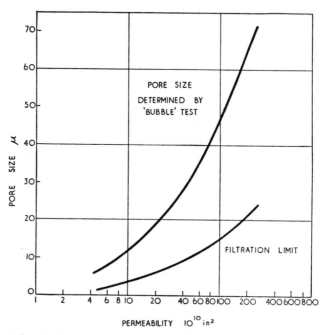

FIG. 60. Relationship between permeability and pore size as determined by the bubble test and filtration limit.

empirical guide is to specify at least twice the calculated filter area. Once the surface area is known (together with filter material and the characteristics of the chosen grade) the form of the filter is finally decided. This final stage, designing the best form, may be the most difficult since porous products are made in a limited number of basic forms, flat sheet, discs, simple cylinders, cones, etc., from which the more complex shapes must be fabricated.

On occasions the results of the elementary calculations of surface area may give unreasonably large results, usually because it has been necessary to choose a grade of low permeability in order to remove particles of small size.

In such cases consideration can be given to the use of filter aids, i.e. the addition to the fluid of particles of some substance to form a filter cake. This method allows the use of a higher permeability metal, the filter cake removing the fine particles. Although the filter cake itself may act as a low permeability body, it is often found that the total permeability of the system is greater than when the whole of the particle removal has to be effected with low-permeability porous metal.

The applications of metal filters are numerous and it is not possible here to mention more than a few. Filtration of water is frequently accomplished with metal filters, a typical example being the removal of pipe scale from water intended for photographic process. In this application metal filters are particularly convenient because they will operate for long periods without attention. Other important filtration applications are found in the chemical and pharmaceutical industries. Metal filters are often used for collecting samples from both liquids and gases. Dust samples for recording atmospheric pollution is an example, and similarly combustion products may be examined for fuel particles. Liquid-fuel filtration is another important application, particularly in high-performance engines. Hydraulic liquids used in critical applications, such as are found in aircraft, may also need filtration through permeable metals.

The great corrosion resistance of porous metals leads to their finding many applications involving the filtration of corrosive liquids. A number of designs of Buchner funnel having porous-metal filters have been proposed for laboratory filtration. The use of these is justified only in special circumstances because they are much more expensive than conventional paper or sintered glass filters. Bishop and Collins[4] mention the use of a 30-in. diam. stainless-steel Buchner funnel for the lecithin coating of a crystalline penicillin salt.

A further example of use in highly-corrosive environments is the filtration of liquid sodium. Sodium is a very efficient heat-exchange medium and is used in a number of nuclear reactors such as the Dounreay fast-breeder reactor. Liquid sodium will reduce the oxides of many metals because of its affinity for oxygen. The oxygen in the sodium will, however, attack metals such as niobium that are used for canning the fuel, and it is therefore essential to remove the oxygen from the sodium as it is circulated throughout the reactor. An elegant method of accomplishing this is to cool the sodium to just above its melting point, at which temperature solid sodium oxide is formed and then filtered out with stainless-steel filters. Purification to 4 p.p.m. of oxygen has been claimed for this method.

Porous metal filters are employed as permeable supports in a number of applications. The use of porous bronze to support kieselguhr beds in water filtration is cited by Sinclair.[11]

A porous metal can also act as a filter in a more subtle manner than the simple mechanical stopping of solid particles. If two immiscible liquids are presented to a metal filter and the filter is wetted by one of the liquids, the other will not pass through. In this manner it is possible to remove traces of water from certain liquid fuels.

Flow Distribution

There are a number of important applications in which permeable metals act as distributors for both gases and liquids. In these applications the fluid being passed through the permeable metal is broken into discrete, small streams. After leaving the porous plate the streams may remain discrete, as in the case of a gas emerging as bubbles into a liquid. Alternatively, the streams may recombine to give a thin surface layer. One of the simplest examples of the use of permeable metals in this manner is aeration. Air passed through a permeable body can also be used to 'fluidize' solid particles. Permeable heat-resisting alloys have been produced for high-temperature fluidization. Oliver and Sands[5] have given short-time creep properties for such a material (Table 22). The fluidization and distribution of cement powder using a porous metal has been described by Frehn, Hotop and Stempel.[12] The breaking-up of fluid into fine streams and droplets is, of course, an admirable way of mixing it with some other substance. There are a number of important applications of porous metals in which rapid and intimate mixing is involved. Sinclair[11] mentions such uses in yeast fermentation and in the production of cresylic acid.

Table 22. Short Time Creep Strength of a Permeable Nickel-Base Alloy

Permeability coefficient (10^{10} in^2)	100 h rupture stress at 800°C (tons/in^2)
300	0·8
100	1·5
50	2·0
10	3·3
5	4·0

Porous bronze has been widely used in aircraft deicing. Strips of permeable metal are located in the leading edge of the wing through which deicing fluid is forced to prevent ice formation.

An application which has frequently been suggested for permeable metal is transpiration or effusion cooling. The idea is that certain components which must be metallic, because of the requirements of shape, size, thermal-shock resistance, etc., and which are exposed to severe overheating conditions, should be made permeable and a relatively cold fluid passed through them. The cooling fluid would reduce the temperature by conducting heat away, forming also a continuously-replenished surface layer which would reduce heat transfer. Furthermore the latent heat required to volatilize the effusing liquid would be lost to the system. Much of the stimulus for the advancement of porous-metal technology came from the hopes of effusion-cooled turbine blades[8, 9, 10] which would allow higher turbine-inlet gas temperatures with consequent increases in thermodynamic efficiency. However, no instance of the active use of such turbine blades is known. More recently the subject has been revived with speculation as to the merits of effusion-cooled walls for rocket combustion chambers.

Flow Restriction

The restriction to flow owing to the presence of a porous body in a fluid stream results in either a reduction in the flow rate or a pressure drop across the obstruction. The magnitude of these effects, at least below the critical Reynolds number, can be calculated from Darcy's equation. One of the simplest examples of the use of permeable metals in this way is the protection of instruments from the detrimental effects of a transient pressure wave. Provided that the pressure wave is of only short duration the porous metal will attenuate the pressure and protect the instrument. The pressure drop which occurs when a gas passes through a permeable metal has been used to lessen noise in a variety of pneumatic equipment. Since the pressure drop which arises in a porous metal is analogous in some ways to that caused by an orifice the effect may be used for metering fluid flow rate. The method seems particularly applicable to small flow rates.

Surface Area

There are a number of applications in which the large surface area of porous metal is utilized, the use of metals for catalysing chemical reactions being perhaps the best known example. A property such as mechanical strength is usually unimportant in these applications, the chief consideration being the amount of surface available for reaction and the activity of the surface. It should be appreciated that the fine surface fissures which are present in the unsintered powder mass are preferably retained for the most efficient catalysis. Production of catalysts therefore usually involves minimum sintering temperatures to preserve the maximum surface area and either close control of the sintering atmosphere or a post-sintering treatment in order to confer the greatest possible activity to the surface.

The extended surface area of porous metals also offers potential application in heat exchangers. Some exploratory work carried out to assess the usefulness of porous metals in heat-transfer applications has been reported by Zemo.[13] The usual arrangement consists of tubes, sometimes having a spiral configuration, around which powder is sintered. The future of porous metals in heat-exchange applications is at the moment uncertain.

Electrical Applications

There are two applications for porous metals in electric power generation, the first and more important at the present time being the use of porous nickel electrodes in nickel–cadmium batteries. The second is their use in fuel cells. As yet these applications represent only a minor use for permeable metals.

The manufacture of porous electrodes for nickel–cadmium batteries by loose sintering carbonyl nickel into high-porosity plates was referred to earlier in this chapter. Frequently the nickel is sintered on to a supporting wire mesh. The positive plates are impregnated with nickel nitrate, which is subsequently converted to nickel hydroxide. The negative plates are made from a similar porous plate but are impregnated with cadmium chloride to deposit cadmium hydroxide. The cells are formed by assembling positive and negative plates alternately, and adding potassium hydroxide electrolyte. The power is generated by transference of a hydroxyl ion from the positive to the negative plate forming cadmium hydrate.

These batteries, which may be recharged, are mainly used where light weight and compactness are important, for instance, in high-speed aircraft, missiles and space vehicles.

Porous metals are also vitally important in fuel cells. In these cells porous electrodes are the physical medium within which gas-electrolyte reactions take place. Metal electrodes are stronger than the ceramic or carbon alternatives, although their electrochemical activity is low. Higher catalytic activity combined with mechanical strength is obtained with the double-skeleton electrode (DSK) which is prepared from a mixture of nickel and Raney alloy (50% Al, 50% Ni). After sintering the Raney alloy is attacked with potassium hydroxide, leaving behind nickel with a very large surface area. With these electrodes 100 mA/cm^2 of geometrical electrode area have been obtained. An alternative active electrode material is palladium–silver.

The well-known, high-pressure, hydrogen–oxygen cell, with which the name of Bacon is particularly associated, also uses porous nickel electrodes. In this type of cell there are corrosion problems and for this reason nickel is preferred to iron. Precious metals, although having better corrosion resistance, are too expensive if the fuel cell is to become commercially acceptable. Certain difficulties in the corrosion of nickel above 100°C have had to be overcome, because the oxide, NiO, which is a poor conductor, is formed in the presence of potassium hydroxide and oxygen. This problem has been overcome by impregnating the electrode with dilute lithium hydroxide, and drying and oxidizing. The lithium decreases the cation deficiency of the nickel oxide and thereby greatly increases its oxidation resistance and electrical conductivity.

REFERENCES

1. Arthur, G. *J. Inst. Met.*, **83**, 7, 329 (1954/55).
2. Kopelman B. in *The Physics of Powder Metallurgy*, W. Kingston (ed.), McGraw-Hill, New York (1951).
3. Morgan, V. T. Symposium on Powder Metallurgy, 1954 (*Special Rept. No. 58*), 81, 1956; London (Iron and Steel Institute).
4. Bishop, E. and Collins, G. M. in *Chemical Engineering Practice*, **2**, Butterworth, London (1956).
5. Oliver, D. A. and Sands, R. L. in *Powder Metallurgy in the Nuclear Age*, Benesovsky (ed.), 692 (1962).
6. Tracey, V. A. and Perks, R. P. *Powder Metallurgy*, No. 12, 54 (1963).
7. Mowen, H. C. and Fruda, T. R. *Progress in Powder Metallurgy*, **18**, 166 (1962).
8. Lenel, F. V. and Reen, O. W. *A.S.T.M. Spec. Pub.* 140, 24 (1952).
9. Duwez, P. and Martens, E. *Trans. A.I.M.E.*, 848 (1948).
10. Sugarman, B. Symposium on Powder Metallurgy, 1954 (*Special Rept. No. 58*), 184, 1956; London (Iron and Steel Institute).
11. Sinclair, C. E. Symposium on Powder Metallurgy (*Special Rept. No. 38*), 105, 1947; London (Iron and Steel Institute).
12. Frehn, F., Hotop, W. and Stempel, G. *Achema*, xi, Frankfurt/Main (1955).
13. Zemo, F. *Progress in Powder Metallurgy*, **19**, 183 (1963).

CHAPTER 9

SINTERED FRICTION MATERIALS

The friction elements used in early brake and clutch mechanisms were usually made from organic materials such as wood and leather. As operating conditions became more arduous these organic substances were found to be inadequate and were replaced by resin-bonded asbestos. For many years the asbestos-based materials have served well and are still adequate for most purposes. However, in certain heavy-duty applications the friction elements may be heated to temperatures at which the asbestos-based materials are unsuitable. The main reason for this is that when such materials are heated above a certain temperature they lose their friction properties or 'fade'. At even higher temperatures the resin bond breaks down and the asbestos dehydrates. These deficiencies are accentuated by the poor thermal conductivity and low thermal capacity of asbestos materials.

For heavy-duty applications, therefore, a material having high thermal conductivity and thermal capacity, coupled with heat resistance, is required. Metals, particularly copper, meet these requirements, but when working under frictional conditions metals tend to cold-weld and gall giving rise to excessive chatter, unpredictable friction properties and eventually complete seizure. To be suitable for friction applications the properties of the metal must be modified to prevent galling and seizing. Additions of solid lubricants will reduce the tendency to gall, while hard particles will abrade the small cold-weld areas from the mating material before serious build-up occurs. Such a composite friction material may only be conveniently fabricated by powder metallurgy.

The most widely used metal matrices for high-duty friction materials are copper and bronze, although iron matrices are used where service temperatures are likely to exceed 1000°C. Batchelor[1] considers that tungsten or molybdenum matrices may have to be used for certain applications in the future.

Many materials have been used as the abrasive component, including silicon carbide, silica, mullite, bentonite, asbestos, spodumene, feldspar and kyanite.

Graphite is the most popular solid lubricant, but molybdenum disulphide, molybdenum trioxide and boron nitride have also been used. Lead is often added, although its exact function is not clear. It certainly acts as a binder during pressing and probably also as a lubricant in service.

It is obvious that a great many combinations of metals, abrasives and lubricants could be evolved and indeed a large number of formulations have been tested under a variety of conditions. A typical composition that has found commercial application is shown in Table 23.

Table 23. Typical Composition of Sintered Friction Material

Composition (weight per cent)					
Copper	Tin	Lead	Graphite	Iron	Silica
68	7	8	6	7	4

When sintered friction materials are operated under dry conditions, particularly in brake applications, the surface of the friction element becomes covered with a film or glaze which seems to be necessary for efficient and consistent operation. According to Hewitt and Blackwell,[2] this film forms in two stages. First, matrix material smears across the surface and is work-hardened and annealed in a cyclic manner, and secondly oxides of both the friction and mating material may appear and contribute to the formation of the film. Hewitt and Blackwell also consider that solid lubricants promote glaze formation, while Batchelor[1] states that it is frequently necessary to add a small amount of low-melting-point ceramic to ensure film formation at low energies. It seems that, as yet, the mechanisms of film formation are not well understood. However, the formation of a stable film is essential to achieve consistent braking conditions. Film formation is unlikely to occur in wet conditions, such as those under which many clutches operate.

Sintered friction materials generally have lower friction coefficients (0·1–0·5) than their asbestos counterparts, so that higher applied pressures are required. The actual value of the coefficient of friction varies with rubbing speed, applied pressure and conditions (wet or dry) (see Fig. 61).

Production Techniques

Individual powders are mixed together and blended, usually in double-cone blenders, for the minimum time necessary to achieve uniform distribution of

14

the ingredients. Compacting pressures are usually in the range 10–20 tons/in², and the usual mechanical presses are used for small components. However, a

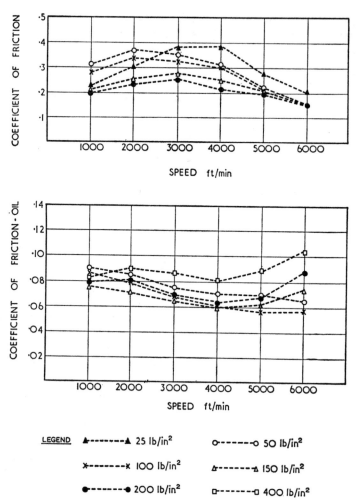

FIG. 61. Variation of coefficient of friction with speed and load for dry (*upper*) and wet (*lower*) conditions.
(*Hewitt and Blackwell*[2])

considerable proportion of sintered friction material is required in the form of discs, rings or plates of large area (up to 200 in²) for which large-capacity hydraulic presses are necessary. Dies are often loaded by hand with pre-weighed charges. In some cases two layers are charged, the first one being a backing layer containing little or no additions to the metal matrix and the second layer being of the friction composition. The backing layer gives added strength and facilitates bonding to a solid support.

Green compacts are relatively weak because of their shape and the high proportion of brittle non-metallic constituents; consequently special ejection techniques are used to prevent breakage due to ejection stresses. It is common practice to keep the part under light compression between the punches while the die and cores are stripped. Close tolerances on parallelism across the thickness of the part must be maintained. Hewitt and Blackwell[2] quote tolerances of 0·002 in. on 5 in. diam. discs and 0·004 in. on 15 in. diam. discs. Such tolerances demand precision tooling with minimum clearances and accurately set press rams.

Owing to their low strength, sintered friction materials are almost invariably joined to a solid back-up plate to give adequate support. The joining operation may be combined with sintering. Backing plates are blanked from steel sheet and, where the quantities required allow, the blanking die also generates gear teeth, etc. For lower quantities such forms are machined after blanking. The steel plates are deburred, stress relieved to avoid distortion and nickel- or copper-plated to facilitate good bonding of the friction element.

Friction parts and backing plates are placed face to face and are stacked on the hearth of the sintering furnace which is usually of the bell type. Individual assemblies are separated from one another by graphited stainless-steel spacers and a pressure of up to 300 lb/in^2 is applied to the stack during sintering by means of a flexible diaphragm arrangement. Sintering temperatures range from 700–850°C for copper-base and 900–1100°C for iron-base materials. During the sintering of a bronze material the tin and lead melt, giving liquid-phase sintering conditions, and the tin is gradually absorbed by the copper particles. The non-metallic additions are not affected by the sintering process and are merely mechanically locked in the matrix as it shrinks around them. This is not entirely true for iron-base materials, because some of the graphite addition is absorbed by the iron particles during sintering.

The efficiency of the bond between friction and backing members is dependent upon the cleanliness of the interface and the purity of the atmosphere, as well as on the sintering time, temperature and applied pressure.

After sintering, various finishing operations are carried out on the composite plates. Surface grinding is often necessary to ensure complete flatness and, where parts are to be operated wet, grooves may have to be machined on the friction faces to ensure the retention of an oil film between plates. Such grooves also facilitate the removal of detached particles and foreign dirt. For special shapes, such as the friction elements of internally expanding drum-brakes, roll-forming machines have been used of the type shown by Kane.[3]

Applications

Sintered friction materials are mainly used under heavy-duty conditions where their high thermal conductivity enables them to dissipate the heat generated by friction. A particularly arduous application is the aircraft brake which may, in certain circumstances, be required to absorb vast amounts of energy. Batchelor[1] points out that in the case of a rejected take-off of a DC 8 the brakes are required to absorb $3 \cdot 2 \times 10^8$ ft/lb, or 410,000 Btu, which is generated in 30 seconds at the friction interface; this heat must be rapidly dissipated to avoid gross melting. This is an excellent example of the type of conditions with which resin-bonded materials could not possibly cope. Even in normal operation, temperatures of up to $1400°C$ may be generated in aircraft brakes, so that iron-base friction materials are essential.

Other braking applications for sintered friction materials are found in vehicles such as trucks, ambulances, police cars, certain sporting vehicles and on railway rolling stock. For most of these applications a copper-base material is used. Sintered friction materials have not yet found wide use in the general automobile industry, although drum brakes with segmented shoes of sintered material are offered as an alternative on several American cars. Reinsch[4] has described their application in this field. The use of the single-disc brake, which is able to dissipate heat very rapidly and in consequence exhibits little fade even under arduous braking conditions, has probably postponed the general introduction of sintered friction materials in the automobile industry for some time to come.

Sintered friction materials are widely used in both wet and dry clutches. A typical example is the multi-disc steering clutch used on crawler tractors. In clutches of this type the maximum torque is governed by the diameter of the clutch, the number of discs and the coefficient of friction of the facing materials. Although sintered materials have a lower coefficient of friction than asbestos materials it is possible to use much thinner discs (and hence a larger number) because of their very low rate of wear.

Other clutch applications are found on heavy-duty engines, aircraft starters and various machine tools.

Some typical sintered friction parts and applications are shown in Plate 19.

It seems likely that in the future there will be a continued expansion of the use of sintered friction materials on aircraft, earth-moving equipment and machine tools. New materials based on higher melting-point matrices will probably be required. The automobile industry (the largest single market for friction materials) seems unlikely to make much increased use of sintered materials following the introduction of the single-disc brake.

REFERENCES

1. Batchelor, C. S. in *Powder Metallurgy*, Leszynski (ed.), 825, Interscience, New York (1961).
2. Hewitt, J. C. and Blackwell, R. I. *Engineering Materials and Design* (Nov., 1961).
3. Kane, L. P. *Proceedings of the Sixth Annual Meeting of the Metal Powder Association*, 59 (1950).
4. Reinsch, E. W. *Progress in Powder Metallurgy*, M.P.I.F., **18**, 131 (1962).

CHAPTER 10

ELECTRICAL AND MAGNETIC MATERIALS

In this chapter the various electrical and magnetic materials produced by powder metallurgy are discussed. The materials involved are extremely varied, as are the techniques necessary to produce them. Indeed, in no other field is such a wide range of powder-consolidation techniques employed. For instance, compacting pressures may reach 100 tons/in² in some applications, whereas use may be made of loose powders in others. The type of bonding is also suitably varied. In some instances liquid-phase sintering and infiltration may be employed to produce high-density parts, or unsintered powders (sometimes plastic-bonded) may be used.

The various materials can be conveniently dealt with in three groups: (i) materials used in electrical contact applications, (ii) soft magnetic materials and (iii) permanent-magnet materials. Some of the applications of porous powder-metal components in electrical power generation were discussed in Chapter 8.

ELECTRICAL CONTACT MATERIALS

The importance of powder metallurgy in electrical contact technology is due to the ability to form two-phase materials. Such duplex materials combine the desirable characteristics of each phase, e.g. the high current-carrying capacity and low resistance of metals such as copper with the wear resistance and refractoriness of tungsten or the low coefficient of friction of graphite. It is not possible to produce these duplex structures other than by powder metallurgy. Materials produced from metal powders are used for both sliding and switching contacts.

Sliding Contacts

Sliding contacts are found in many types of electrical machinery, where they are used to transfer current between moving and stationary parts. Brushes in electric motors, generators and rotary convertors, contacts in rheostats and power collectors for electric trams and trains are typical and well-known examples of the use of sliding contacts.

The important requirements of sliding contacts are low electrical losses across the contact interface and high wear resistance. The contact material must therefore have good electrical conductivity, a low coefficient of friction and resistance to arcing, as well as adequate mechanical strength. Which of these properties needs to be dominant depends upon the application. Pure metals and single-phase alloys do not satisfactorily meet these requirements. Although the electrical conductivity of many pure metals is adequate, their high friction coefficient leads to large mechanical losses and rapid wear. (Liquid lubricants cannot be used because of their high electrical resistance.) Stronger alloys, although having acceptable wear resistance and low coefficients of friction, are unsuitable because of their low electrical conductivity.

Graphite is a satisfactory sliding contact material in many respects; it has good friction and wear properties but its electrical conductivity, although much higher than most non-metals, is too low for many applications. Nevertheless, graphite is suitable for high-voltage low-current applications and is widely used for these purposes. Apart from its low conductivity graphite is also unsuitable in low-pressure environments. For instance, in certain aviation applications it has been found that graphite is rapidly pulverized at high altitudes, the wear rate being many times greater than at sea level.

Although pure graphite cannot be used for contacts carrying high currents, its properties, in particular low-friction coefficient, are so important that duplex graphite–metal materials have been developed. The current-carrying capacity of these graphite–metal materials increases as the amount of metal is increased. Graphite by itself may be used up to current densities of 35–50 A/in^2 and small additions of metal will increase this to 70 A/in^2, while 125–250 A/in^2 can be used with high metal contents. Momentary loads of 450–500 A/in^2 can be withstood by the high metal-content materials without damage. Although increasing the metal content raises the maximum allowable current density, it also increases the friction coefficient and the rate of wear.

The most important of the graphite–metal materials are graphite–bronze, graphite–brass, graphite–copper and graphite–silver, these materials containing 5–70% graphite. Bronze is the most widely applied of the four matrices, being preferred where strength is important and, for a given graphite content, having the best wear resistance. Usually the 10% tin–bronze alloy, sometimes with small amounts of zinc and lead (which confer additional self-lubricating properties) is preferred. Silver- and copper-containing materials are more suitable than bronze when the highest possible electrical conductivity is required. The high cost of silver is a deterrent to the use of graphite–silver, although in certain applications, e.g. precision instruments, it is chosen because of its very low contact resistance and good anti-welding properties at low contact pressures.

The manufacture of graphite–metal contacts consists of compacting the mixed powders and sintering in the temperature range 750–900°C. Graphite–bronzes are prepared from graphite, copper and tin powders and in this temperature range a liquid phase is formed, from which originates the superior strength of these materials. The sintered parts are readily machined to their final dimensions. Normal die-pressing of the high-graphite materials produces compacts of low green-strength which usually necessitates the use of a binder.

Switching Contacts

Switching contacts are used to make or break electrical circuits. Sometimes these circuits are of high power and the contacts in them may be required to operate many thousands of times without maintenance. Many factors influence the performance of such contacts (twelve factors are listed by Jones[1]), but three will suffice here: (i) the characteristics of the circuit (a.c. or d.c., voltage and current), (ii) the contact material and (iii) the dielectric medium. It appears that the principal factors that limit the life of a contact are arcing and mechanical wear. Arcing will occur in d.c. circuits with a minimum potential of 10–20 V and an arc current of 0·2–2 A. An important feature of arcing is that it can lead to material transfer across the contacts; short arcs cause evaporation of the anode, whereas long arcs result in ionization of the dielectric and evaporation of the cathode. The amount of material transported by an arc is, of course, determined by the contact material and the quantity of electricity involved; for a given contact and circuit it is therefore dependent upon the speed of operation of the contact. According to Hausner and Blackburn[2] every voltage has a definite current (critical current) which just permits the circuit to be interrupted without producing an arc. The critical current is dependent upon the contact material and the dielectric medium. An increase in the temperatures of the contact, owing to the passage of current or to arcing, for instance, lowers the critical current.

Another factor which has an important bearing on switching contact performance is the tendency for contact faces to weld together. Such welding is restricted by the presence of oxide films on the contact surface, also metals with high melting points have less tendency to weld. While the presence of a surface film inhibits welding, it also raises the contact resistance which leads to increased electrical losses. For contacts which operate in air and corrosive environments it is important that thick surface films do not build up. It is apparent that all of the requirements for a contact material will not be met by a single metal or alloy. The great advantage of producing these components by powder metallurgy is that duplex structures can be formed from metals having complementary desirable attributes.

The majority of switching contacts produced by powder metallurgy consist of either tungsten or molybdenum to confer resistance to wear, arcing and welding, in combination with copper or silver to provide high electrical and thermal conductivity. In these duplex materials the refractory metal generally comprises 40–80 wt-% of the body. Molybdenum–silver materials have high thermal and electrical conductivities but relatively low wear resistance, and they are therefore generally used for low-voltage high-current applications. For lower-current applications, particularly where frequent switching occurs, advantage may be taken of the better wear resistance of tungsten–silver, which has lower conductivity than molybdenum–silver. In high-voltage applications where pitting (material transfer) is the chief consideration tungsten–copper materials are used. A further improvement in wear resistance is obtained from tungsten–copper–nickel materials, the nickel promoting resistance to material transfer in addition to increasing the hardness. Tungsten–copper contacts (with or without nickel) are frequently operated under oil, which not only limits the formation of oxide films which would increase the contact resistance but also rapidly extinguishes the arc and therefore minimizes material transfer. Other measures for minimizing arc duration are the use of an air blast or the introduction of a condenser across the contacts. In some applications it is advantageous to use multi-layer contacts, a hard wear-resisting face being backed by layers with better conductivity.

These duplex materials are manufactured by one of two methods: (i) compacting and sintering of a refractory metal powder followed by infiltration with the low melting point metal, or (ii) compacting the mixed powders, sintering and machining if necessary. In the second method hot working is sometimes used to densify the sintered compact prior to machining.

In addition to the metal-powder contact materials described above there is at least one other type of some importance. This is also a duplex material and consists of cadmium oxide dispersed in silver (about 40% CdO). This material is used extensively in heavy-duty relays and maintains unusually low contact-resistance over long periods of time. It also has good resistance to welding during inadvertent overloads and has good arc-quenching characteristics. It is interesting to note that a silver–cadmium alloy while satisfactory in many respects has a much lower conductivity than the oxide-silver mixture.

'Hard metals' are also used for certain contact applications requiring extreme wear resistance. Tungsten carbide–cobalt and tungsten carbide–osmium contacts have been used for telephone relays.

Table 24 gives some properties of various contact materials.

The duplex materials that have been developed for switching contacts have also found other important uses where the combinations of wear and erosion

Table 24. Properties of Contact Materials

Material	Density (g/cm³)	Hardness (HV)	Electrical conductivity (%IACS)	Thermal conductivity (Silver = 1·0)
Silver	10·5	26	106	1·0
Silver–CdO	9·8–10·0	58	75–82	0·85–0·88
Silver–graphite	8·7–9·7	30–40	55–86	0·9
Silver–molybdenum	10·4	170	50	0·6
Silver–tungsten	12·5–15·6	110–220	36–61	0·6
Copper	8·9	35	100	0·94
Copper–tungsten	12·8–15·2	140–240	28–41	0·4
Tungsten	19·3	290	31	0·39

resistance together with high electrical conductivity are required. One such application is the contact electrodes of flash-butt welding equipment. Another use for tungsten–copper is as spark-erosion electrodes. In this application high-tungsten content materials give long life, while high-copper materials give faster cutting rates.

SOFT MAGNETIC MATERIALS

The use of powder-metallurgy techniques has enabled the range of available soft magnetic materials to be considerably extended. The principal contributions of powder metallurgy are (i) the production of iron and iron–silicon alloy components of complex form at low cost, (ii) the ability to produce iron–nickel alloys of higher initial permeability than can be achieved by more conventional manufacturing methods and (iii) the production of powder cores ('dust' cores). It should be noted that whereas the first two of these products are competitive with similar materials produced by other means, the dust cores can only be produced from powder.

Before discussing the various soft magnetic products some elementary features of these need to be recalled. Consider Fig. 62, in which the strength of the induced magnetism B is plotted as a function of the applied field strength H. Materials that are suitable as a soft magnet have some combination of the following: high saturation B_{max}, low coercivity H_c or high permeability $\mu = B/H$. The permeability value that is of importance is either the initial permeability μ_0 or the maximum permeability μ_{max}. The significance of permeability is that it represents to some extent the efficiency of the material because the field strength H is a measure of the applied energy and B is the energy induced into the magnet. Since it is desirable in all cases to keep the field strength to a minimum and to get the maximum work from this, the importance of permeability is clear. Initial permeability represents the efficiency at very small applied field-strengths, while μ_{max} is the maximum efficiency.

Moulded Components

Sintered iron and iron–silicon alloys have been widely used for moulded pole-pieces, armatures and similar components. In these applications the moulded parts must compete with components produced by machining from the solid or built-up from laminations. The sintered materials, although having inferior magnetic properties to those produced by the alternative methods, offer certain advantages; for instance, they are usually considerably cheaper.

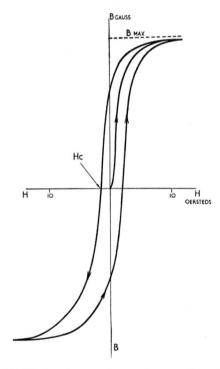

FIG. 62. Hysteresis curve for a soft magnetic material.

In addition there is a greater shape flexibility. For example, round hubs which are particularly desirable for ease of coil winding cannot be produced simply from laminations, whereas such shapes can easily be pressed from powders.

In the applications for which moulded parts are used, the magnetic-property requirements are not too severe. Usually the most important property is permeability. To achieve maximum permeability a high density is necessary, and this means that the compacting pressures must be high and the powders chosen for their compressibility. Consistency of permeability is often more important than the absolute level in many of the applications for which sintered parts are employed. Table 25 gives typical properties obtained in moulded components.

Table. 25. Typical Properties of Moulded Iron

Density (g/cm^3)	μ_{max}	H at μ_{max} (oersted)	Tensile strength (tons/in^2)	Elongation (%)
6·0	600	15	10	8
6·5	1100	—	12	12
7·0	1500	5	15	18
7·3	2000	—	17	25

Iron–silicon alloys, rather than plain iron, are preferred for a few a.c. applications where eddy-current losses are important. Silicon, by raising the electrical resistance, limits the eddy-current losses. Silicon contents of 1–4% are normal, although up to 6% may be added in exceptional cases. The a.c. applications for which moulded parts can be used are those where there are large air-gaps, as in small electric motors and generators and various a.c. instruments.

Although it is well known that soft magnetic properties are optimized in 'pure' alloys, purity is rarely the major consideration when choosing an iron powder for these magnetic applications. More important features are compressibility (for greater density and permeability) and cost. For many applications electrolytic iron powder is preferred; silicon is preferably added in the form of fine ferro-silicon powder. Production techniques are basically the same as those employed for iron-base engineering components. Such techniques are described in greater detail in Chapters 3 and 5. Compacting pressures are preferably in the range 20–35 tons/in^2, although 50 tons/in^2 may be employed in some cases. Sintering temperatures range from 1100°C to 1350°C. To avoid carbon pick-up dissociated ammonia atmospheres are better than those which contain carbon monoxide and hydrocarbons.

High Permeability Alloys

Some of the alloys of iron and nickel have very high initial permeability (μ_0 up to about 30,000). These alloys, basically 80% nickel–20% iron, sometimes with small molybdenum and copper additions, also have comparatively high magnetic saturation. The alloys can be produced by the normal techniques of melting, casting and rolling, but it has been found that when produced from powders somewhat better properties are obtained. (More recently the availability of vacuum melting has changed the position. Vacuum-melted alloys seem to be at least equal to the best produced from powders.)

Alloys of this type are very sensitive to changes in composition of the major elements ($\pm 0.1\%$), and undoubtedly the accurate compositional control that is possible is one of the reasons for the superiority of the powder product. The accuracy of composition of the powder-metallurgy alloy is limited only by the accuracy with which the constituent powders can be weighed. It is possible that a more important reason for the higher permeability of the sintered alloys is their freedom from inclusions. Inclusions occur in cast alloys as a result of deoxidation with silicon, calcium or magnesium compounds, while further inclusions may be formed during hot rolling by internal oxidation. A comparison of the initial permeability of alloys produced by air melting and from powders is given in Table 26. The powder product is clearly superior after annealing in wet hydrogen. Annealing in dry hydrogen gives about the same mean permeability values as the melted product, but there is very much less scatter in the values obtained from the sintered material.

Table 26. Comparison of Melted and Powder Metallurgy Alloys[3]

Type	Initial permeability	
	Annealed in pure hydrogen	Annealed in wet hydrogen
Powder-metallurgy alloys	27,000–32,000 (mean 29,000)	27,000–34,000 (mean 30,000)
Melted alloys	18,000–33,000 (mean 28,000)	13,000–20,000 (mean 17,000)

Results such as those given in Table 26 have led to claims that alloys prepared from powders have greater consistency of initial permeability and are also more tolerant to variations in the annealing atmosphere (and annealing temperature). As Lynch[4] has pointed out, users of magnetic materials must design for the worst properties they are likely to get, and in this respect the consistency of the sintered alloy is obviously important and allows substantial material savings. Another advantage claimed for alloys prepared from powders is the better retention of permeability in thin strip (30,000 μ_0 at 0.0006 in. has been obtained). The absence of the internally oxidized zone characteristic of the hot-rolled alloys appears to be responsible for this feature. The production of these alloys from powders is characterized by the great care which is taken to prevent contamination by interstitial elements. The raw materials are carefully selected and may be pre-reduced before being blended together.

Although the normal techniques of die compacting and sintering are usual, a recent step has been to produce strip by direct rolling. Recent work by Walker[5] suggests that silicon–iron strip might also be produced with advantage by techniques similar to those used for the nickel–iron alloys.

Powder Cores

The efficiency of an inductor is greatly increased by filling the air space with a suitable ferro-magnetic material, i.e. a core. A satisfactory material for a.c. cores needs to have a high effective permeability, coupled with low hysteresis and eddy-current losses. For a given material and flux density the hysteresis loss is proportional to the frequency, whereas the eddy-current loss is a function of the square of the frequency. Eddy-current losses are also proportional to the resistance. The cores of interest here are those produced from metal powders, often called 'dust' cores. A very important property of these cores is their high electrical resistivity which may reach 10^6 times that of the parent metal. This high resistivity is achieved by insulating the powder particles from each other. The properties of the insulator are therefore important in determining the eddy-current loss by their influence on the resistivity, while the temperature stability of the insulator determines the operating temperature range of the core. In addition to their high resistivity, powder cores are also characterized by almost constant permeability over a wide range of operating frequencies. The frequency-permeability relationships of powder and solid metal cores are compared in Fig. 63.[6] This permeability stability is due to the large number of air gaps within a powder core. Since it is essential to minimize porosity in order to maintain a high permeability, the compressibility and packing characteristics of dust-core powders are of great importance.

The methods used to manufacture powder cores reflect the need to achieve high density (for maximum permeability) while preventing interparticle bonding (to keep the resistance high, etc.). An outstanding feature of producing dust cores is the use of extremely high compacting pressures (up to 100 tons/in²) and the addition of special binders to the powders which can, after curing, give adequate bonding. These binders contain insulators such as silica or magnesia or other compounds whose decomposition products have a high resistance. The binder film must have sufficient strength to prevent it being ruptured during the compacting operation.

The powders used for dust cores are either the hard or annealed grades of carbonyl–iron or iron–nickel–molybdenum alloys. Variations in density, etc., can alter the properties of the cores; for use at low frequencies, eddy-current losses must be low and permeabilities of about 10 are acceptable. At higher frequencies even lower permeabilities must be accepted in order to minimize the losses. Some typical values for powder cores are given in Table 27. The loss factors given in the table refer to the parameters occurring in Legg's analysis,[7] in which the series loss resistance R due to the core is assessed in terms of three loss parameters; a the hysteresis loss, c the residual loss and e the eddy-current loss:

$$R = 2\pi f L \mu_0 \left(\frac{aB}{10^4} + c + ef \right)$$

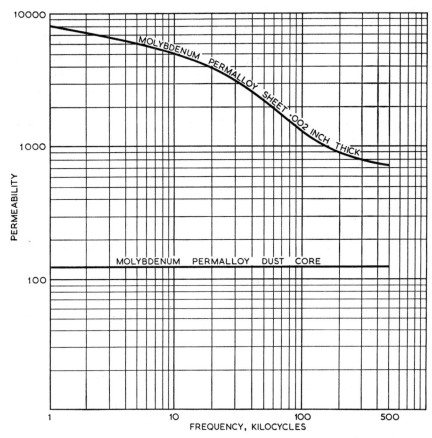

FIG. 63. The effect of frequency on the magnetic permeability of Mo-Permalloy.
(*Reproduced from Reference 6 by courtesy of the Iron and Steel Institute*)

where f is the frequency, L the effective inductance and B the r.m.s. flux density.

Table 27. Loss Factors for Powder Cores

	Permeability	Loss factors		
		$a \times 10^6$	$c \times 10^6$	$e \times 10^9$
Electrolytic iron	35	200	1000	20
Carbonyl iron 'E'	12–15	3–8	1000	0·2
Carbonyl iron 'C'	15–55	50	200–600	1–2
Molybdenum Permalloy	125	1·6	30	19
Molybdenum Permalloy	26	6·9	100	8
Molybdenum Permalloy	14	11·4	140	7

A different type of core from the dust cores just described is the flake-iron core. Flake-iron cores were developed as substitutes for iron–silicon laminations for operation at 50 c/s. At such low frequencies, normal dust cores are unsuitable because of their low permeability. For this application flake-iron powder, about 25 μ thick and of high purity, is produced by rolling. These flakes, having length to thickness ratios of about 25:1, are introduced into dies in such a manner that the flakes are preferentially orientated. As with dust cores maximum density is needed to get the highest permeabilities, and again the properties of the binder are important.

Flake-iron cores have been used in a number of television applications, for example, squegging, line and E.H.T. transformers and scan coils. Other uses are for radio-interference suppressors and audio-frequency output transformers. The material seems no longer to be used for the 'E' cores of ballast chokes in fluorescent-lighting units, the application for which it was developed. Table 28 gives the properties of flake-iron cores.

Table 28. Properties of Caslam Flake-Iron Cores
(*Courtesy The Plessey Co. Ltd.*)

	Grade 3	Grade 4	Grade 5
DC μ_0	250	220	170
DC μ_{max}	950	560	470
H_c (oersted)	1·8	2·0	2·1
Saturation flux density (10^3 gauss)	15·5	14·0	13·0

PERMANENT-MAGNET MATERIALS

The reasons why some permanent magnets are produced from metal powders are similar to those given for soft magnetic materials. The range of useful permanent-magnet materials has been extended by the development of special materials that can only be produced by powder metallurgy, while some magnets are most economically produced by powder-metal techniques.

A *B-H* curve for a permanent-magnet material is given in Fig. 64. The properties which are important in a permanent-magnet material are a high value of remanence, (B_r, the residual magnetism retained in the material after removal of the magnetizing field), high coercivity (H_c, the reverse field required to demagnetize the magnet) and maximum-energy product, BH_{max}. The maximum-energy product represents the greatest amount of useful energy which the magnet can provide and numerically is the largest value of $B \times H$. It should be noted that the useful properties of permanent magnets are described by the second quadrant of the *B-H* curve, whereas for soft magnets (see Fig. 62) it is the first quadrant that is of most interest.

Alnico Magnets

The magnets commonly known by the name Alnico have been developed from the discovery by Mishima[8] that a 30% nickel, 12% aluminium, 58% iron alloy possesses outstanding permanent magnetic properties. Alnico alloys are today the most important of all the permanent-magnet materials and have, to a very large extent, replaced the hardenable steels. A survey of magnet usage in the U.S.A.[9] showed that this class of magnets accounts for almost 90% of the total permanent-magnet production. This widespread use of Alnico magnets results from their excellent magnetic properties, their low

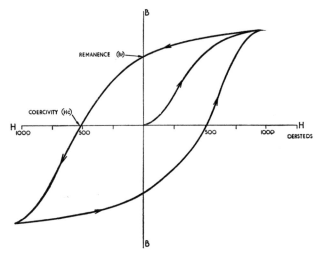

FIG. 64. Hysteresis curve for a permanent-magnet material.

cost and low density. A further important characteristic is their metallurgical and magnetic stability. Their use, however, is sometimes limited by their brittleness and high hardness which make machining difficult.

All of the Alnico alloys require a precipitation heat-treatment to produce optimum magnetic properties. Certain of the alloys are heat treated in a magnetic field which greatly enhances their magnetic properties. Since such magnets are anisotropic, the magnetic field must be arranged so that the best properties are obtained in the required direction. In cast alloys a further improvement in magnetic properties can be obtained by inducing structural anisotropy, which is achieved by controlled directional cooling. The structurally anisotropic alloys have the highest energy product of any commercial magnets at the present time; for instance, Ticonal XX, BH_{max} 11×10^6 gauss-oersteds.

15

Many additional alloying elements have been added to the basic iron–aluminium–nickel composition discovered by Mishima; four elements are important, cobalt, copper, titanium and niobium. Cobalt increases the residual saturation induction of the alloys and also raises the Curie temperature. The increase in the Curie temperature is extremely important where heat treatment in a magnetic field is being applied. Coercivity is increased by copper additions, which are also reputed to assist in obtaining consistent properties. Titanium is an important addition to some of the 'higher' Alnico alloys. It combines with residual carbon, which would otherwise cause a loss of saturation induction in the iron phase. Titanide phases may also be formed (Fe_2Ti, Co_2Ti, Ni_3Ti) which give increased coercivity. Niobium increases coercivity without adversely affecting the remanence or the maximum-energy product.

Iron–aluminium–nickel alloys are mechanically as well as magnetically hard and can only be machined by grinding. Because of this it is necessary to produce the magnets as near as possible to the finished shape. Two production processes are used, precision casting and powder metallurgy. Casting accounts for about 95% of current production. Powder metallurgy is generally applied to magnets smaller than about 50 g, and the usual condition that large production runs are necessary to justify tool costs, applies. At the present time it appears that powder metallurgy is increasing its share *vis-à-vis* casting, and magnets considerably larger than 50 g are being produced in limited quantities. The advantages claimed for sintered magnets are that they are free of oxide and other inclusions such as are found in castings, are homogeneous and free of cracks and blowholes, and the grain size is small. A consequence of these characteristics is that sintered magnets are magnetically more homogeneous than those which are cast and they are also somewhat stronger. Sintered magnets always contain a small amount of residual porosity which may cause up to 10% reduction in remanence and coercivity, and result in up to 20% lower maximum-energy values compared with cast alloys of the same composition. Nevertheless, the compositional and magnetic homogeneity of the sintered alloys is such that in practice the magnetic performance is usually comparable with cast material. In Table 29 the compositions and magnetic properties of cast and sintered alloys are given. It will be seen that the density of the sintered alloys is some 5–6% less than that of the cast alloys.

Alnico alloys are produced from mixtures of iron, nickel, cobalt and iron–aluminium or nickel–aluminium powders. Early in the production of the alloys it was found impossible satisfactorily to sinter mixtures containing aluminium powder which, even in the best 'commercial' sintering atmospheres, had a surface oxide which could not be reduced. The use of aluminium-rich master alloys overcomes the problem of alumina formation, but for satisfactory results the sintering atmosphere must still be either purified hydrogen

Table 29. Properties of Sintered and Cast Alnico-type Magnets

Type	Composition wt-%*							Properties			
	Al	Ni	Co	Cu	Nb	Ti	Si	B_r (gauss)	H_c (oersted)	BH_{max} (M.G.O.)	Density (g/cm³)
SINTERED											
Alnico 1305	12	26	5	4	—	—	—	5,100	600	1·25	6·6
Alnico 1605	11	24	9·5	3·5	—	—	—	5,750	570	1·28	6·8
Reco 3A	10	19	12	6	—	—	—	6,500	530	1·5	7·0
Alnico 1905	11	24	16	4	—	—	—	6,450	640	1·6	6·9
Alinico 2505	7	19	24	3	—	5	—	5,600	915	2·03	6·9
Alcomax II	8	11·5	21	4	—	—	—	10,700	550	3·4	7·0
Alcomax III	8	13·5	24	3	0·5–0·8	—	—	10,800	600	4·1	7·0
Alcomax IV	8	13·5	24	3	2–2·5	—	—	9,000	700	3·5	7·0
Ticonal S	8	14	3	3	—	—	—	11,100	620	4·2	7·0
Hycomax	9	21	20	2	—	—	—	7,900	790	2·6	7·0
CAST											
Alnico 130	12	26	5	4	—	—	—	5,700	650	1·4	7·0
Alnico 160	11	24	9·5	3·5	—	—	—	6,400	630	1·45	7·1
Reco 3A	10	19	12	6	—	—	—	7,250	580	1·7	7·3
Alnico 190	11	24	16	4	—	—	—	7,200	700	1·8	7·2
Alnico 250	7	19	24	3	—	—	—	6,200	1,000	2·3	7·2
CAST ANISOTROPIC											
Alcomax II	8	11·5	22–24	3	0·2	—	0·4	13,000	580	5·4	7·35
Alcomax III	8	13·5	24	3	0·5–0·8	—	—	12,600	650	5·4	7·35
Alcomax IV	8	13·5	24	3	2–2·5	—	—	11,500	750	4·5	7·35
Alnico U AB (U.S.A.)	8	14·5	24	3	—	—	—	12,300	685	5·0	7·3
Hycomax	9	21	20	2	—	—	—	9,500	830	2·3	7·25

* Balance iron.

or vacuum; the latter is finding increasing application. Completely pre-alloyed powders are not used for sintered magnets because their hardness makes them impossible to compact satisfactorily. Compacting pressures are usually modest, about 20 tons/in² being common. The sintering temperature is about 1350°C and the liquid phase formed by the 'master-alloy' promotes densification and homogenization.

Since a precipitation heat-treatment is necessary to develop the magnetic properties, rapid cooling from near the sintering temperature is desirable, otherwise a separate solution treatment is required. The desirability of rapid cooling means that sintering in hydrogen is carried out in continuous furnaces rather than batch furnaces. Where anisotropic magnets are being produced, it is usual to arrange for cooling from the sintering temperatures to take place in a magnetic field.

A recent development in this field is the use of pre-alloyed Alnico powder bonded with thermoplastic or thermosetting resins. About 3–6% of binder is normal and compacting pressures are low, usually 7–8 tons/in². Some properties of these bonded magnets are given in Table 30. Anisotropic-bonded magnets have been produced but have not yet found wide commercial application.

Table 30. Properties of Bonded Magnets

	Composition wt–%*					Properties		
Type	Al	Ni	Co	Cu	Ti	B_r (gauss)	H_c (oersted)	BH_{max} (M.G.O.)
Tromalit Alni 090	12	22	—	—	—	4,400	250	0·40
Tromalit Alni 120 P	13	27	—	—	—	3,400	465	0·50
Tromalit Alnico 160	11	24	9·5	3·5	—	3,800	600	0·70
Tromalit 800	7	19	24	3	5	3,500	850	1·0

* Balance iron.

The density of these alloys is usually 5·2–5·5 g/cm³, but a higher density form of Tromalit 800 is produced (5·7–6·2 g/cm³) in which the remanence and maximum-energy product are each increased by about 20%.

Single-Domain Particle Magnets

The development of single-domain particle magnets stems directly from the theoretical studies of Néel[10] and of Stoner and Wohlfarth,[11] who showed that particles sufficiently small to contain only a single domain ought to have a very high coercivity, since the easiest mechanism of demagnetization, domain boundary movement, would not be available. Practical single-domain particle magnets are made from iron or iron–cobalt alloys, because the very high saturation induction of these alloys leads to high remanence. The first commercial production of single-domain particle magnets used spherical powders, about 150 Å diameter, obtained by reducing iron, or mixed iron–cobalt, formate with hydrogen. The powder was bonded with an organic binder to give a high-coercivity low-density magnet, or compacted to give a modification having higher remanence. Typical properties of magnets produced from formate powders are given in Table 31.

Table 31. Properties of Magnets Produced from Reduced Formate Powders

	Composition	B_r (gauss)	H_c (oersted)	$B.H._{max}$ (M.G.O.)
Gecalloy MC	Fe	4,000	500	0·6
Gecalloy MR	Fe	7,000	330	1·0
Gecalloy HC	Fe–Co	5,200	640	1·1
Gecalloy HR	Fe–Co	9,000	350	1·5

Production of magnets from spherical formate powders has now ceased, the probable reasons, according to Jones,[1] being expense of the formate process, occurrence of internal oxidation and low maximum-energy values. More recently single-domain particle magnets have again been produced commercially. These newer magnets are produced from elongated particles which enable the shape anisotropy factor to be utilized to give better properties: these are termed E.S.D. magnets (elongated single domain) by Luborsky, Mendelsohn and Paine,[12],[13] who have pioneered their production.

The production of E.S.D. magnets is undoubtedly a triumph of technology. The principal steps in processing are: (i) electrodeposition of particles (iron or iron–cobalt alloy) into a mercury cathode using additives to give shape control, (ii) concentration of mercury-powder slurry (excess mercury being returned to electrodeposition cell), (iii) concentrated slurry compacted in the presence of a magnetic field giving simultaneous particle orientation and further mercury removal, (iv) remaining mercury removed by vacuum distillation and (v) particles embedded in a matrix which serves to protect them from oxidation and also insulates the individual particles. The matrix may be either an organic substance which produces a magnet of low density and high energy-to-weight ratio, or a metallic matrix which gives high maximum energy values and greater resistance to environmental attack. The most popular matrix is lead or a lead alloy.

In Table 32 typical properties of E.S.D. magnets are given, together with the theoretical limits towards which they may ultimately be developed to give higher energy values than the structure-orientated Alnicos.

Table 32. Properties of E.S.D. Magnets

	Composition	B_r (gauss)	H_c (oersted)	BH_{max} (M.G.O.)
E.S.D.30	Fe	5,700	1,500	2·9
E.S.D.50	Fe	8,800	715	3·3
E.S.D.45	Fe	9,000	700	3·5
E.S.D.40C	Fe–Co	9,050	1,025	5·0
Theoretical	Fe	14,300	3,600	39·0
limits	Fe–Co	16,300	16,300	50·0

Manganese Bismuthide

Heusler[14] showed that certain alloying additions to manganese caused its exchange integral to change from negative to positive. Only one alloy based on this concept is of commercial importance, manganese bismuthide, the important magnetic properties of which were discovered by Guillaud.[15] This material possesses exceptionally high coercivity, which is the reason for its use; it also has low residual induction. The alloy does not find wide use mainly because it is highly susceptible to corrosion, and the coercive force being very sensitive to temperature; also the high-purity bismuth from which it is made is expensive.

Manufacture of manganese bismuthide consists of heating finely powdered manganese with an excess of solid bismuth at 450°C. After milling to reduce to single-domain particles (about 9 μ) the powder is hot pressed (100–450 lb/in² at 240–300°C) in a strong magnetic field of up to 20,000 oersted. Properties of manganese bismuthide fall in the range, B_r 4,000–4,800 gauss, H_c 3,000–3,800 oersted and BH_{max} 3–5 × 10⁶ gauss-oersteds.

REFERENCES

1. Jones, W. D. *Fundamental Principles of Powder Metallurgy*, 766, Arnold, London (1960).
2. Hausner, H. H. and Blackburn, P. W. in *Powder Metallurgy*, Wulff (ed.), 470, A.S.M., Cleveland (1942).
3. Walker, E. V., Worn, D. K. and Walters, R. E. S. Symposium on Powder Metallurgy, 1956 (*Special Rept. No. 58*), 204, 1956; London (Iron and Steel Institute).
4. Lynch, A. C. ibid., 363.
5. Walker, E. V. and Howard, T. *Powder Metallurgy*, No. 4, 32–42 (1959).
6. Buckley, S. E. Symposium on Powder Metallurgy (*Special Rept. No. 38*), 59, 1947; London (Iron and Steel Institute).
7. Legg, V. E. *Bell System Tech.*, 3, 15 (1), 39–62 (1936).
8. Mishima, T. B.P. 378478.

9. Parker, R. F. and Studder, R. J. *Permanent Magnets and Their Applications*, John Wiley, New York (1962).
10. Néel, L. *Compte rendu Acad. Sci., Paris*, **224**, 1488–1490, 1550–1551 (1947).
11. Stoner, E. C. and Wohlfarth, E. P. *Phil. Trans. Roy. Soc.*, 240A (826), 599–642 (1948).
12. Luborsky, F. E., Mendelsohn, L. J. and Paine, T. O. *J. appl. Phys.*, **28**, 344–351 (1957).
13. Luborsky, F. E., Mendelsohn, L. J. and Paine, T. O. *Powder Metallurgy*, No. 4, 57–78 (1959).
14. Heusler, F. *Z. angew Chemi.*, **17** (9), 260–264 (1904).
15. Guillaud, C. *J. des recherches du C.N.R.S.*, **2**, 267–278 (1948/49).

CHAPTER 11

REFRACTORY METALS

The word 'refractory' is defined by the *Oxford Dictionary* as 'difficult to fuse (or to work in any way)'. Thus, those metals with melting points above about 2000°C, for example, tungsten, molybdenum, tantalum, niobium and some of the precious metals, are commonly termed refractory metals. As stated in Chapter 1, when man wanted to fabricate a metal which he found difficult to fuse he adopted the powder metallurgy approach, that is, he extracted the metal from its ore as a powder and then consolidated the powder into usable forms. With the introduction of the electric furnace most metals could be melted, but there remained some metals which could not be fused because the materials used for furnace linings and crucibles either reacted with the molten metals or themselves fused. However, with the introduction, shortly after World War II of commercial vacuum consumable-electrode arc furnaces and later of electron-beam melting furnaces, the way was open for the melting even of tungsten with a melting point of 3410°C. Thus ingots of all metals can now be produced without resort to powder metallurgy.

At the turn of the century, when tungsten was required in the form of fine wire for the electric-lamp industry, means for its fusion did not exist and it was necessary therefore to use powder metallurgy. The first attempts used paste-extrusion techniques whereby mixtures of the metal powder with substantial amounts of various binders, such as starch or dextrin, were extruded through diamond dies. However, on sintering a porous product was obtained and the wire was very brittle. Despite these drawbacks it was the only type of wire available at that time for electric-lamp filaments, and it was certainly superior to the carbon filaments that it replaced. This position continued until about 1910 when a revolutionary method for the fabrication of tungsten was devised by Coolidge.[1] Tungsten powder was pressed into a bar which was

Table 33. Properties of Refractory Metals

Property	Tungsten	Molybdenum	Tantalum	Niobium
Melting point, °C	3410	2610	2996	2468
Density, g/cm³	19·3	10·2	16·6	8·57
Linear coefficient of expansion/deg C (0–100°C)	$4·6 \times 10^{-6}$	$5·7 \times 10^{-6}$	$6·5 \times 10^{-6}$	$7·2 \times 10^{-6}$
Specific heat, cal/g/deg C (20°C)	0·034	0·058	0·036	0·065
Thermal conductivity, cal/cm²/deg C/sec	0·397(0°C) 0·322(1427°C) 0·362(1627°C)	0·346(17°C) 0·259(927°C) 0·173(1627°C)	0·13(20–100°C) 0·174(1430°C) 0·198(1830°C)	0·125(20°C) 0·140(500°C) —
Vapour pressure, mm Hg	4×10^{-8}(2200°C) 4×10^{-6}(2500°C) $6·5 \times 10^{-3}$(3150°C)	$2·5 \times 10^{-8}$(1600°C) 5×10^{-4}(2200°C) 1×10^{-2}(2500°C)	$9·5 \times 10^{-11}$(1727°C) — —	1×10^{-3}(2539°C) — —
Electrical resistivity, μΩ-cm	5·65(27°C) 46·78(1427°C) 60·06(1827°C)	5·78(27°C) 41·2(1327°C) 53·5(1727°C)	15·5(20°C) 71·0(1430°C) 80·0(1830°C)	15–22(20°C) — —
Temperature coefficient of electrical resistivity /degC	0·00482(20–100°C)	0·0047(20–100°C)	0·00382(0–100°C)	0·00396(0–600°C)
Work function, eV Positive ion emission, eV Electron emission, mA/cm²	4·55 11·93 1·0(1950°K)	4·20 8·60 1·0(1900°K)	4·10 10·0 19·5(2000°K) $4·7 \times 10^{-3}$(1500°K) 1×10^{-6}(1273°K)	4·01 5·52 —
Tensile strength, lb/in² 0·50 mm diam. 0·10 mm diam. 0·05 mm diam. cold worked annealed	260,000 420,000 485,000	140,000 153,000 190,000	110–180,000 50–100,000	96–130,000 48–59,000
Elongation, % cold worked annealed	1–4	25 (max.)	2–3 25–40	1 30
Modulus of elasticity, lb/in² × 10⁶	50	42	27	15

then sintered. The sintered bar was sufficiently ductile to be swaged at about 1500°C, and Coolidge found that as the degree of consolidation increased so the working temperature could be decreased. After swaging to rod further reductions were effected by hot drawing. Coolidge's method was soon found to be applicable to molybdenum and later to tantalum and niobium, although, in fact, these metals are sufficiently ductile to be cold worked after initial hot consolidation.

In recent years the need for refractory-metal alloys for missiles and other applications has led to widespread use of melting processes such as consumable-electrode arc and electron-beam. Nevertheless, substantial quantities of tungsten, molybdenum, niobium and tantalum are still processed into rod, wire and sheet by the techniques of powder metallurgy, and since the method has an economic advantage over melting it seems likely that for a large number of applications the refractory metals will be processed in this way for many years to come.

Table 33 gives some of the important properties of tungsten, molybdenum, tantalum and niobium.

TUNGSTEN

Consolidation

The basic method of Coolidge is still followed in most cases. Rectangular bars up to 2 in. square by 2 ft long are pressed in split dies on large hydraulic presses, side rams being usually necessary to keep the die closed during compaction. Compacting pressures of 15–30 tons/in² are used and both single and double-acting presses are employed, although the former are more usual. Isostatic pressing is used to produce even larger bars or billets.

The usual heating method employed in sintering is direct resistance because of the temperature requirements. This involves clamping the tungsten bars between water-cooled electrodes; the as-pressed bars are usually too fragile to withstand this operation and pre-sintering at 1100–1300°C in hydrogen provides the necessary increase in strength. Resistance sintering is carried out in a water-cooled bell-jar through which is passed a stream of dry hydrogen. The pre-sintered bar is clamped at the top between a fixed pair of heavy water-cooled copper blocks which are faced with tungsten strips. The lower end of the bar is attached to tungsten or molybdenum clips which are either spring loaded or immersed in a water-cooled trough of mercury to allow for movement due to shrinkage of the bar on sintering. Some sintering facilities are designed to take a number of bars in one bell-jar.

Sintering temperatures for tungsten, using this method, range from 2650–3100°C, but the upper end of the range is more commonly used. To attain such temperatures requires substantial currents, the actual magnitude of which depends on the dimensions of the specimen; a bar one inch square by ten inches long, for example, would require about 9000 A to reach 3000°C. Potentials rarely exceed 20 volts.

Although the resistance-sintering technique will provide suitable material for conversion to wire and sheet, 'space-age' demands for large complex parts have necessitated the use of indirect methods of heating. For example, both indirect resistance heating, using tungsten elements, and induction heating, using a graphite or tungsten susceptor, have been used to sinter large tungsten parts. The temperatures used in these methods are lower than those attained in direct resistance sintering; Wong et al.[2] quote sintering temperatures for tungsten of 2350–2400°C for induction heating and 2500°C for indirect resistance heating.

In view of the difficulties in obtaining the high temperatures necessary for the efficient sintering of pure tungsten, attempts have been made to activate the process by various means. The use of a 'wet' hydrogen atmosphere has been found to be useful[3] in promoting sintering at relatively low temperatures. A small addition of nickel (as low as 0·25%) has also been shown to have a remarkable effect and Brophy et al.[4] using such additions were able to obtain densities of 98% of theoretical by sintering for 16 hours at 1100°C. However, tungsten containing even small amounts of nickel is much too brittle to be fabricated, so that the process is only suitable for parts which are to be used in the as-sintered condition.

Fabrication

Providing the density is over 90% of theoretical, sintered tungsten may be safely worked at about 1400–1500°C. Preliminary hot working is normally by swaging and for the production of rod and wire this operation is continued down to about 2 mm diameter from a 25-mm square bar. Further reductions, if required, are then achieved by wire drawing. For the production of sheet the sintered bar is swaged to flatten the corners, then hammer-forged and finally hot-rolled.

Before hot-working the ends of resistance-sintered bars are cropped, since they are of low density and unworkable. The bar is then heated to about 1500°C in a molybdenum-wound furnace under an atmosphere of hydrogen or cracked ammonia. When the temperature is equalized the bar is transferred rapidly to the swaging machine, the feed being manually controlled at this stage. The minimum working temperature for tungsten decreases as the bar is reduced in section. Typical working temperatures for various reductions are shown in Fig. 65. It will be seen that very fine wire may be drawn at temperatures as low as 550°C. All of these temperatures are below the recrystallization temperature so that the metal is actually cold-worked. However, during the early stages of swaging it is common practice to anneal the material at 2500°C (again by direct resistance) to homogenize the structure. Such a treatment, which recrystallizes the tungsten and also embrittles it, must be followed by working at the top of the working temperature range, i.e. 1400–1500°C. Working temperature may then be gradually reduced again with increasing reduction. When the length of the swaged rod reaches about 1 metre further swaging is carried out on a machine with a mechanical feed. In this case the rod is fed through a tube furnace with no protective atmos-

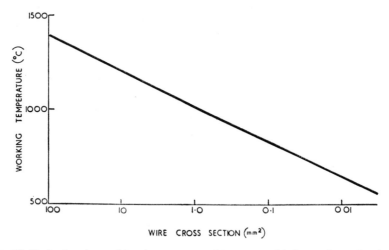

FIG. 65. Reduction in working temperature of tungsten with increasing reduction in wire cross-section.

phere and it is necessary to coat with graphite to prevent oxidation. This also reduces wear on the swaging hammers, which are usually of high-speed steel, although cemented carbides are finding more use in this field.

During swaging a graphite–tungstic oxide film is formed on the surface of the rod which must be removed when swaging is complete. The usual method is to burn off the graphite by heating in air or oxygen and then to pickle off the oxide in boiling caustic soda solution; the rod is then finally rinsed in water.

Wire-drawing operations replace swaging at a diameter of between 1 mm and 5 mm depending on the size of the original sintered bar. For most applications of tungsten wire it is necessary to carry out a number of drawing reductions in order to obtain a satisfactory surface finish and uniform diameter. Cemented-carbide drawing dies are used down to diameters of about 0·25 mm, below which diamond dies become necessary. Graphite is used as a drawing lubricant and the resulting film is removed in a boiling caustic soda or caustic potash solution. Drawing temperatures are slightly higher than those used in swaging (for equivalent diameters) and even wire of 0·1 mm diameter must be drawn at about 600°C. In the later stages of drawing it is necessary to heat the die block to ensure that the wire is not chilled below the required drawing temperature.

In the production of tungsten sheet initial consolidation of the sintered bar is effected by hammering at about 1550°C, although this may be preceded by a swaging operation to remove sharp corners and minimize edge cracking. Where narrow strip or ribbon is required then swaging may be continued until a suitable diameter is reached, after which the rod or wire is rolled. Rolling of a hammered ingot is conducted at gradually decreasing temperatures, starting at 1300–1400°C and continuing down to 700–800°C when the sheet thickness is about 1 mm. At this stage the sheet is cleaned to remove oxide and further rolling takes place at about 250°C, at which temperature oxidation is not a severe problem, although where very clean sheet is required pack rolling between molybdenum sheets may be employed. When the thickness of the sheet is below 0·2 mm further rolling is conducted at room temperature and the resulting sheet has a high polish and good ductility.

Tungsten sheet may be formed by the usual processes such as pressing, deep drawing, spinning and flow turning, but elevated temperatures (sometimes as high as 1000°C) are usually required for such operations.

The joining of tungsten presents problems due to both the lack of oxidation resistance and the severe embrittlement resulting from recrystallization. Welding processes such as argon-arc, electron-beam and resistance welding are suitable for tungsten, provided a brittle joint is acceptable. Brazing at temperatures below the recrystallization temperature is not often used since tungsten is rarely employed at such low temperatures; furthermore, it must be remembered that the constituents of many brazing alloys may lower the recrystallization temperature. The high modulus of tungsten is a disadvantage in welding and brazing, because small strains due to differential thermal contractions will give rise to high stresses. At present the preferred method of joining for assembling complex tungsten components is pinning by rivets, bolts or fasteners.

Properties and Applications

Tungsten has the highest melting point of all the metals, 3410°C, and it is natural that many of its applications should be based upon this property. In fact the original application of fabricated tungsten, the electric-lamp filament, remains today the major commercial use to which the metal is put (though its use here is also a result of the metal's very low vapour pressure). Also, because of the poor oxidation resistance of the metal, it must always be operated under vacuum or in a protective atmosphere when used at elevated temperatures.

Drawn tungsten wire owes its ductility to its extremely fibrous structure, although tungsten single crystals also display remarkable ductility. It seems that the brittleness of the recrystallized structure is associated with the presence of recrystallized grain boundaries. Work by Jones[5] using electron microscopy shows that the large numbers of dislocations in the 'as-drawn' structure start to order themselves into a sub-grain structure on annealing at temperatures in excess of 1100°C. This 'polyganization' is associated with a reduction in ductility. True recrystallized grains appear on annealing at 1,500°C and above, and this leads to complete brittleness. Actually Jones's work was carried out on one particular sample of tungsten wire and the temperatures of polyganization and recrystallization are likely to vary with the past history, i.e. working programme, of the wire.

The service temperature of an electric-lamp filament is far in excess of its recrystallization temperature, so that the wire becomes severely embrittled. In fact, at the usual filament-operating temperatures of 2000–2500°C rapid grain growth occurs and the wire becomes a series of large grains which occupy the whole of the cross section. In service a straight-wire filament deforms under gravity by grain boundary movement which results in what is termed 'off-setting'. Fig. 66, which is taken from Smithells,[6] is a diagrammatic representation of the process of recrystallization, grain growth and off-setting. Such a wire is reduced in section at the off-set boundaries and therefore tends to overheat and eventually fuses at one of these points.

Coiled filaments are not prone to off-setting, but on grain growth they tend to sag and lose their efficiency. In practice, various additions are made to the tungsten, either to the metal powder or to the oxide before reduction, in order to overcome the effects of grain growth. Three general types of additions are made: (i) a substance which is relatively stable at the service temperature and maintains a stable structure by restricting grain growth. In practice additions of 0·5–1·0% thoria are usually made. Although grain growth is not eliminated, the effect is such that the grain size after heating for about 1000 hours is similar to that obtained in pure tungsten after a few minutes. Since at service temperatures the thoria is gradually reduced to thorium these filaments are not stable over very long periods, but they are useful in lamps which are subject to vibration or shock. (ii) Volatile substances, usually silicates: such additions do not restrain grain growth but result in a coarse polycrystalline structure in which the grains are very elongated in the axis of the wire. Grains tend to overlap so that grain boundary movement is difficult. The effect is greatly exaggerated when the wire is coiled, presumably due to the additional strain imposed during the coiling operation. These filaments find use in vacuum lamps, usually as a single coil. (iii) If a second less volatile oxide such as alumina is added together with the silicate then the elongated grain structure is obtained in even more exaggerated form. The structure is found to be stable over very long periods, so that this type of wire is usually employed as a coiled-coil filament in gas-filled lamps where long term stability is essential.

Tungsten also finds widespread use as a cathode material in radio valves and similar devices. This is not because the metal is a particularly good

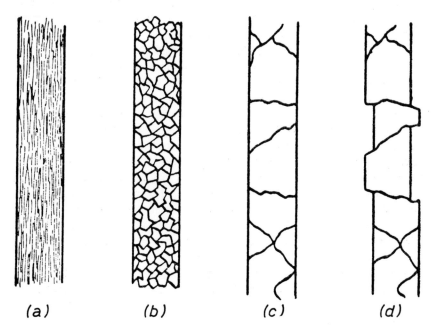

(a)　　　(b)　　　(c)　　　(d)

FIG. 66. Diagrammatic representation of the stages leading to offsetting in tungsten filaments
(a) As-drawn wire with fibrous structure (b) Recrystallized (c) Grain growth (d) Off-setting
(*Reproduced from 'Tungsten' by C. J. Smithells,*[6] *Chapman and Hall, by courtesy of author and publisher*)

electron emitter but rather because of its low vapour pressure and high-temperature stability. In many cases tungsten with an addition of about 1% thoria is used in valve applications. By a suitable 'activation' heat-treatment a thin layer of reduced thorium is obtained on the filament and this enhances the electron emission. An activation treatment consists of flashing the filament to about 2500°C, followed by holding at about 1900°C until emission remains constant.

Again because of its high melting point tungsten is used as an electrode material in the inert-gas arc-welding technique, often known as TIG (tungsten-inert-gas) welding. Thoriated material is usually employed because of its high-temperature stability.

Tungsten wire is used as a resistance element material in certain special furnaces, usually vacuum furnaces, and tungsten tubes, heated by direct resistance, have been used in similar applications.

The low coefficient of thermal expansion of tungsten (4.4×10^{-6}/degC) has led to its use as a lead-in wire in valves and other devices where a glass-to-metal seal is necessary. Swaged wire is usually employed since its surface finish is more suited to this type of application.

Because of its high density (19.3 g/cm^3) tungsten makes a very good γ-radiation shield. With the advent of γ-sources in medicine it was necessary to develop a method of producing tungsten in massive form with low porosity. Owing to the difficulties in obtaining temperatures of 3000°C in massive tungsten shapes, a liquid-phase sintering technique was developed for the production of heavy alloys. These materials are prepared by mixing tungsten powder with 2–4% copper and 5–6% nickel, pressing to shape and sintering above the melting point of the copper–nickel alloy; densities in excess of 17 g/cm^3 are thus obtained. These alloys are fairly readily machined and, in addition to their original application as radiation shields, have also been extensively used as balancing weights on rotating machinery (particularly where space is at a premium), as tool holders in lathe turning (because of their good damping capacity) and as electrodes in certain spark-erosion applications.

The uses of tungsten in the production of cemented carbides and electrical contact materials have been discussed in Chapters 6 and 10 respectively.

MOLYBDENUM

Consolidation and Fabrication

Molybdenum is produced in rod, wire and sheet form in much the same way as tungsten. Bars up to $2\frac{1}{2}$ in. square by 2 ft long are pressed from powder on large hydraulic presses and are sintered by direct resistance at 2000–2400°C in hydrogen. Hot working begins at about 1200°C and, because the metal is more ductile than tungsten, working can continue without annealing down to room temperature. In fact very thin foil may be produced by cold rolling. Since sintering temperatures are lower than those required for tungsten it is easier to sinter large molybdenum shapes by induction or indirect resistance heating. Sintering in a 'wet' hydrogen atmosphere gives a high density at temperatures as low as 1500°C, but the times required are fairly long.

Molybdenum sheet, like tungsten, may be formed by the usual sheet-forming processes; elevated temperatures are often necessary but operations involving only a small amount of plastic deformation may be conducted at room temperature. The joining of molybdenum poses similar problems to those outlined for tungsten. Unless very well protected from oxidation, fusion welds are likely to suffer from hot-tearing due to the formation of a Mo–MoO$_2$ eutectic. Welding under water (or other protective liquid) minimizes the extent of the recrystallized zone and reduces oxidation; resistance welding under water also reduces problems due to electrode sticking. As with tungsten, however, pinning is the preferred method for joining fabricated molybdenum sheet assemblies.

Properties and Applications

Like tungsten, molybdenum has very little oxidation resistance at elevated temperatures and it may only be used above 300°C under a protective atmosphere or in vacuum. Molybdenum has a lower melting point (2610°C) and higher vapour pressure and is therefore used at lower temperatures than tungsten. However, its ductility permits the fabrication of much more complex forms than may be achieved with tungsten. Additions such as thoria are rarely made to molybdenum (other than to improve thermionic emission) since the metal is used at lower temperatures and recrystallization does not have quite so drastic an effect on ductility as it does in the case of tungsten.

Molybdenum is widely used in electric lamps as supporting parts for tungsten filaments and in valves in the form of anodes, supports and grids. Because of its ductility molybdenum wire is particularly suitable for the manufacture of very fine grids.

Furnaces heated by molybdenum windings or elements are widely used for operation at temperatures up to about 1700°C. The elements must be protected, of course, and they are usually operated under an atmosphere of hydrogen or cracked ammonia. Molybdenum sheet is often used as radiation shields in vacuum furnaces, and molybdenum bars are used as electrodes in some glass-melting furnaces.

TANTALUM

Consolidation and Fabrication

The melting point of tantalum (2996°C) lies between those of molybdenum and tungsten. The properties of tantalum, however, differ in many respects from the two other refractory metals so far discussed. Tantalum oxide is not reduced by hydrogen and the metal easily forms a hydride on heating in hydrogen so that vacuum sintering is essential. Ductility is so good that the ingot may be cold worked immediately after sintering.

Details of commercial practice in the preparation of primary forms in

16

tantalum have been given by Pochon[7] and by Schussler *et al.*[8] Powders to be sintered are carefully selected to give the best carbon:oxygen ratio to ensure maximum elimination of these elements on sintering. Powders prepared by hydriding contain hydrogen which is also eliminated on sintering. Tantalum powders are pressed into bars at pressures of about 30 tons/in², the bars being sintered by direct resistance or in tungsten resistor furnaces at temperatures of 2400–2600°C under a vacuum of about 10^{-4} torr. Various outgassing stages are observed during sintering: hydrogen and water vapour are evolved between 400 and 600°C; the carbon–oxygen reaction proceeds over the range 1400–1600°C; at 2000–2200°C excess tantalum oxide is volatilized; and the nitride decomposes above 2300°C. Temperature is held relatively constant during each stage to ensure complete elimination of each impurity. The final sintering temperature is held for about three hours.

After this first sintering the unsintered ends are cropped and the bar cold worked by rolling or hammering. This is followed by a further sintering treatment at 2000–2500°C for 3 hours, and final densities substantially equal to theoretical (16·6 g/cm³) are obtained.

Bars are then cold-worked by swaging, rolling, drawing, etc. to the desired forms. Hot-working is undesirable owing to oxygen pick-up which causes hardening and embrittlement. Tantalum does not work harden rapidly, but when intermediate annealing operations are necessary these are conducted under a vacuum of about 10^{-3} torr at 1200–1260°C. Annealed tantalum sheet may be satisfactorily spun or deep drawn at room temperature using standard techniques. Unlike tungsten and molybdenum, tantalum is not embrittled by recrystallization so that this is not a problem in welding. However, tantalum is embrittled by interstitials, such as oxygen and nitrogen, which it rapidly absorbs, unless precautions are taken to avoid their presence in the welding atmosphere. Heli-arc welding is said to be superior to argon-arc because of the lower nitrogen content of helium. Tantalum has also been successfully welded by carbon-arc under carbon tetrachloride, and by spot and seam welding under water.

Properties and Applications

Most of the present applications of tantalum are a result of its excellent corrosion resistance rather than its high melting point. Tantalum is one of the most versatile of corrosion-resistant materials and Stern and Bishop[9] list over one hundred environments that are reported to have little or no corrosive effect on the metal. Among the few corrosive media which do attack tantalum are environments containing fluorides, strong alkalis, fuming sulphur trioxide and concentrated sulphuric and phosphoric acids at high temperatures. Accordingly tantalum is widely applied in the chemical industry. Because its ductility permits rolling to thin sheet and fabrication into complex shapes its greatest single use in this field is in the form of heaters, heat exchangers and condensers.

Electronics is the other important field of application for tantalum, where it is widely used in capacitors, valves and tubes. The use of the metal in capacitors is due to the very thin and stable oxide film (dielectric) which may be developed on it and the fact that very thin foil (0·0005 in.) may be obtained by cold rolling. Because of its high melting point, low vapour pressure, good gettering properties and fabricability, tantalum is widely used in electronic valves and tubes as cathodes, grids and supports.

Tantalum like tungsten and molybdenum has poor oxidation resistance, but it finds application at elevated temperatures in vacuum furnaces where it is used as supports, resistors, heat shields and susceptors.

Because of its chemical inertness, strength and tissue acceptability, tantalum has become recognized as one of the most desirable materials for body implants and is widely used in surgery.

A good review of the various applications of tantalum is provided by Buttner, Bacon and Bancroft.[10]

NIOBIUM (COLUMBIUM)

Niobium is very similar to tantalum in most respects (chemical behaviour, valency, ionic radius, etc.) and the metals are always found together in nature. The production of niobium wire, rod and sheet from powder follows exactly the techniques used for tantalum, but because of its lower melting point (2468°C) niobium requires lower sintering temperatures. As with tantalum it is necessary to hold the temperature constant at various stages to allow the removal of impurities. The final sintering temperature of 2300°C is held for 3–4 hours. After a cold reduction of about 20% the bar is re-sintered and then, like tantalum, may be cold worked by standard techniques.

Although niobium has excellent resistance to corrosion it is generally considered to be somewhat inferior to tantalum in this respect and has not, as yet, been widely used in the chemical industry.

Because of its fabricability, strength and low capture cross-section for neutron absorption, niobium is used as a nuclear-fuel cladding material, for example, in the Dounreay fast reactor.[11]

Niobium is also used in the electronics industry, but only to a limited extent. It is sometimes preferred to tantalum for various parts in electronic tubes, usually because of its superior welding properties. Niobium becomes superconducting at a higher temperature (9·1°K) than any other element, while the compound Nb_3Sn (which may be prepared by powder metallurgy) becomes superconducting at 18·0°K. Wires of these materials are finding increasing application in the various devices that are being developed to take advantage of this remarkable phenomenon.

OTHER REFRACTORY METALS

Small amounts of the so-called refractory noble metals, rhenium, rhodium, iridium, ruthenium, platinum, palladium and osmium are prepared by powder metallurgy, although for platinum, the most widely used of this group, melting techniques are usually employed. Details of consolidation and fabrication techniques are given by Jaffee, Maykuth and Douglass.[12] After sintering, the metals may be fabricated by hot and cold working, except for rhenium which is hot-short and may only be cold worked and osmium which is completely unworkable.

Refractory Metals as High-Temperature Structural Materials

There is a rapidly increasing demand, particularly in the missile and aircraft industries, for materials to operate under stress at higher and higher temperatures. The nickel- and cobalt-base 'superalloys' appear to be nearing the limit of their development, and for operation at temperatures above about 1100°C, under oxidizing conditions, new creep-resistant materials are required. The inherent brittleness of ceramics and the failure of high-temperature cermets to live up to early expectations have forced the materials technologist to look at the refractory metals, despite their lack of oxidation resistance. Early attempts to overcome this problem by alloying and coating were not particularly successful, but more promising results are now being obtained. Owing to its low density (8.57 g/cm^3) niobium shows most promise on a strength-to-weight basis. It seems likely that, to succeed in this field, a refractory metal will need a coating to give oxidation resistance and alloying to give optimum creep resistance (and to prevent catastrophic oxidation should the coating fail).

Because of the accent on alloying most of the developments in this field have been based on materials prepared by fusion. However, dispersion-strengthening techniques also look promising so that powder metallurgy may still have a part to play.

REFERENCES

1. Coolidge, W. D. *J. Amer. Inst. elect. Engrs.*, **29**, 953 (1909).
2. Wong, J., Christopher, S. S. and Worcester, Jr., S. A. in *Refractory Metals and Alloys II*, Semchyshen and Perlmutter (eds.), 351, Interscience, New York (1963).
3. Jones, D. J. *J. Less Common Met.*, **2** (2), 76 (1960).
4. Brophy, J. H., Shepard, L. A. and Wulff, J. in *Powder Metallurgy*, Leszynski (ed.), 113, Interscience, New York (1961).
5. Jones, F. O. in *Niobium, Tantalum, Molybdenum and Tungsten*, Quarrell (ed.), 66, Elsvier, Amsterdam (1961).

6. Smithells, C. J. *Tungsten*, Chapman and Hall, London (1952).
7. Pochon, M. L. in *Columbium and Tantalum*, Sisco and Epremian (eds.), 72, John Wiley, New York (1963).
8. Schussler, M., Mincher, A. L., Wilson, J. L. and Dufendash, H. E. ibid., 132.
9. Stern, M. and Bishop, C. R. ibid., 304.
10. Buttner, F. H., Bacon, F. E. and Bancroft, R. K. ibid., 560.
11. *Symposium on the Dounreay Fast Reactor*, Institution of Mechanical Engineers, London (1960).
12. Jaffee, R. I., Maykuth, D. J. and Douglass, R. W. in *Refractory Metals and Alloys*, Semchyshen and Harwood (eds.), 383, Interscience, New York (1961).

CHAPTER 12

MISCELLANEOUS APPLICATIONS OF POWDER METALLURGY

The ability of powder metallurgy to produce controlled, and sometimes unique structures, to compete economically with other forming processes, to provide materials with special properties or to fabricate materials that are difficult or impossible to fabricate by more conventional techniques, has led to its widespread use in many fields. The principal present-day fields of application have been discussed in previous chapters, but the techniques of powder metallurgy are constantly being used to solve new problems. This is particularly true in the aircraft, space and nuclear fields where there is a virtually insatiable demand for new materials with special properties.

HIGH-TEMPERATURE MATERIALS

Since World War II, the amount of effort expended on the development of materials capable of operating under stress at elevated temperatures has been phenomenal. Much of this development has been due to the ever increasing demand for improved efficiency in the aircraft gas-turbine, which is most readily achieved by the use of higher operating temperatures. The rotating turbine blades are the most highly stressed of the very high-temperature components and a material for this application has heavy demands placed upon it: the creep life must be adequate (and predictable) under the stress-temperature conditions prevailing in the turbine and there must be adequate resistance to failure by oxidation, corrosion, fatigue, impact and thermal shock. Impact resistance is particularly important, because with a brittle blade material the entry of a foreign body or the failure of a single blade could be disastrous (failure of a high proportion of the blading could occur).

The demands of the gas turbine have led to the development of many nickel- and cobalt-base 'superalloys' and these materials have also found widespread use in fields outside the aircraft industry but, as is often the case the turbine designer is ahead of the materials technologist and the super-alloys appear to be nearing the limit of their development. Improvements in the nickel- and cobalt-base alloys have been brought about by increased alloying to improve solid-solution- and precipitation-strengthening effects. In general this has tended to lower the melting temperature of the alloy, thus the maximum operating temperatures have been getting closer to this obvious upper limit, while the range of forgeability has tended to become diminishingly small. Much work has been carried out in attempts to overcome the deficiencies of the superalloys by developing materials that are mixtures of metal and ceramic components prepared by the techniques of powder metallurgy. Thus far the superalloys have kept ahead of this competition by constant development.

Sintered Superalloys

Some advantage is to be obtained by the use of powder metallurgy techniques in the fabrication of superalloys. Because of their high-temperature 'stiffness' these alloys are inherently difficult to forge, while the casting techniques do not allow close control of structure. Powder metallurgy does not suffer from either of these problems. Early attempts[1, 2] to sinter cobalt-base alloys from elemental and master-alloy powders were not entirely successful, although showing some promise. Not until suitable atomization techniques[3] were available for the production of completely pre-alloyed powders was it possible to produce sintered superalloys with properties similar to the wrought material. Poyner, Tracey and Watkinson[4] using pre-alloyed nickel-base powders, of the Nimonic 90* and 100 types, and closely controlled vacuum sintering, were able to produce materials which compared favourably with the corresponding wrought product in terms of stress-to-rupture and thermal-shock properties, but were somewhat inferior in terms of ductility, fatigue and impact properties. Small additions of zirconium and boron were shown to have a pronounced effect on stress-to-rupture and also to improve significantly the ductility, fatigue and impact properties. These workers attributed the properties of the sintered material to the presence of small amounts of alumina at the grain boundaries which maintained a fine, uniform and very stable grain size, although it seems likely that some degree of dispersion strengthening due to an internal oxidation mechanism (see later) also occurred.

The hot working of a pre-form prepared from powders has also shown

* Nimonic 90 and Nimonic 100 are trade names of Henry Wiggin & Co. Ltd.

promise as a method of fabricating superalloys. One advantage of this method is that it avoids the necessity for a critically controlled sintering cycle.

Cermets

That the superalloys based on nickel and cobalt would be limited in terms of maximum operating temperature was obvious, although the extent of their development has been greater than most would have prophesied. Much work has been carried out on the development of materials eventually to replace the superalloys and it was equally obvious that these should be based on materials with high melting points. Two types of material immediately suggested themselves, the refractory metals and ceramics, i.e. oxides, carbides, nitrides, etc. The refractory metals display little or no oxidation resistance but even so a considerable development effort has been expended upon them in terms of alloying and coating protection. The main reason for this has been the failure of materials based on ceramics to live up to early expectations. Many ceramics have excellent oxidation resistance and it was thought that this could be combined with the ductility of a metal (using techniques similar to those employed in the hard-metal field) to provide a material (cermet) of adequate high-temperature strength and impact resistance. Unfortunately this has not proved to be the case and the early hopes have been largely frustrated; strength and oxidation resistance have proved relatively easy to achieve but to combine this with adequate impact resistance has so far proved impossible. In general two types of cermet have found some application as high-temperature materials (though not, as yet, as turbine blades); these are titanium carbide bonded with nickel- or cobalt-base alloys and alumina bonded with chromium, tungsten or molybdenum or alloys of these metals.

Of the cemented carbide-type materials only those based on titanium carbide have shown promise as materials for applications under stress at high temperatures. Many such materials have been developed with nickel or nickel-alloy binders and a few with cobalt-alloy binders; binder contents between 30% and 75% have been used. The higher binder contents give improved impact properties, but the stress-rupture properties generally decrease rapidly with increasing binder content above about 50%. Alloy additions to the binder, giving solid-solution-or precipitation-strengthening effects, lead to increase in creep properties but the impact properties are impaired.

Wambold[5] has reviewed the properties of a number of nickel-alloy-bonded titanium carbide cermets, while Goetzel[6] gives data on nickel-alloy- and cobalt-alloy-bonded materials produced by the infiltration technique. Both authors show that 100-hour stress-to-rupture figures of about 12 tons/in² at 980°C are obtainable in titanium-carbide cermets. However, it is apparent that impact strengths are limited to about a third of the values attained by the superalloys.

Many oxide-metal type cermets have been investigated but materials based on alumina (Al_2O_3) have shown most promise. Chromium or its alloys has achieved most success as the metal component of alumina-based cermets, owing to the good bonding that may be achieved. This strong bond is apparently due to the formation of a solid solution between the alumina and the tightly adhering oxide film (Cr_2O_3) on the chromium-rich component.

Alumina cermets are not prepared by liquid-phase sintering as are the carbide materials, and in fact few metals would adequately wet the oxide; instead the milled oxide-metal mixture is pressed, or slip cast, and sintered in dry hydrogen at about 1550°C. There is usually sufficient oxide on the chromium particles to ensure good bonding, but in some cases a 'wet' hydrogen atmosphere may be necessary in order to achieve the desired thickness of chromium-oxide film. According to Shevlin[7] a Cr_2O_3 content of 3–7% in the alumina is desirable.

Several variations on the basic chromium-alumina material have been developed. For example, an 80% chromium–20% molybdenum alloy has been used instead of chromium; not only does this raise the high-temperature strength but the thermal-expansion coefficient of the alloy is more closely matched to that of alumina so that better thermal-shock resistance is obtained. The addition of some titania (TiO_2) to the alumina is also said to improve high-temperature properties. Marshall[8] quotes a modulus of rupture of 11,800 lb/in² at 1320°C for a $Cr–Mo–Al_2O_3–TiO_2$ composition, compared with 4,600 lb/in² for a $Cr–Al_2O_3$ material. If most, or all, of the chromium is replaced by tungsten or molybdenum excellent high-temperature strength is obtained (e.g. modulus of rupture at 1320°C of 25,000 lb/in² for a $W–Cr–Al_2O_3$ composition[8]) though at the expense of oxidation resistance.

Although cermets have thus far not been applied as turbine blades their properties, such as oxidation and corrosion resistance, good thermal shock resistance and adequate high-temperature strength, have led to their use in a number of somewhat less exotic applications. In the foundry the oxide-based cermets are gaining popularity as pyrometer sheaths, pouring spouts and flow-control valves. The carbide grades have found application where there is a demand for wear resistance and high-temperature strength combined with thermal-shock resistance. Typical applications include high-temperature bearings, mechanical seals and valve seats.

Dispersion-Strengthened Materials

Although the cermets have not lived up to early hopes as high-temperature materials, new materials are showing great promise in which a smaller addition (up to 15% by weight) of a very fine dispersion of a refractory compound is made to a metal. It has long been recognized that a dispersion of a hard second phase in a pure metal or alloy matrix produces a significant strengthening effect; this in fact occurs in steel wherein the strengthening effect is obtained from a dispersion of cementite.

The fact that fine eutectic or eutectoid structures are stronger than coarse ones is well known. Orowan[9] was one of the first to consider the effect of interparticle spacing using dislocation theory. He suggested that a dislocation line, on meeting a row of dispersed hard particles, will tend to bow out between them, finally connecting beyond the particles and leaving a dislocation loop around each particle. The stress required to bow out a dislocation is inversely proportional to the radius of curvature of the bow, and this stress therefore reaches a maximum when the bow is a semicircle of radius $d/2$, where d is the interparticle spacing. The yield strength of a dispersion-strengthened material is thus inversely proportional to the interparticle spacing. For a given volume percentage of hard-phase, the interparticle spacing is proportional to the particle size of the hard phase which, therefore, should be as fine as possible for maximum effect. An increase in the volume percentage of the second phase will also decrease the interparticle spacing (particle size remaining constant), but in general this results in a loss in ductility.

Conventionally, dispersions of a second phase are produced by a liquid or solid-state reaction, for example, eutectic or eutectoid reactions, or precipitation from a solid solution. In the precipitation-hardened alloys the effective interparticle spacing is decreased by the stress fields due to coherency between particle and matrix. Dispersions produced by precipitation or solid-state reaction suffer from the disadvantage that with increasing temperature their solubility in the matrix leads to agglomeration, an increase in interparticle spacing and drastic reduction in the strengthening effect (overageing). Thus, for high-temperature stability, it is essential that the dispersed phase exhibits negligible solubility in the matrix.

Phases which exhibit negligible solubility in the solid state may be soluble in the liquid state. An example is found in the aluminium–iron system where the maximum solid solubility of $FeAl_2$ (θ) is only 0.03%. However, it is impossible to obtain a suitable dispersion of this phase in an aluminium matrix by conventional casting and working techniques. In fact the problem has been solved by powder metallurgy; by atomizing an aluminium–iron alloy a very fine dispersion of $FeAl_2$ is obtained in the particles and this dispersion is maintained when the powder is consolidated by extrusion.

Many of the hard, inert phases which are desirable for dispersion strengthening are, however, insoluble in both solid and liquid metals, so that powder metallurgy is almost essential for the fabrication of materials containing these phases.

Many dispersed-phase systems have been investigated and of the dispersed hard phases used the stable oxides appear to be the most popular, because of their very low solubility in most metals. Many carbides, nitrides, silicides, borides and other intermetallics have also been studied.

The first successful dispersion-strengthened material to be prepared by powder metallurgy was sintered aluminium powder (S.A.P.) where the hard phase is the naturally occurring oxide on the aluminium particles. S.A.P. was discovered accidentally by the laboratories of Aluminium-Industrie—A.G. in Switzerland. Accounts of the development of this material have been given by Irmann[10] and more recently by Bloch and Hug.[11] The production of S.A.P. is critically dependent upon the milling process in which flake aluminium is treated in a Hametag-type mill under controlled oxidizing conditions with small additions of lubricant. The natural oxide film on aluminium is about 100 Å thick, and during milling fresh surfaces are exposed and oxidized while welding and entrappment of oxide within particles also occurs. Thus, a relatively coarse aluminium powder (about 100 μ) is produced in which each particle contains a fine dispersion of oxide. This powder is cold compacted, wrapped in aluminium sheet and sintered at about 500°C in air. Little shrinkage or increase in strength occurs during this process, but it seems that dehydration of the oxide takes place. Billets are subsequently hot pressed and hot extruded. Several grades of S.A.P. with oxide contents up to 13% are commercially produced. Bars of the higher oxide-content materials may only be further shaped by hot working or machining, but S.A.P.'s containing 10% oxide or less may also be cold worked, the severity of the operation depending on the oxide content. Sheet material is produced by extruding slabs which are subsequently hot or cold rolled to plate and sheet.

The most remarkable features of S.A.P. are its retention of properties and stability at elevated temperatures. For example a S.A.P. with 13% oxide has a tensile strength of about 7 tons/in² at 500°C, even after soaking for one month at this temperature. Under such conditions the best of the conventional aluminium alloys have strengths of only 1–1·5 tons/in². In fact, because the precipitation-hardened aluminium alloys rapidly overage at temperatures above about 200°C, S.A.P. is superior at all temperatures above this. Even at the melting point of aluminium, S.A.P. parts will retain their general form and become only pasty, but such a treatment destroys most of the strength properties. Because melting destroys the properties, the joining of S.A.P. presents some problems. Since fusion welding cannot be used it is necessary to employ solid-state-bonding techniques, such as hot or cold pressure welding, hammer welding or spot welding. Flash-butt welding, in which the molten and softened material produced by the arc is squeezed out by the subsequently applied pressure, is also suitable, while friction welding is very useful for rods and tubes. The fabrication of S.A.P. sheet into complex assemblies, however, is best achieved mechanically using S.A.P. rivets.

Because of its remarkable properties S.A.P. has found various applications in the aircraft and other industries where there are requirements for light-weight materials to operate at 200–500°C.

The success of S.A.P. has led to much investigation of other dispersion-strengthened systems. An excellent review of the preparation and properties of various dispersion-strengthened materials has been given by Smith.[12] Unfortunately, unlike aluminium most metals do not form an extremely stable, thin oxide film with very low solubility in the matrix, so that in most instances it is necessary to introduce the stable oxide of another metal. Various methods have been used to achieve this aim. Direct mixing is the simplest approach and usually the most economically feasible. However, in order to achieve a satisfactory dispersion by simple mechanical mixing of the two phases it is necessary that both powders should be extremely fine. Oxides, being brittle, are easily comminuted to sub-micron sizes, but metal powders are not usually easy to obtain in such fine size ranges. The ball milling of metal powders to very fine sizes and the use of surface active agents to prevent welding have been discussed in Chapter 2. Having obtained the two powders in the required size range it is necessary to blend them. Perfect distribution is extremely difficult to achieve by mechanical blending and dispersion-strengthened materials prepared by this method tend to contain oxide agglomerates.

A better distribution of oxide may be obtained by using a solution of a nitrate, acetate or similar salt which will yield the oxide on subsequent heating. It is usual to add the metal powder to the solution, with continuous stirring, to form a slurry which is subsequently dried carefully. Conversion to oxide occurs during the sintering operation.

Where the oxide of the matrix metal is easily reduced in hydrogen it is often convenient to form an intimate mixture of the two oxides and then to reduce the less stable one. An intimate mixture of oxides may be produced by co-precipitation of, for example, hydroxides which are subsequently converted to oxide on heating. Alternatively, a solution of the nitrate of one metal may be mixed with fine oxide of the other.

A technique that has received much attention in recent years is internal oxidation. This method relies on the fact that a metal contained in dilute solid solution in a more noble metal will be preferentially oxidized by oxygen diffusing through the lattice. By careful control of the oxidizing conditions a fine dispersion of the solute metal oxide is obtained. The rate of oxide formation is governed by the rate of oxygen diffusion through the lattice, so that for solid metals the technique is limited to thin sections, such as strip and wire, which may be internally oxidized in reasonable times. Further, there is a tendency for the oxide particles to become coarser with increasing distance from the surface. In order to prepare larger sections with an adequate oxide distribution in economic times it is therefore necessary to start with powdered alloys. When powders are used several oxidation techniques are possible. The powder may be heated under controlled conditions before compaction, or a low-temperature 'scaling' treatment may be used to put an oxide film on each particle, the oxygen being diffused in by heating under an inert atmosphere, either before compaction or during sintering. A third possibility is to mix the oxide of the matrix metal with the alloy powder to provide an oxygen source during sintering.

It seems that in order to obtain useful properties from dispersion-strengthened materials produced by powder metallurgy, consolidation by hot working after sintering is essential. Hot extrusion is most convenient and gives the best results.

Many dispersion-strengthened materials have been investigated, including lead, tin, silver, copper, nickel, nickel–chromium alloys, iron, stainless steels and various refractory metals. The stable oxides such as alumina, silica, magnesia or thoria usually provide the dispersed phase. There is a vast amount of information in the literature and the reader's attention is directed particularly to a recent symposium on the subject.[13]

One material, in addition to S.A.P., to have found industrial application is a 2% thoria-strengthened nickel (T.D. Nickel*). This material is produced by depositing on to fine thoria particles nickel-oxide which is subsequently reduced to nickel. The product is converted to rod, wire and sheet, by powder metallurgy and conventional working techniques. An extremely fine and uniform distribution of thoria is obtained (Plate 20).

The room-temperature properties of T.D. Nickel although much superior to pure wrought nickel are not outstanding, but the properties at elevated temperatures are remarkable and, as Fig. 67 shows, the creep properties of T.D. Nickel are increasingly superior to those of the conventional superalloys at temperatures above about 1000°C. Because of its high resistance to recovery and recrystallization T.D. Nickel retains the effects of cold work up to about 1150°C.

Fibre-Strengthened Materials

It is well known that small diameter fibres and, in particular, single crystal whiskers, can possess strength properties far in excess of those displayed by the same material in bulk form. It is recognized, however, that these properties are not directly due to the size of the fibres, but are a second-order effect resulting from the absence or near absence of lattice defects and, particularly, surface flaws. For some years high-strength fibres have been used to reinforce a weaker matrix in the field of glass-fibre reinforced plastics

---

* T.D. Nickel is a trade mark of E. I. du Pont de Nemours & Co. (Inc.).

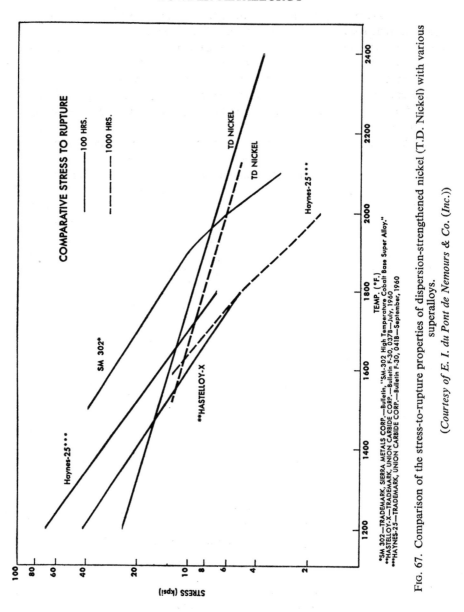

FIG. 67. Comparison of the stress-to-rupture properties of dispersion-strengthened nickel (T.D. Nickel) with various superalloys.

(*Courtesy of E. I. du Pont de Nemours & Co. (Inc.)*)

and it is natural that the principle should be extended to metals with a view to improving high-temperature strength properties. Much work has been carried out in the United States in this field and progress up to 1961 has been reviewed by Machlin.[14] Several workers have studied model systems such as tungsten fibres in copper[15] and stainless-steel fibres in aluminium[16] and have concluded that strength is directly proportional to fibre content. It is generally assumed that the relatively soft and ductile metal matrix acts to transfer load between fibres by shear forces at the interface. The strengthening effect increases with increasing aspect ratio, i.e. the ratio of fibre length to fibre diameter. Maximum strength is obtained when all the fibres are orientated in the direction of stress. The use of ceramic whiskers is very attractive because of their very high strength. Sutton and Chorne[17] prepared composites of alumina whiskers in silver and compared them with silver dispersion-strengthened with alumina particles by internal oxidation. They found that, whereas the whisker reinforced material had slightly lower strength than the dispersion-strengthened material at room temperature, it became increasingly superior at temperatures above 370°C.

Various methods may be used to incorporate fibres in a metal matrix; for example, a 'felt' of fibres may be infiltrated with molten matrix metal. For large-scale production, however, mixing the fibres with metal powders and consolidating by the techniques of powder metallurgy would appear to offer the widest scope. A technique described by Cratchley and Baker[18] in which silica fibres are coated with aluminium and then consolidated by hot pressing has produced material with a strength of about 70 tons/in² at room temperature.

BERYLLIUM

The metal beryllium has been the subject of many major researches over the last 15 years. The interest in this metal has stemmed from its remarkable combination of properties, in particular its rigidity/weight ratio (specific stiffness), low capture cross-section for neutron absorption, corrosion resistance and melting point. The suitability of beryllium for two fields of application, canning of nuclear fuel elements and structural applications in aerospace vehicles, has been widely explored.

Table 34. Thermal Neutron-Absorption Cross-Section

Metal	Microscopic absorption cross-section (barns/atom)
Beryllium	0·010
Magnesium	0·059
Zirconium	0·180
Aluminium	0·215
Niobium	1·1
Iron	2·43
Chromium	2·9
Nickel	4·5

The interest in beryllium as a fuel-canning material for nuclear reactors arises mainly from its exceptionally low thermal neutron-absorption cross-section. Table 34[19] compares the absorption cross-section of beryllium with other metals.

In addition to low capture cross-section, beryllium also has good elevated temperature strength that makes it attractive for gas-cooled reactors.

The origin of the potential application of beryllium in aero-space vehicles is its unusually high specific stiffness. The specific stiffness of beryllium is compared with values for some other metals and compounds in Table 35.

Table 35. Specific Stiffness of Various Materials

	Density ρ (g/cm³)	Elastic modulus E (10⁶ lb/in²)	$\frac{E}{\rho} \cdot 10^6$
Magnesium	1·7	6	3·6
Beryllium	1·8	44	24
Aluminium	2·7	10·5	3·9
Titanium	4·5	17	3·8
Iron	7·8	30	3·8
Molybdenum	10·5	40	3·9
Silicon carbide	3·2	80	25
Silicon nitride	3·2	55	17
Aluminium nitride	3·3	50	15
Carbon whiskers	2·3	140	61

Owing to the very high value of specific stiffness, the use of beryllium for the load-carrying struts of aircraft could decrease the structural weight to less than a half that necessary with conventional materials.

Despite apparently compelling advantages, beryllium has not yet found commercial use in either of the fields cited. Essentially this is due to its extreme brittleness. There are, in fact, two forms of brittleness in beryllium; that which occurs at temperatures below 200°C and that found between 200–600°C. It is now well established that the embrittlement found in the 200–600°C temperature range is due to impurities, particularly iron, and can be overcome either by overall purification or by heat treatment. Neither purification nor heat treatment has, however, succeeded in alleviating the low-temperature (<200°C) brittleness. It appears that this low-temperature brittleness is due to the restricted number of deformation modes which operate in the hexagonal close-packed beryllium structure. The practical consequence of this is that any fabrication process which produces either a coarse-grained structure or one which has preferred orientation of the grains will give a material which will be brittle when subjected to tri-axial stresses.

The most successful approach to obtaining fine-grain, randomly-orientated beryllium has, so far, been by powder metallurgy. Beryllium powder is produced by machining vacuum-melted ingots, the machining swarf and chippings being then ball-milled to powder. Since beryllium dusts are highly toxic, machining and milling have to be carried out in enclosed working spaces. Controlled atmospheres are needed to prevent excessive oxidation.

The consolidation of beryllium powder is most usually achieved by hot pressing, although high-density material has been produced by sintering. Hausner and Pinto[20] have shown that vacuum sintering at about 1200°C gives a low porosity product, while Martin and Ellis[21] have shown the relationship between powder properties and sintering behaviour. Martin, Knight and Ellis[22] also showed that hollow shapes could be produced by loose sintering. The hot pressing of beryllium powders is carried out *in vacuo* at 800–1050°C using pressures of 100–1,500 lb/in^2, graphite dies being normally employed. The hot pressing of beryllium is notable for the large sizes that have been produced, e.g. billets up to 72 in. diameter and weighing up to 1 ton have been produced in the U.S.A.

Where tri-axial ductility is required it is necessary to machine components directly from the hot-pressed billet. This approach has been adopted for various experimental space-vehicle components. It has been established that further working of hot-pressed billets, by forging, extrusion or rolling for instance, rapidly develops preferred orientation with consequent brittleness in two directions.

At the present time it is believed that the low-temperature brittleness of beryllium is an inherent property. It therefore appears that if beryllium is to be exploited commercially it will most likely have to be produced by powder metallurgy.

ATOMIC ENERGY APPLICATIONS

In the development of nuclear power reactors a whole new field of materials has been required. In this development, powder metallurgy has played a significant role. Indeed, a very large proportion of the powder metallurgy research which has been carried out over the past twenty years, has been stimulated by the needs of nuclear engineering. This work has not been confined to establishing new materials, but also to developing new processes for consolidating powders.

Much of the powder-technology research for nuclear engineering has been concerned with ceramics and thus falls outside the scope of this book. The development of entirely metallic systems, such as niobium and beryllium, particularly for fuel canning, is related to the processes used to produce such metals for other applications and has been covered elsewhere in this book. There has also been a demand from nuclear engineering for a unique range of

17

composite materials. These are applied in various fuel elements and control-rod systems. In the fuel-element applications the metallic phase is generally continuous and is required to provide the strength and structural integrity of the element during burn-up. Often these are very searching requirements, since the dimensional changes and release of fission gases which occur during burn-up impose high stresses on the metallic matrix. Similarly, in composite control-rod materials, it is the metallic phase that provides the essential strength of the body.

In these composite bodies the proportion of the metallic phase is usually between 50 and 90 volume %. The exact composition is determined by reconciliation of the conflicting needs for the highest possible content of the active (non-metallic) phase necessary for utilization of the available volume, and the strength considerations that require maximum metallic content. The maximum volume fraction of active material which can be incorporated is dependent to a large extent upon particle shape and upon the way it is distributed. Particle size is also important because, for a given volume fraction and particle shape, it controls the thickness of the metallic web between the non-metallic particles. The importance of web thickness is that when radiation damage occurs the properties of a certain thickness of metal surrounding the particles are altered and this portion of the metal phase may no longer be able to provide adequate ductility.

It is also necessary that the composite bodies are of high density. Not only is this a prerequisite for maximum strength and volume efficiency, but also because the metallic phase is required to conduct heat to the fuel can.

There has thus been a series of processes developed by which composite materials of critically controlled characteristics can be produced. These processes include (i) the production of materials, such as fissile oxides and carbides, rare-earth oxides, etc., as high-density powders of closely controlled size and frequently having a spherical form; (ii) techniques for coating these or mixing them with metal powder in order to produce homogeneous dispersions; and (iii) techniques for consolidating the mixed powder into high-density bodies often of a form, such as a long rod, which is considered difficult to achieve in more conventional powder-metallurgy fields.

Probably the most intensively studied systems are the various cermet fuels based on uranium dioxide or uranium–plutonium oxide. The most usual metallic matrix is an austenitic stainless steel, although refractory metals have also been studied. Cope[23] has described a refined method, involving die-compacting, sintering and multiple coining, for producing 50 volume % cermets of less than 4% porosity. The details of the process had to be carefully balanced to produce maximum density without fracturing the oxide particles. A similar material was produced by Menny et al.[24] by a route involving hot extrusion. Cunningham et al.,[25] who produced material with a higher fissile oxide content by hot pressing, noted the great promise of the gas-pressure bonding technique for this type of material. Similar cermets with smaller oxide contents have also been fabricated by hot rolling, although heavy reductions, which may be necessary to achieve high density, may fracture the oxide particles; working in one plane also destroys the distribution uniformity. A similar range of techniques has been necessary for other cermet fuel-element materials.

A wide range of critically controlled techniques has been applied also to control rod materials. In these the dispersant has a high neutron absorption, the most usual materials being boron compounds or some of the rare-earth oxides. Again stainless steel is frequently chosen for the matrix.

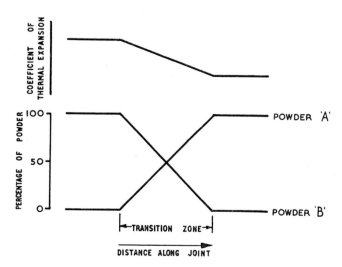

FIG. 68. Method of mixing two powders to obtain a smooth transition in coefficient of thermal expansion.

TRANSITION JOINTS

In industry there are many applications which involve the joining together of materials having widely differing coefficients of thermal expansion. Where the joining is accomplished at elevated temperatures, stresses are set up at the interface on cooling. Unless one of the members (or a filler material) is sufficiently ductile to relieve the stresses by plastic deformation, cracking may occur. Where the joint is subject to thermal cycling failure by fatigue is possible.

One way of reducing the stresses in a joint of this type is to arrange a gradual change or 'transition' in thermal-expansion coefficient between the two members being joined. This involves interposing between the two members a component with a gradual transition in thermal-expansion coefficient from one face to the other. A method of producing such a 'transition joint' by powder-metallurgy techniques has been proposed by Zimmer.[26] Powders are prepared (usually by atomization) having the expansion coefficients of the two members being joined; the powders must be compatible with each other when sintered together and must be readily joined to the two members. The transition joint is then prepared by arranging, between outer layers of the 'straight' powders, graduated mixtures of the two powders so as to give a gradual change in composition, and, hence, in thermal-expansion coefficient (Fig. 68). The joint is then pressed and sintered, and often further worked.

Such joints, which may be prepared in all manner of forms, such as bar, tube and plate, have many possible fields of application. One possible application, the joining of large carbide tips to shanks, was mentioned in Chapter 6. The electrical generating industry also has many instances where austenitic steels (expansion coefficient $\sim 18 \times 10^{-6}$) must be joined to ferritic steels (expansion coefficient $\sim 14 \times 10^{-6}$). Many instances also occur in the nuclear and 'space' fields where cermets, ceramics or refractory metals must be joined to metals of much higher thermal-expansion coefficient.

REFERENCES

1. Buswell, R. W. A., Pitkin, W. R. and Jenkins, I. in *High Temperature Steels and Alloys for Gas Turbines, Iron and Steel Inst. Special Rept. No. 43*, 258 (1952).
2. Harris, G. T. and Child, H. C. Symposium on Powder Metallurgy, 1954 (*Special Rept. No. 58*), 257, 1956; London (Iron and Steel Institute).
3. Watkinson, J. F. *Powder Metallurgy*, No. 1/2, 13 (1958).
4. Poyner, G. T., Tracey, V. A. and Watkinson, J. F. in *Powder Metallurgy*, Leszynski (ed.), 701, Interscience, New York (1961).
5. Wambold, J. in *Cermets*, Tinklepaugh and Crandall (eds.), 122, Reinhold, New York (1960).
6. Goetzel, C. G., ibid., 130.
7. Shevlin, T. S., ibid., 97.
8. Marshall, C. L., ibid., 109.
9. Orowan, E. *Symposium on Internal Stresses in Metals and Alloys*, Inst. Metals, 451 (1948).
10. Irmann, R. Symposium on Powder Metallurgy, 1954 (*Special Rept. No. 58*), 236, 1956; London (Iron and Steel Institute).
11. Bloch, E. A. and Hug, H. in *Powder Metallurgy*, Leszynski (ed.) 371, Interscience, New York (1961).
12. Smith, G. C. *Powder Metallurgy*, No. 11, 102 (1963).
13. *Symposium on Non-Metallic Dispersions in Powder Metallurgy, Powder Metallurgy*, No. 10 (1962).
14. Machlin, E. S. *Materials Research Corporation*, Contract NOW 61–0209C, 1961, AD–265943.

15. McDanels, D. L., Jech, R. W. and Weeton, J. W. *N.A.S.A. Technical Note*, N.A.S.A. TN D–1881.
16. Cratchley, D. *Powder Metallurgy*, No. 11, 59 (1963).
17. Sutton, W. H. and Chorne, J. *Metals Engng. Quart.*, 3, 1, 44 (Feb., 1963).
18. Cratchley, D. and Baker, A. A. *Metallurgia*, 69, 414, 153 (April, 1964).
19. Bold, M. *Nuclear Engineering*, 296 (July, 1958).
20. Hausner, H. H. and Pinto, N. P. *Trans. A.S.M.*, 43, 1052 (1951).
21. Martin, A. J. and Ellis, G. C. *Powder Metallurgy*, No. 7, 120 (1961).
22. Martin, A. J., Knight, R. A. and Ellis, G. C., ibid., 268.
23. Cope, L. H. *Metallurgia*, 59 (Aug., 1964).
24. Menny, L., Buffet, J. and Bauve, Ch. *Powder Metallurgy in the Nuclear Age*, Metallwerk Plansee, 566 (1962).
25. Cunningham, G. W., Kizer, D. E. and Paprocki, S. I., ibid., 483.
26. Zimmer, F. *Metal Progress*, 101 (Jan., 1963).

AUTHOR INDEX

SUBJECT INDEX